By John Taylor:

Big Game and Big-Game Rifles

African Rifles and Cartridges

Pondoro

JOHN TAYLOR

LAST OF
THE IVORY
HUNTERS

SIMON AND SCHUSTER, NEW YORK, 1955

FIRST PRINTING
LIBRARY OF CONGRESS CATALOG CARD NUMBER: 55-10049
DEWEY DECIMAL CLASSIFICATION NUMBER: 916.9104
MANUFACTURED IN THE UNITED STATES OF AMERICA

To Aly Ndemanga, tracker and gunbearer,

steadfast friend and companion of the African bush

Acknowledgments

The author and publishers of *Pondoro* wish to express their thanks to the editors of *The Field, Game and Gun, The American Rifleman, Safari,* and *The Times Weekly of India* for permission to work into the following pages various articles which were originally published in those journals. Gratitude must also be expressed to John C. Dawkins of Virginia, South Australia, for kindly permitting the use of photographs taken on his first African safari with the author.

Note

The author adheres to the hunter's preference for the singular form for
game animals (elephant, buffalo, lion, kudu, etc.). Non-game animals
(crocs, hyenas, baboons, etc.) are given the customary plurals.

CONTENTS

PROLOGUE

Those readers whose acquaintance with Africa consists of a short safari through Kenya, British East Africa, may fancy that the following pages read like the yarns of the old-timers who hunted in the years between the eighties and the outbreak of the first World War. In those happy days guns were cheap even if not so reliable as today, game of all kinds was plentiful and still unsophisticated, ivory was a good price, and there were no restrictions or officials to impose them. A man could wander whithersoever he wished, then, and there was no one to say him nay—and territorial boundaries and frontiers were about as clearly defined as the equator. Those must indeed have been happy days. But I would remind such readers that there are, even today, vast tracts of Africa over which the Union Jack has never flown—where the natives have never heard a word of English spoken and wouldn't recognize it if they did, and wherein it is still possible for the keen hunter to live, as in my opinion he should, entirely on his rifles. I am typing this right now in the heart of such country—one of the very best elephant-hunting districts in all Africa. One of the best, that is, from the ivory hunter's point of view. The period covered by my story includes the years between the two world wars and up to the present day. Although by no means so young as I was close on thirty-three years ago when I first started hunting, I am not a senile wreck mumbling his reminiscences of the last century. I am still actively engaged in elephant hunting and cannot begin even to imagine myself quitting while I'm still capable of handling a rifle and tramping the elephant trail. Elephant hunting gets into a man's blood even more tenaciously than gold seeking; it becomes an obsession. And I know of few things in this world that give a man such satisfaction as the sight and memory of a decent pile of gleaming tusks shot by himself—legitimately or otherwise.

But I would like to slip in a word, here and now at the start—a word of warning: if you imagine you are going to sit back and have your hair standing on end from the first to the last page of this book, as thrill follows thrill and one hairbreadth escape follows another, you are due for a disappointment. What makes me put that in right here is that I have recently been reading a book by another hunter who frequently refers to the "hundreds of hairbreadth escapes" he experienced on each of his expeditions and mentions how "death in a hundred different forms" was always waiting ready to spring out on him as he made his way through the forest or bush. That sort of thing is plain buncombe. I would willingly undertake to walk from the Cape to Cairo armed with nothing more lethal than a walking stick and a good sheath knife. And the latter is not to enable me to out-Tarzan Tarzan when in hand-to-hand combat with lion and gorillas, but simply because it is a thing every bushman should carry since it will supply him with food and drink from various plants, shrubs, trees, roots, vines, and creepers that provide one or other or both. That fellow was talking about the life lived by the hunter who leaves the more beaten tracks of the automobile "champagne" safaris and wanders out into the blue. He overlooks the fact that the farther you get from human habitations the less likely are animals to attack you: to a very great extent they have not yet learned that man is inimical. Few animals will wantonly attack a human being.

Naturally, hunting all the year around as I do—I hunt from eleven and one-half to twelve months a year, every year, and have frequently been away for three-, four- and five-year stretches (my safaris seldom last less than three years) without even seeing a white man, much less setting foot in such civilization as exists out here—in such circumstances it is almost inevitable that from time to time I will have an adventure which the stay-at-home would describe as "hairbreadth," and that many of the ordinary everyday incidents of hunting he would consider "thrilling." But what I want to make clear is that adventures wherein someone's life was saved by a timely shot are very definitely high lights in the hunter's life, and there may be literally years of more or less uneventful hunting between them. When a hunter comes to write about these things, however, it is almost inevitable that one story will lead to another and the inexperienced reader will gain the impression that elephant hunting consists of eternally leaping out of possible deathtraps into even more dangerous situations—that big-game hunting consists of a never-ending round of saving one's own or someone else's life. It is nothing of the sort. Big-game hunting can be just as dangerous as you wish to make it—but only the born fool deliberately makes it more dangerous than it need be. If you go the right way about things, I consider it less dangerous than crossing the street in a big city nowadays. The man who consistently hunts dangerous

1

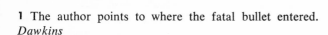

2
3

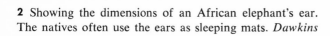

1 The author points to where the fatal bullet entered. *Dawkins*

2 Showing the dimensions of an African elephant's ear. The natives often use the ears as sleeping mats. *Dawkins*

3 Jama, Southern Sudan.

4 Aly Ndemanga and the author in camp, Nyasaland. *Dawkins*

5 Butchering an elephant raider. The meat is some compensation to the natives for the damage done to their crops by such marauders. *Dawkins*

5

4

6   7

6 Velvet monkey. *South African Railways*

7 King vulture with a wing span of about seven feet. *Dawkins*

8 Giraffe. *South African Railways*

8

9 10

9 Greater kudu; a fine trophy. *Dawkins*

10 Elephant. *South African Railways*

11 Zebras and wildebeest. *South African Railways*

11

12 Bald-headed kopje, Central Africa. *Dawkins*

13 The author at a water hole, Central Africa. *Dawkins*

14 Reconnaissance, Central Africa. *Dawkins*

15 Roan antelope. *Dawkins*

16 Aly Ndemanga and a young kudu which had lost its mother. *Dawkins*

17 Giraffe. *Dawkins*

18 Cheetah. *South African Railways*   19 Lion. *South African Railways*

20 Aly Ndemanga bartering surplus meat to native women for meal, tomatoes, and eggs, while the author looks on. *Dawkins*

21 Typical road scene, Central Africa. *Dawkins*

22 Buffalo. *South African Railways*   **23** Wildebeest. *South African Railways*

24 An elephant which will do no more marauding. *Dawkins* [The author says his turban is the coolest, lightest head covering he has found. Moreover, it catches sweat (which hats and helmets do not), and sweat makes the eyes bloodshot and sore.]

25 A troop of bull elephant, showing some fine tuskers. *Dawkins*

26 Aly Ndemanga, to whom this book is dedicated. *Dawkins*

27 The author today—1955.

28 The author and John Dawkins with an elephant which had been raiding natives' crops.

29 Aly Ndemanga in happy mood, Central Africa, 1953. *Dawkins*

game will have all the narrow escapes any man in his right mind could possibly want without actually asking for them. But they will not be a matter of daily occurrence.

It has been my earnest hope throughout this book that my writing may be of assistance to beginners and those with less experience than I have had. I well know how much I would have appreciated some genuine advice when I was starting on my career. In those days I knew nothing, nothing at all, about big-game hunting: I knew there was plenty of game in Africa, but reckoned it was just a millionaire's sport; I did not know if there were a single elephant left in the whole continent; I did not know one rifle from another, never having used anything but .22 rim-fires and service rifles; I did not know that there were other hunters actually engaged in hunting who had written books which I might have read. Nobody could have known less than I did when I first started out. And I was afraid to ask questions, afraid of the howls of ribald laughter which such questions would probably arouse. I was very shy and had always been a somewhat solitary boy given to living in my dreams. Those dreams, many of them, had been inspired by the late Rider Haggard's romances, and it had been my secret ambition almost ever since I could remember to be an elephant hunter. That Africa might not be the same place it was in the days of which Haggard wrote was something I did not consider.

Perhaps a few words about my beginnings would not be out of place here. I was born in Dublin, Eire, at the start of the century. My father, the late Sir William Taylor, was generally acknowledged to be one of the four or five great surgeons of his day. My mother was born in Louisiana, in the United States, but her family of I don't know how many generations back was of Irish stock. I had my own small library as a boy and insisted that every volume in it have at least one Negro character. Most of the books dealt with Africa and African tribes. (I did not care whether they were fact or fiction.) It was at my preparatory school in Eire that I discovered Rider Haggard's *Nada the Lily,* an extremely well-illustrated edition. From that day I knew there was only one country for me—Africa. Later I came across *Golden Glory* by Horace Rose, which only deepened my determination to live among the Africans. The years I spent in Shrewsbury—one of the Big Five of the English public schools—in no way lessened my determination. Neither did a winter spent in Canada. In fact, it was when I returned from Canada that I first mentioned to my mother and father my determination to go to Africa. They were the kindest of parents, as their most customary remark to me clearly shows:

"All right, son. So long as you are happy, we are."

It might be of interest to mention that when I arrived in Africa I did not feel a strange man in a strange land; on the contrary, it seemed to me I was returning home after a long absence. And the odd affinity I had felt for Africans before I saw one in the flesh was enormously enhanced when I found myself surrounded by them. Thirty-three years of intimate contact have merely increased that affinity.

When I first set foot on African soil, with twenty golden British sovereigns and a Harley-Davidson motorcycle, I was not discouraged by the settled and peaceful atmosphere of the Cape. I mounted my Harley and rode north. I guessed that all Africa could not be civilized, like this; so I just continued riding until I had no more money left with which to buy gasoline. I thereupon sold my motorcycle and proceeded to jump freight trains—always heading north—as I wanted to save my money for the rifle I hoped soon to be buying. On arrival in Bulawayo in Southern Rhodesia I passed a sports-goods store with rifles in the window, and went in. The fellow behind the counter did not seem to know much more about them than I did, and as I did not know the difference between the various Mausers and their calibers I plumped for a brand-new BSA .303 sporter and a hundred shells. With this and my old Webley .455 revolver, which I was carrying in my knapsack, I jumped more freight trains until I reached the famous Victoria Falls on the Zambezi River. Here I parted from the railway with the intention of wandering away up the Zambezi.

I did not know where I was going or what I was going to do when I got there. I was not actually making for anywhere in particular; I had no plans. But I knew from seeing maps that Barotseland was native territory, that there was no civilization there, and that away out to the west lay Angola, Portuguese West Africa. The Zambezi flowed through those parts on its long wandering way down from the mysterious Belgian Congo, where it rose, and I could see no very good reason why I shouldn't follow it right up and then maybe return in Livingstone's footsteps and follow them right through to Portuguese East. Anyway, I would be seeing something of Africa. But the first thing was to get a native companion. So I asked one of the English-speaking room boys in the Falls hotel to get me a cheery youth who would be willing to come with me for a cruise and who would buy me a small canoe when we struck the first kraals, or villages. I had visions of canoeing up the river, my visions being of light handy Canadian canoes—I had yet to make the acquaintance of the Zambezi variety of dugout. (Some of the Congo and Sudanese canoes are beautiful and graceful craft; the Zambezi ones are not!) At this period, of course, I spoke not a word of any African language. Hence my wish for a native companion: he could teach me his tongue and help me out if I wanted anything, such as this canoe, from the local natives; but above all, I would almost certainly be able to learn a great deal of African bushcraft from him.

And so the cheery, ugly, faithful Joro came into my life. Black as the ace of spades, and naked except for a minute strip of loincloth worn solely to conform with the conventions around the hotel and instantly discarded when we left, he was probably two or three years younger than I was in actual age, but was a self-reliant man when on his own in the veld and when showing me the ropes. He was absolutely at home in the wilds: he knew every tree and creeper, vine and shrub—which roots and fruits were edible and which were not. The spoor of the different animals was an open book to him, which he could read as easily as I could read print; and he was as much at ease in or on the water as he was on land. He knew the habits and customs of all animals, birds and fish, and how to trap them. At first he was shy and diffident, not being accustomed to a white man like me; but when he realized that I had no highfalutin ideas about "white herrenvolk," and really wanted to learn, he took an immense delight in teaching me both his language and the ways of the wild. His shyness disappeared as his trust and confidence grew, and he became that rare thing, a real friend and companion. I could not possibly have had a better teacher or a finer introduction to the life that was to be mine.

I might mention here that I had no licenses or permits whatsoever: I did not even have permission to be in the territory, not having called at the Immigration Office when I was in Bulawayo. (I had guessed I wouldn't have enough money to satisfy them.) Thus my very first shot fired in Africa made me a poacher.

But at first I simply could not see the animals. There would be Joro looking at them, pointing and whispering, but for the life of me I could not see them. Then one of them would move, flip an ear or swish a tail, and there they were as large as life right in front of me. When I learned what to look for it was easier; but to start with I did not know the native names and therefore could not tell what my companion had spotted. However, I knew what the commoner species looked like from reading Fitzpatrick's charming *Jock of the Bushveld* and studying the excellent marginal illustrations that were in it, so when I learned the native names I knew what to expect. My slow introduction under the tutelage of such a keen companion was a never-ending source of delight and interest to me. We poled and paddled our canoe up the river week after week, until the weeks ran into uncounted months.

You may wonder how the two of us managed, since it is customary for whites to be accompanied by innumerable porters and servants when trekking through Africa. All I had were the clothes I wore—a hat, a khaki shirt, a pair of khaki shorts, a pair of stout shoes—a cutthroat razor (my leather belt served as a strop for it), a rifle and revolver with their ammunition carried in a bandolier over my shoulder, matches in a water-proof box, a hunting knife, and a couple of three-legged pots. I also had about a hundred and fifty assorted fishhooks and a small bag of salt. I gradually removed my clothing until I was well tanned all over and then, since I knew I'd need them again some day, I rolled up my shirt and shorts and stuffed them into our cooking pot when we were on the march or (when we got it) traveling in our canoe.

I had very little money, which didn't matter because the natives way out here had no use for it. But I have yet to find Africans who have no use for meat. I would shoot a buck, and Joro would have a great time bartering the meat to local villagers for meal and eggs and any vege-tables they had. That was how we obtained our canoe, too: I shot a large buck and gave it to the owner of the canoe in exchange.

We had no bedding, nor did we need any. If the nights were cold we use a couple of armfuls of dry grass as a mat or mattress, lit two fires, and lay down together between them. I learned then, and subsequent ex-perience has corroborated it, that one does not suffer from the heat during the day when one is not wearing clothes and yet seems somehow to absorb heat so that one does not feel cold by night—especially when two or three sleep together. There are no mosquitoes to worry about during the dry season, except near lakes with reedy growth around the edges. When the rains came we always tried to reach some native kraal where we would be sure of a roof over us, even though we usually had to share the hut with several others. But that didn't worry me—it was all part of the life I had chosen and everything was of interest. Besides, had I tried to hold myself aloof I could never have made friends with these people. And since I wanted to be friends with them why should I be standoffish?

One evening Joro and I had pulled in rather earlier than usual be-cause I wanted a look at the surrounding country. Naturally we took the rifle with us, even though we were not hunting. It was close to sundown when we came back to where we had left the canoe. I was in front; Joro was a little way behind and was carrying the rifle. I was following a small-game trail which led down to the river, and just as I turned around a fairly thick bush something made me look up. There was a leop-ard in the act of launching himself down on top of me from the branch of a tree that grew out over the trail. Whether he had been waiting for some small animal to come along for a drink and got himself so ready to spring that he overbalanced or whether he figured he had been cornered and attack was his only hope, I cannot say—there must have been some reason for his spring as the average unprovoked animal rarely attacks man. Because the breeze had been blowing across he could not have known I was coming, and surely he would have cleared for his life had he known it was man: so I assume that one or the other of those explanations must contain the answer. His face was only about two or three feet from mine when I saw him; he was actually in the air and coming down. I just had time to draw my revolver and shoot him in the chest when he landed on top of me. His weight brought me down and the back of my head made contact with a stone or something which scattered my wits. I can just dimly remember moving my head slightly to one side so that he would not chew my ear off, as his jaws were clashing immediately beside it. I could feel his claws busy on chest and thigh, but curiously enough felt no pain. Then there came a splintering crack and thump: Joro, hearing the report of the revolver, had bounded forward and brought the butt of the rifle down with a crash on the leopard's head. It was an extremely plucky thing to do, because he had no means of knowing that the beast was at his last gasp. He could see me underneath, and that was enough for him. His blow smashed the butt off the rifle, but it put a stop to the leopard's antics—which was maybe just as well, because all the ribs down the right side of my chest were exposed and my left thigh was in ribbons.

Joro rolled the leopard off me, not deigning to give it another look, and then set to to examine my injuries. I had some difficulty in managing the leg, which did not seem to belong to me, but with Joro's help and my arm around his shoulders got the rest of the way to our bivouac. I suggested Joro fetch some water from the river to wash the wounds. Although I now had a smattering of his language my suggestion mostly took the form of gestures—Africans are remarkably quick at understanding what you want. I don't doubt that the river water would have done. (Although it was considered suicidal by the Portuguese, as I afterward learned, to drink Zambezi water unboiled and unfiltered, I have drunk it ever since I have been on it and have never boiled it except to make tea or coffee. My view is that since the natives drink it, why can't I?) However, Joro pointed out how muddy and discolored it was and indicated that he had something better and cleaner. Whereupon, in the most matter-of-fact manner, he commenced washing the wounds with his own urine, straight from its source. It stung and smarted but was certainly gin clear, which was more than could be said for the river water. It did not occur to me to protest. Joro, as I well knew by now, was clean and healthy; besides, he had proved himself such an experienced bushman and was doing this in such a natural manner that I decided it must be the correct procedure. After he had finished he grinned, patted me on my undamaged shoulder, and told me to lie still for a short while. He disappeared and returned after ten or fifteen minutes with various leaves and roots and the soft inner bark of some tree. He pounded the roots until they bled a thick white milk. This he smeared on and into the wounds, and I found it most soothing. He then looked around until he found a spot where some white ants were working. He stirred them up and got hold of the big warriors from among them. These he grasped tightly between his fingers until their powerful jaws opened wide. Then, drawing the lips of the deep gashes in my thigh together, he fixed the ant on the lips and broke off the body, leaving the jaws pinching together the edges of the wound. He set a row of them along each deep cut and then used the leaves he had brought as a dressing and the soft inner bark as bandages. His strong black fingers and hands were as gentle as those of any trained hospital nurse, and—dare I say it?—as skillful.

With a double armful of grass he made me a bed, and then, after he had given me some soup and fed himself, he dragged the carcass of the leopard down and proceeded to skin it.

Next morning he removed my dressings and gently pressed and probed here and there until he was satisfied no pus had formed in any of the wounds. That done he replaced the dressings with fresh ones and left them there for the following three or four days. He then removed the ant-jaw stitches and told me I was all right. During the days I was laid up he tended and washed me as tenderly and carefully as any mother her infant. I found his treatment most efficacious. My wounds healed up without the slightest trouble or complications. The medical fraternity might have something to say about it—but they are a conservative lot. And it is worth bearing in mind that certain African tribes, the Masai, for instance, knew that malaria was carried by mosquitoes when our own learned professors were still struggling in their entanglement with witchcraft. If seventy-five or a hundred years ago some traveler had asked one of those men, suffering from malaria, what was the matter with him and heard the answer, "I've been bitten by a mosquito," he would have treasured that remark as a delightful example of heathen superstition.

I have described this incident in some detail because I have heard so many discussions as to the amount of pain a man must suffer when being mauled by a beast. Apart from my own experience I know personally some seven or eight others who have been mauled by lion, tiger, or leopard, in addition to the many others I have heard or read about; and they all say the same thing: that they felt no pain at all during the actual mauling. I myself had a curious detached feeling, quite impersonal, as though I were withdrawn and watching the predicament in which some other fellow found himself. (It was exactly the same some years later, under a wounded and very angry elephant.) It is true that I was somewhat dazed by the leopard's sudden attack. However, I was quite conscious and could definitely feel his claws busy. But there was no pain. So the softhearted who bemoan the mouse's sufferings as the cat plays with him and crushes a few ribs from time to time before finally killing him can take comfort from the thought that in all probability the mouse is too numbed to feel anything. Terror doubtless has a great deal to do with it; yet I can definitely say that I was not scared on this occasion. It was all too sudden.

As soon as my wounds healed we continued our cruise, stopping over for a while with the swamp dwellers in Angola. Simple, kindly, hospitable folk we found them. They lived on fish which they caught in traps and nets and on homemade hooks which were not too good. We were able to requite their hospitality with a gift of about a hundred of the hooks I had with me. Seldom have I seen such gratitude as they expressed—I feel certain that the pair of us could have lived among them as honored guests for the remainder of our lives had we wished to do so. And with this in mind I had to smile when in later days I happened to mention them—in the township of Livingstone in Northern Rhodesia, I think it was—and was greeted with cries of consternation from my listeners. "Oh, but those are a wild, savage, murderous gang of outlaws! No official ever dares attempt to collect hut tax from them. They're bad." It is the same everywhere. I have heard almost identical remarks about the swamp dwellers of the Upper Nile, the Nuer. Yet I found them just the same: simple, kindly, friendly people whose only desire was to be let alone. It would seem that the proper definition of the word "savage" is: Someone with a dark skin who has not yet taken to wearing trousers.

With my rifle out of action my hunting activities fell off, but not my interest or enjoyment in our leisurely journey. Joro made a fishtrap (slivers of bamboo painstakingly cut) that never failed to hold our breakfast when we hauled it up in the morning, and I set night lines with our hooks which also generally had something on them to add to the feast. And then there were the geese, duck, partridge, and guinea fowl that Joro trapped so cunningly. (I describe such traps later: they are essentially the same all over Africa, and native youngsters learn how to set them at an early age.) Every day held something of interest, something new to learn. The one regret I experienced was that I had not been born and bred in the wilds like my companion. As I noted each new example of his resourcefulness and ingenuity, and his ability to lay his hands instantly on whatever it was he wanted, no matter where we happened to be, I could only shake a sorry head to think of my own costly and useless school and college education that left me so helpless beside him. He would have been

described as an ignorant savage. But no cultured, civilized gentleman of
the days of chivalry could possibly have been more kindly, more considerate, or more essentially gentle than that same ignorant savage.

It can, I'm sure, be readily appreciated that two youths living as he
and I were living—sharing everything, eating the same food out of the
same pot, sleeping together on the same armful of grass to keep warm—
must inevitably come either to like or to detest each other. I had liked
Joro the instant I set eyes on him. He had that peculiar kind of ugliness
that is attractive: you see it in a well-bred bulldog or boxer. His nose was
a small pug, he had round, beautifully symmetrical ears set close to a fine-
domed skull, and his somewhat puckered face was more than redeemed
by his eyes. Clear, deep-set and steady, frank and honest, they looked
fearlessly out between lashes that any woman of any color would have
envied. His body was perfect: small and lightly boned, wide in the shoulder and tapering to a tiny waist and narrow hips, not an ounce of superflu-
ous flesh, but every muscle in its place under a black skin glistening with
health and vitality. He was truly a handsome sight, yet he seemed totally
unaware of his physical beauty, for no one could have been more unself-
conscious.

My liking for him changed to genuine admiration after the episode
with the leopard. Remember, he had no notion of how to fire a rifle, he
couldn't have known that I had shot the beast through the heart—that
for all practical purposes it was dead—yet he hadn't run but had done all
in his power to save me. Then, afterward, there was the calm and confident manner in which he took charge of the situation. Is it any wonder
that I developed a real affection for him? And I think it awakened a similar response in him.

I finally had my rifle put into shape again by a native bush gunsmith.
He made a remarkably good job of it when one considers how little he had
in the way of tools. I paid for the work by shooting a beast for him
with the weapon he had repaired.

We pushed on until eventually the fishermen we met told us that we
were now in the Congo. Had we had a light Canadian canoe we would
undoubtedly have gone farther, but the portaging of the heavy ironwood
dugout began to become a trifle wearisome. So we swung around and
paddled downstream again. Returning to our swamp-dwelling friends we
gave them our canoe, as I did not want to return by the same route.
We now struck out overland through the Mashakulumbwi country, more
or less following Livingstone's footsteps. (Unless memory fails me it was
these same Mashakulumbwi who attacked Selous' camp one time so that
he only just managed to escape with two or three of his men and one
rifle, everything else having been lost. Selous, for those who do not know,

was without question the best of the old-time hunters, and his name is familiar to all who have read much about African hunting.) We experienced no trouble of any kind. Ninety-nine times in a hundred it is the white man's own fault if he gets himself attacked—witness the fact that in all his wanderings, throughout most of which he was the first white man the natives had ever seen, Livingstone only once had to fire a shot at "savages" in self-defense. And that was on the eastern border of Angola when the local tribes held up his porters and demanded tribute. It was the usual procedure in those days, and the Arab slavers and traders always paid it; but Livingstone's men from the coast apparently did not know of it. When it looked as though things were going to happen, Livingstone fired his shotgun in the air and that was the end. He had no further trouble all the way across to Portuguese East Africa. And neither did we. Right across Northern Rhodesia we strolled, and then across the Portuguese border and down along the Zambezi valley. No matter where you want to go in Africa you will almost always find a small native footpath winding its leisurely way more or less in your direction. This is followed, not only because the walking is easier, but also because such a path will invariably lead to water and kraals.

In due course we arrived in Tete, said to be the oldest inland township south of Cairo, and thence headed south toward Southern Rhodesia. In Southern Rhodesia I took on a job shooting lion off a cattle ranch where they were preying on the stock, and later got a similar job in Northern Rhodesia. (I shall not take time here to tell you about those lion— they appear in a later chapter.) But it was elephant I wanted. Joro was still with me when in my youthful exuberance I wiped out the lion and was told that there was no longer any need of my services. But I didn't care; now I could afford to go after the big fellows.

I have typed this rather lengthy prologue for the benefit of any youngsters—and surely there must be plenty of them—who fancy this sort of wild free adventurous life but may have been told by their elders that that is all a thing of the past, that such days are gone, never to return. There are many who think that, who know only the Africa of the towns and cities and the motor roads of the various British colonies. There are plenty of people living in those same colonies who haven't the remotest notion of conditions across the border. I have been looked at in speechless astonishment when I happened to mention that the fellow I was speaking to was the first white man I had seen for maybe three or four years. People just cannot believe it. When I (very foolishly) volunteered early in World War II and was giving particulars about myself, I mentioned that the first I had heard about the war was from a scrap of old newspaper which happened to be wrapped around some odds and ends that one of my runners had gone and bought for me, and that I hadn't heard a radio or seen a paper for the previous three years. And they looked at me as though I had grown a second head.

Now, to close this prologue, let me tell you of two incidents that occurred sometime in 1935 or '36. I was hunting in Portuguese territory just south of the Nyasaland border. It was a bad area, the tsetse fly swarming and sleeping sickness (*trypanosomiasis*)* prevalent. Of the five hunters who had tried to work the district before me, four had died, three of them of sleeping sickness, and the fifth had one foot in the grave with the other expected to follow it shortly. The natives who inhabited it were outlaws and runaway criminals (so-called) who acknowledged no authority and paid no taxes. They were desperately poor, for the land was too infertile and the rainfall too scarce and uncertain to permit them to raise enough to feed themselves; and when, maybe once in five or seven years, they *did* manage to get a good year, the locusts that looked on the district as a breeding ground ate everything. The people lived by setting traps and snares around water holes, drying the meat they caught and trading it across the Nyasaland border in the fertile land along the Shire River for grain.

There came another hunter to try his hand in this neck of the woods, an Englishman. He was broke and had no license. (Neither had I, for that matter.) I came across his camp one day and stopped to have a yarn with him. I found him mightily pleased with himself. It seemed that that morning he had found a buck caught in one of the local native's traps and had killed the beast and taken it himself. He had then gone around destroying all the traps and snares he could find. I asked him why, and his reply, made in a highly indignant and virtuous tone, ran somewhat as follows: "Damn it, man, don't you realize that it's a serious offense to trap game? By jove, I'll put a stop to it while I'm here! These bastards mustn't be allowed to think they can get away with that sort of thing. I've a good mind to report them to the *Chefe de Posto* at Benga."

"Oh, yes," I said, "and if he asks you what the hell you've been doing up here yourself during the last eight or nine months, are you going to tell him you've been poaching his game all that time? He knows these people trap game, and he also knows he can't stop them."

"Hell! It's no good talking to you," he shouted. "You're half a nigger yourself the way you live among them and take their part. I'm a white man and can do what I like and you ought to remember you're white too."

---

* I have been asked what precautions I took against sleeping sickness: only those taken by the majority of Africans themselves, to wit, keeping perfectly fit and not worrying, which prescription seemed to work.

I left him fuming and sputtering to himself. But this is typical of the attitude of a certain kind of Britisher in Africa. Because he was doing something it was automatically all right; but when he saw the natives doing similar things he instantly became highly indignant. The fact that taking the meat from a trap and using it made it the same as though he had set the thing himself was a point he was incapable of seeing.

Now for the second episode. A plane passed over one day, heading north. Planes being a rare sight in those days, everybody ran out to watch it. A week or two later some lads I had sent over the border to get me some provisions—tea, coffee, sugar, salt, and soap, all I ever buy—returned with word of the then newly introduced currency and brought some of the new coins with them. Since notices had been stuck up all over the place saying old money must be brought in and exchanged for the new, that after a certain date the old currency would no longer be legal tender, I told my men to advise the locals, any who had money, that they'd better see about changing it. They came running to see the new coins —brand-spanking new, straight from the mint. Instantly there came a yell of joy. Stragglers were shouted at to hasten. They also joined in the chorus of delight: "They're coming! They're coming at last! See, they've sent their fine new coins on ahead of them by plane so that they'll be ready when they come! They don't want the old British and Portuguese money; they'll only use their own. They're coming! *They're coming!* Now we'll all be free! No more hut tax; no more forced labor! *The Americans are coming!*" The drums were hauled out and banged and thumped and rattled till they rolled the glad tidings far and wide through the dim aisles of the forest, across the shallow valley, and away across the low distant hills into the sunset.

That, friend, is no fairy tale invented to round off this prologue. It is a plain statement of what I actually saw and heard in that remote and lonely valley. The Portuguese are disliked because of the forced labor which is a part of their native policy—every able-bodied male must work at least six months every year; but the British are hated even more because of their broken promises and hypocrisy. I know that this doesn't make pleasant reading; but I am concerned solely with truth. Except in a few of the very remotest parts of the hinterland it has been the same wherever I have roamed throughout Africa: an instant brightening of the eyes, and an eager and intense interest in whatever one is saying when the words "America" and "American" are mentioned—so enthusiastic that it is almost embarrassing. I do not think this is sufficiently well known among Americans. Most writers on Africa are British, and naturally they wouldn't notice or mention such a thing; but I certainly think it ought to interest American readers.

No words of mine can hope to convey to you the ringing joy and hope embodied in that spontaneous yell: *"The Americans are coming; at last they are coming!"*

I hadn't the heart to disillusion them.

J. T.

Portuguese East Africa
April 1955

1

MOSTLY ELEPHANT

1: THE FIRST ELEPHANT

I poached my first elephant, the very first wild elephant I had ever seen, in Portuguese East Africa. In those far-off days I had not started to keep any record of my hunting experiences. It was only after some years that I decided to jot down in a rough diary anything of interest that happened or that I observed and later write it up more fully in a hunting journal. Accordingly, when I write now of my first few elephant, and of my very earliest experiences as an ivory poacher, I must do so from memory. But those recollections are indelibly stamped in their appropriate place among my experiences, and I can picture all of them today as though they had taken place only yesterday or the day before—if only because the faithful Joro played his part in them, and I can never forget him, my first guide and mentor, my friend, companion, and instructor in the wilds.

Neither of us had as yet ever seen an elephant. We had come across plenty of elephant spoor during that long fifteen months or more of our first trek, but not the animals that made the spoor. During the remainder of the second year, when I was shooting lion, we had been out of elephant country. However, as my confidence grew I became more and more determined to be an elephant hunter—particularly now that I realized there were plenty of elephant waiting to be shot. I had armed myself with an exquisite little Martini-Henry carbine (.577/.450) which fired black powder and a lead bullet. It was beautifully engraved and inlaid with gold right up to the muzzle of its short octagonal barrel. It had been built to the special order of an Indian prince just before the order prohibiting all weapons of that caliber in India. After that, it found its way to Rhodesia. Since nobody out there wanted a gold-inlaid gun, I picked it up for the proverbial song. It was, of course, a single-shot weapon, but I had found it very satisfactory for lion, which I had shot only at close range and always with my old revolver as a stand-by.

As I was going poaching I decided against taking a crew of Rhodesian porters with me. I fitted myself out with a string of pack donkeys, and Joro and I set out with these. I had had plenty of experience with horses and mules, but this was my first attempt to do anything with "Irish lions." How I cursed them! And how I wished I hadn't bothered with them but had just started out with my companion as we had on our way to cross the continent a few years before. (In view of the fact that a white man is invariably seen with a string of porters toting his kit, it might be asked how the two of us had managed after we abandoned our canoe back on that first trek of ours. Well, the answer is easy: we had no kit for anyone to tote. I had set off, as I have mentioned earlier, merely with the clothes I was wearing, a hunting knife, rifle and handgun, ammunition, and a couple of three-legged pots.)

However, from listening to other men talking during the months I was lion hunting, I had learned that serious elephant hunting was a very different thing from all other kinds of hunting, and that a man needed to be fairly well equipped. I also realized that I had been missing my tea and coffee, and that a pup tent would be a very nice thing to have in the rains. So I had bought a small police patrol tent, normally supposed to be for one man; I reckoned it would just nicely accommodate Joro and me.

Well, I'm not going to weary you with an account of the trials and tribulations of traveling with pack donkeys in bush and forest in Africa; suffice it if I strongly recommend that you not attempt it. In the days of which I write there were no motor roads where I was heading. There are today, and you can get right into the heart of the elephant country by truck with all the kit you want—though you will have to get out and walk if you want to bag your elephant. We finally crossed the border—a little heap of stones marking it—and made for a certain river of which I knew and where I had heard that there were sure to be plenty of elephant. We saw abundant sign as we approached the area: trees broken and pushed down, branches torn off, droppings with their characteristic sweet and by no means unpleasant smell, and great pad marks all over the place. When we reached the river we pitched our little tent under a big shady tree not far from a small kraal. The local natives came to greet us and see who and what we were and what we wanted here. When they heard that we were after elephant they were greatly excited and assured us there were plenty, all, needless to say, with gigantic tusks—they clasped both hands around their thighs, high up, to show us how thick the tusks were. We told them that the first thing needed was something to fill our pot: it was too late this evening, but early next morning I wanted to go out and shoot something to eat. And then I realized another disadvantage of donkeys when there are only two in the party: I would have to get some youngster to herd them when we were out hunting. Joro certainly was not going to remain behind like a woman minding camp, when I was out after elephant.

So next morning at daybreak, having hired a herd boy, the pair of us went out. We did not wander far before I spotted what I took to be a strange reddish variety of lesser kudu or a gigantic bushbuck. I was doubtful about the range, so I just held the sights as they were and aimed at the animal's withers. He dropped instantly to the shot, as I could see through the haze of smoke, and I found that my bullet had taken him exactly where my fore sight had been. Joro chopped down a pole and lopped the branches off it, and we tied the buck to this and swung him to our shoulders. I was greatly puzzled as to what he was. At that time I had never heard of the nyala. (In any case, it was something of a zoological discovery to find this one here as they were not known to inhabit that territory; but I knew nothing of this.) It was only some years afterward that I heard there had been a wealthy American collector offering some hundreds of dollars for a complete skin and skeleton of a nyala ram.

We carried the animal back to camp in triumph, and after butchering him traded the surplus meat to the villagers for meal, eggs, vegetables, and what-have-you, in our usual manner: it was living on the country like this which enabled us to wander around without numerous loads of stores. This business finished, we chatted with the locals and arranged for a couple of them to come around at daybreak next morning so that we could get out after elephant. It was advisable to make use of the local men as guides because they would know to a very great extent where elephant usually halted for their midday siesta, where they usually watered, what elephant were likely to be in the district at any given season, and the best way back to camp if we had gone a long distance—because the most direct way was not always the best, for it might lead into swamps or impossible thickets of thorn. They would also know where the nearest kraals were. Unless you have won yourself a perfectly damnable name among the natives, you will never have the slightest difficulty in getting guides in elephant country. Most of them ask no pay; they know you will give them all the meat they can eat and carry away. That is all they want.

At first crack of dawn Joro had the coffeepot boiling while I was wiping the oil out of my gold-inlaid Martini. By the time we had finished the coffee guides appeared and told us that a big lone bull had been raiding the granary overnight. In this district the granaries for some reason were built out in the lands (in most districts they are built inside the living huts, or immediately outside them in the kraals). The guides led us to where the raiding had taken place, about half a mile away, and showed us how the big bull had pushed the conical thatched roof to one side and had his feed of the stored grain. I felt considerably excited, with a queasy feeling in the pit of my belly which I knew was nervousness: I well remembered the feeling I had so often experienced in days gone by immediately before the gun that started our boat races at school and college; and I was delighted when Joro told me afterward that he had felt exactly the same thing. If any man tries to tell you that he was not a mite scared when tackling his first elephant, and even more so his second and third, you can safely call him a liar or consider him a freak with no more imagination than a hen.

We picked up the spoor and proceeded to follow it. What little breeze there was was favorable, and I had a little tobacco bag full of wood ashes on my belt with which to test it. This is one of the handiest ways of testing the wind: you have only to give the sack a tap with your finger and the particles of ash will instantly tell you how the air is moving, even when there is so little movement that you cannot feel it. Elephant have a keener sense of smell than any other animal, and I have known them to wind me when I was still more than half a mile away. It is absolutely imperative to watch the wind the whole time when hunting them.

How long this silent spooring went on I don't know—perhaps a couple of hours. The local men were very good; I could see that. They worked side by side as a team, each with his long spear stretched out in front of him. There was no sound, no word passed between them, but every now and then one of them would point to some small indication with the blade of his spear. The other would just glance at it and then go on without pausing, to point to something else, himself, a little way on. They were never wrong, and we followed pretty well as fast as we could comfortably walk. It was amazing to see how little indication there was of the passage of so huge an animal as the African elephant. At the time I was not accustomed to following spoor, my eyes were not sharp enough, or rather had not been trained, and more often than not I had not the slightest notion what they were seeing even though they had pointed to it with their spears.

Suddenly, as one man, they stopped and froze. We did likewise. Like four statues we stood in whatever position we had been in. I heard the swish of a branch close in front, but on account of the dense undergrowth could see nothing. We were in heavy forest, the tops of the trees meeting overhead, and there was considerable undergrowth everywhere. Softly and slowly the guides drew back and signed to me to move forward to where they had been. I did so, guessing that they must have seen our quarry and that that branch I had heard swishing must have been he.

One of the men put his hand on my bare shoulder and gently guided me into position, indicating that I should look slightly to my left front. I moved around the bush that had prevented my seeing, and there, sure enough, was my elephant. He looked about the size of a house and was not more than about eleven paces away, standing broadside-on to me.

Now I knew that my lead bullet would be useless for a head shot, and was not sure that it was capable of breaking a shoulder (I had heard an elephant is helpless on three legs). But I did know that any animal could be killed on a shot behind the shoulder provided the bullet finds its way in sufficiently far to hit either the heart or lungs. I had decided long before that I must take only lung shots. All I really knew about shooting elephant was that you must never shoot aft of an imaginary perpendicular dropped from the hindermost edge of his ear when that ear is back against the shoulder. This fellow's huge ear was back against his shoulder, so I took most deliberate aim exactly halfway up his body and right on that imaginary line, hoping my bullet would slip in close up behind the shoulder. I felt not the slightest trace of nervousness now that I had raised the rifle and to my delight found that I was rock-steady. I squeezed my trigger, heard the roar of the black powder, the "clup" of the bullet, and then everything was blotted out by smoke. Here in this heavy forest so early in the morning the sun had not had a chance yet of drying the dew and there was still considerable moisture in the atmosphere—hence the smoke, which is not much worry otherwise, on hot dry days with modern powder. Automatically reloading, I waited for the smoke to clear. I have a notion that I rather hoped to see my elephant lying there like yesterday's nyala, but there was no sign of him when the smoke cleared sufficiently for me to see through it. However, I was perfectly confident of my shot and had no trace of doubt that we would find him somewhere in the vicinity. I looked around and found that Joro was standing right beside me. I asked him in a whisper if he had seen which way the elephant had gone, and he somewhat breathlessly replied that he had gone off after his trunk—in other words, in the direction in which he had been facing. I advanced slowly to where the elephant had been standing, and the trackers caught up with me just as I got there. I told them where I had hit the elephant, and they at once brightened up and assured me that with such a wound he would be dead when found and could not go far. Even as they spoke there came the crash and swish of breaking bush and a long deep groan that was almost a roar from the depths of the forest in the direction in which the elephant had run. We remained motionless waiting for further sounds, but none came. So we took up the spoor again, very carefully and slowly, and found that it was leading directly toward where that groan had come from. Suddenly the leading tracker halted, straightened, stood looking for a moment, and then shouted, "He's down! he's down!" We all rushed forward and there, sure enough, was the mighty fellow flat on his side.

I moved around to examine his tusks, which I had scarcely glanced at before firing, although even in that instant I had seen that they were good. And now, just when I began to gloat at the magnificent sight they presented, I suddenly found that I was trembling from head to foot. I was ashamed to let the trackers see, although I would not have minded Joro's seeing since he knew that this was the first elephant I had ever even seen, much less shot; then to my delight I found that he was trembling just as badly as I was. We both moved around to the other side of the elephant, where only our heads could be seen, and waited there until we had steadied sufficiently. It was, of course, nervous reaction: we had both been scared, although the need for steadiness had helped me in the actual shooting and following-up, and until all danger was past. However, our joy was so great that we soon recovered and were able to examine and admire our trophy.

Apart from mere admiration and satisfaction, what immediately struck me was the creature's enormous proportions, and the miserable little squirt my grand wee carbine seemed beside him. When I looked at that huge head and those massive shoulders and hips, I instantly realized the need for steel- or nickel-covered bullets. I had had more than my share of beginner's luck in getting a clear broadside shot at this big fellow—I could not hope for that every time. I had seen enough of this forest to realize that more often than not all I would get would be glimpses of my elephant. What if only the head were visible? Was there any chance of my lead bullet's getting in far enough to find the brain? What if he were standing behind a tree in such a way that I could not place my bullet immediately *behind* the shoulder: was it capable of breaking the shoulder itself? I doubted it. And then what if he were facing slightly away from me: would my lead bullet be able to shatter those mighty hips or that spine? I did not need anyone to tell me the answer. Above all, supposing I only wounded him with my first shot: there would be the possibility of a charge when following up, and I knew perfectly well that no lead bullet could be relied upon to penetrate the head from in front. It probably would not even turn him.

Another thing that then dawned on me was the extraordinary way in which the bull had faded away when shot, like the smoke from my rifle. I have said that the undergrowth was dense, yet that mighty fellow had cleared off at speed, as his spoor had shown, and there had not been a sound of any sort. I was to see a lot more of this: the elephant's remarkable capacity for silent movement even in thick bush, and that whether he has been shot or not. There are times when the screaming, yelling, trumpeting, and smashing down of trees as a herd stampedes is literally paralyzing—many a hunter has described how he was totally incapable of movement until the noise died down—and other occasions when the herd is there in front of you, close by, and the next instant gone, like a puff of smoke, with not a sound of any sort.

Having cut off the tail as proof of ownership, one of the trackers then tied one of the hairs of the tail around my wrist and another around Joro's. This is invariably done, at least with the first elephant of an expedition, the reason given being that it will prevent the spirit of the dead elephant from leading you into danger, since he knows that a bit of himself is with you and therefore he would be leading himself into the same danger.

We then returned to camp with the object of moving out where the body was lying. I was anxious to see this, my first elephant, cut up; and besides, I knew that everybody would soon be out there to get the meat, and I wanted to win the natives' confidence and gain their friendship. Although I was barely ten miles from the border, I was not much more than a dozen from the seat of the nearest government official—really too close to be pleasant, and certainly too close if I did not succeed in inducing these local natives to help me and give me warning should the official learn of my existence and make any move in my direction. So Joro and I decided to go out to the carcass of the elephant and bivouac there for a day or two. We found a small clearing not far from where the bull lay dead, though the nearest water was about two miles away. However, we were able to obtain a couple of large calabashes, which held all we wanted for drinking and cooking.

There was a seething, shouting, yelling black mass of humanity all over the carcass when we got back to it. They were hacking and jabbing and sawing and slashing at great chunks of meat. Much of the surrounding undergrowth had been cleared away and fires lit all over the place, with rough frames erected over them. The chunks of meat would be roughly cut into strips and partially dried on these. All around the fires were large slabs of the choicest morsels impaled on sticks stuck in the ground to toast, and the owners would start in on them when they were scarcely more than warmed. Even as we arrived two youths, red with blood from head to foot, came crawling out from inside the carcass dragging two kidneys as big as their heads. They danced and kicked up their heels and whooped for joy over their prize.

That evening we got hold of our two trackers—their names are still with me, Kandikori and Mariko—took them along to our bivouac, and explained the position to them. They were reassuring and confident. The *Chefe de Posto* of this district was all right; he did not look for trouble or want it. Provided I did not shoot an elephant in his own backyard, I need not worry. Anyway, they would pass the word around, and I could rest assured that I would be warned in plenty of time if inquiries were made. They would all help me to get my kit and ivory across the border if any move was made against me.

That was eminently satisfactory. I then put my problem to Joro: Should we make back into Rhodesia and get another rifle or should we try to bag another elephant or two with the little Martini? I explained the need for steel-jacketed bullets most carefully; but it was not easy to convince him. He had seen me use the Martini with great success on lion, and had I not killed the elephant with a single shot? There couldn't be much the matter with the little gun. Why not try again since we were here? Rhodesia—at least the towns—was a long way away; if our next attempt or two failed, then maybe it would be time to think of leaving. Well, that so exactly coincided with my own ideas that I did not need much persuading, though I was not any too sure of the wisdom of the gamble. I had no money, and the ivory, having been poached, would bring only about half its market value when I tried to sell it; but the tusks were good ones and the price of ivory well up so I figured I would get plenty to pay for a more suitable gun. However, I had not wanted to overrule my companion, and since he was keen to try again that was good enough for me.

Accordingly, when two days later a breathless and perspiring runner came tearing into camp early in the afternoon and gasped out that he had encountered a small party of elephant with one good bull among them, I immediately reached for the rifle. Our two trackers were visiting with us so there was no delay. As soon as the stranger had recovered his breath and had a drink of water, we set out. We had only about three miles to go, our new guide rushing us through the forest at a great pace. I did not really have time to get scared, although I again felt traces of that queasy feeling in the pit of my stomach; but it was considerably overshadowed this time by keen anticipation.

Long before I realized we had arrived our guide halted, pointed, and whispered excitedly: "There they are, *Bwana.* Look!"

Right at the edge of some old abandoned native lands were several huge gray shapes. They were moving like wraiths, slowly and soundlessly and apparently quite aimlessly, among the low secondary growth that had sprung up in the old gardens. I could see a cow with a calf about four feet high beside her, a young bull with tusks that could not have weighed more than about fifteen or sixteen pounds apiece, several other beasts that might have been either bulls or cows, I couldn't tell which, and that was all. Where was the big bull the runner said he had seen? I began to wonder if it had not existed in his imagination. But just as I was about to ask him he touched my shoulder and pointed up to my right. Sure enough, there, some little distance from the rest of the party, was another gray shape. It was standing motionless under a shady tree at the very edge of the forest and was much bigger than any of the others. A clump of bush between me and him prevented my seeing which way he was facing. All I could see was that he was end-on to me—even when a huge ear swung out and then back with a loud "flop" against his shoulder, I still could not tell. However, it didn't matter. The others were about fifty paces away, but this big fellow was fully sixty or seventy: it was necessary to get around to one side of him. I tapped my little tobacco bag and found that the gentle breeze was blowing across—entirely in our favor. We moved quietly up through the fringe of the forest to get broadside-on to the bull. We had no difficulty in doing so; but when I closed to within some fifteen paces I found that the trunk of the tree under which he was standing covered his shoulder and a good deal of his side. His head and tusks were exposed, as also were his hips; but they were no good to me. His fine tusks excited my cupidity, but it was no earthly use firing unless I could get a lung shot. And then, just as I was wondering if there were nothing I could do to move him slightly without stampeding him, he for no discernible reason took one step forward, nicely exposing the spot into which I wanted to slip my bullet.

I raised my rifle without undue haste, took a steady aim, and squeezed. Again I heard the "clup" of the bullet; and through the haze of smoke, which was not bad on this occasion, I saw the bull throw his trunk up over his head, rush forward, and then slew around and make for the forest. The cow with the young calf loosed a shrill trumpeting blast, and the lot of them broke into a run and made after their leader. For a moment or two there was considerable crashing of bush and sticks; and then suddenly there was silence—utter, absolute, complete silence.

All eyes were questioning me when I turned around. I grinned at them and told them that this fellow had gotten it exactly where the other one had. They each and all loosed a gasping breath of pent-up tension, and smiles broke out on their faces. The first bull had run some hundred and fifty yards after receiving the bullet and, as his spoor had shown, had then done quite a bit of staggering before falling. There was no reason to believe that this one would have run much farther. However, we found that he had covered fully two hundred and fifty yards, had then halted and, as it were, just lain down. The undergrowth was not so dense here, and we were able to see him when we were eighty or ninety paces away. He was lying down like a cow taking her ease and chewing the cud—he was not flat out. He gave vent to a deep groan as we came in sight of him, and when I was about forty paces away he heaved to his feet and stood broadside-on to me. I at once halted and gave him another bullet in the same place as the first one, but from the opposite side. He took not the slightest notice. Instantly reloading, I closed in until I had about halved the distance between us.

Kandikori and Mariko were greatly excited. "Shoot, *Bwana!* Shoot!" they kept repeating in hoarse whispers.

But I could not see any need to: I knew my two shots had been perfectly placed. That darned bull was dead on his feet—he must be. Otherwise, why had he halted? All the same, I gave him yet another which took him within two inches of the second one. At that, he swung his head slowly around until he was looking right at me but did not move his feet. For all the world it was as though he were saying: "Get on with it, man; what are you playing at? Finish the job!"

What more could I do? Had I had suitable bullets I would naturally have taken a brain shot; but that was out of the question with my lead slugs.

And then he began to sway. For several moments he swung drunkenly from side to side, then staggered heavily and flopped down into the same attitude he had been in when we first spotted him. Without warning he now keeled over on his side, his head hit the ground with a resounding thump, and he stretched out trembling. That was the end. No sooner had I realized it than I also started trembling. The relief was enormous: it was only now that I fully realized how great the tension had been. After all, he *might* have been capable of a charge when he heaved to his feet that time and took no notice of my second shot; and then, when he looked right at me barely twenty paces away and right out in the open—all the gold inlay in the world would not have helped my little Martini stop him had he come then. I had, of course, been fully aware of all that right along; but although I knew something of African game's remarkable tenacity to life, I could not get away from those two perfectly placed lung shots—they *must* kill. Both second and third, I am still convinced, were entirely needless; the first had mortally wounded him, otherwise he would not have pulled up so soon. It was quite in order to give him the second; the third was just a wasted shell.

But what did it matter? In those days shells were cheap enough. I felt Joro's hand squeeze my upper arm gently as he murmured: "And who said the little rifle was no good?"

It was certainly most gratifying; but I began to feel we were too close to that *boma* (official residence). I wanted to get farther out. The meat of these two elephant would be distributed throughout the district and inevitably the native police and messengers from the *boma* would get to know of it. I am a firm believer in riding my luck, but as we say in Eire and Australia, you can ride a good horse too hard. I then and there decided to make for the border as soon as the ivory had been chopped out and see if I couldn't get a more suitable rifle. Moreover, even if this official were a decent stick, there was no good in riding *him* too hard—and poaching his elephant within ten or twelve miles of his *boma* was really an insult.

2: RUMBLINGS OF THE STORM

Having disposed of my ivory at a far better price than I had expected or dared hope for, I then sold my burros—I had had far more than enough of them! I had left my tent and all other odds and ends with Kandikori, bringing along only my rifle and cooking pots in addition to the ivory. There was an old fellow living close by, I heard, who had done some hunting in days gone by: he might have a rifle for sale. Since I did not want to go all the way down to Salisbury if I could avoid it, I went to see him. This old chap said yes, he had done some hunting over the border long ago and had a double .600 which he would be glad to sell me. He admitted that he had long given up hope of ever being able to sell it because it had been a cheap-grade weapon to start with, was very heavy—eighteen pounds—and, worst of all, had developed the nasty habit of double-discharging: the firing of one barrel jarring the other off simultaneously. It was decent of him to tell me that because, having been brought up to be honest myself, I was still young enough to have the ingenuous belief that all other men were equally so. My long and intimate association with a raw, unspoiled "savage" from "Outside" had, of course, done nothing to shake that belief.

I was not particularly concerned by the report of the gun's double-discharging; I could always use it as a single-loader if I found it misbehaved (anyway, the old boy assured me that it didn't *always* happen). And, being a husky youngster, the thought of an eighteen-pound single-loader didn't worry me. So I made a deal and the .600 became mine. Now I felt I really was an elephant hunter. I could not picture any elephant wanting more than one of those great slugs, or at the most two. All the same, I had sense enough to realize that they would have to be placed in the right spot.

Since the gun was in a case, Joro carried it on his head with our two three-legged pots upside down on top of it, and I carried the Martini. Because we had no mokes this trip we were able to make good time and in a few days were back across the border again. We had no difficulty collecting all the porters we needed to carry our tent and kit, while our two old trackers were determined to come along with us no matter where we went. I presented Kandikori and Mariko with the blanket apiece they had asked me to buy for them and then, after the usual decent interval in which we all exchanged our news, they produced a disturbing piece of information. It appeared that the easygoing official had left and another man had been sent to take his place. This new incumbent was of a different caliber. He had arrived with a bad reputation from wherever he had previously been posted. Everybody disliked him, black and white; and he professed a hatred for Britishers. I did not consider myself a Britisher, but around this part of the world anybody who spoke English was automatically classed as British so that would be enough for him. I was advised to watch my step.

Well, this was all right, just so long as I knew. I had intended to get away from the immediate vicinity of the *boma* anyway. So we packed up and headed for a place where our guides assured us we would find plenty of elephant at that season. During the evening of the third day they told us we were there now and were making for the headman's kraal; but I decided it would be much better to have our own little camp someplace where stray travelers would not see us and spread the word around. Since nobody knew of a suitable spot we camped that first night at the headman's kraal, and he was able to suggest one of the finest camping sites imaginable, where a delicious little spring of pure sweet cold water gushed merrily out of the rocks at the foot of a small *kopje,* or hillock, and where there was a great wild fig tree that threw a deep cool shade all the year around. We moved out there next morning—it was about three miles away—after I had shot a kudu bull and divided the meat with the headman. Having pitched camp and had a feed, I sent all our carriers home. We did not need them any longer.

The headman had sent his son along with us to show us the elephant's favorite resorts. This was thanks to having Kandikori and Mariko, local men known to the headman, along with us. The fact that they were with us and could vouch for us established us with him.

I had great hopes of this place. We had passed abundant elephant signs, both when approaching the village and when coming out to where we were camped. Moreover, this forest was considerably more open than it had been where we shot the first elephant. We took a prowl around, our first afternoon, and spotted some very big pad marks. There were at least two really big bulls among the elephant that had been picnicking here for what must have been months, as we could judge from the quantity of old and fairly old spoor underlying recent droppings.

A lion paid us a visit that first night. I was fast asleep when Joro rolled over and put a hand on my shoulder. (We were sleeping in the open, not having bothered to pitch our little tent: there was small likelihood of rain at that season.) I was awake in an instant and, sure enough, even as my companion whispered "lion," I heard the singsong roar not far away. Presently it came again, and then again. It was obvious that the lion was heading our way. However, the chances were that he was only coming for a drink at the spring. From the very fact that he was roaring I knew there was little need to worry about him: it was in the last degree unlikely that he had any evil designs on us, even supposing he knew of our existence (You frequently read of the lion's "hunting roar" and it's a pity writers don't use a little common sense. The lion is no fool; he knows very well that he would go on mighty short rations if he advertised his presence by roaring when he was looking for a feed. You do not need to worry about the lion you hear; it's the one you *don't* hear that may cause you grief).

My loaded Martini was on the edge of the blanket beside me. The fire had died down to glowing embers. Joro shared my blanket, the two trackers were rolled up together on the opposite side of the fire, while the headman's son snored lustily on the third side. It did not seem necessary to awaken them.

The night was still and dark; there was no moon. Presently we heard a grunt and a low purr which seemed to come from the far side of the lower pool into which our stream ran. I could imagine the lion looking up and spotting us for the first time. I reached over and threw a few sticks on the fire. It blazed up, and again there came a low purr from out of the darkness beyond. Then for what seemed a long time there was no sound. I could picture the big cat standing there gazing toward us in mild curiosity, with that steady, wide-eyed, unwinking stare so characteristic of his species. Then we heard him lapping up the water, with evident enjoyment. A deep sigh told us when he was finished—it was exactly the kind of long-drawn sigh you will hear a child give after a long draught of milk. Again there was a spell of silence; and then once more the lion gave his singsong roar as he wandered away. Each succeeding roar was fainter as the distance increased. My companion and I went back to sleep.

The birds had scarcely got the sleep out of their eyes when Joro woke the fire to life and put our coffee on. I wiped the oil out of the .600 and assembled it, and we started out as soon as it was light enough to see spoor. We had not gone half a mile before we struck fresh elephant droppings— so fresh that they were still moist and almost steaming. Kandikori rolled one over with his foot and, sticking his bare toes into it, told us it was hot and that therefore the elephant must be very close. Since the droppings were in a heap it was clear that the elephant had stopped to relieve himself. Therefore he was in no particular hurry. It was heavy forest we were in, but the trees were not too close together and the clumps of undergrowth, though big, were quite well separated. It looked like fairly easy hunting country, the main difficulty being that my quarry might take it into his head to force his way into a clump with a clear space in the center big enough for him but not for me to share it with him. Still, there would be time enough to cross that bridge when I came to it. On account of these clumps of bushes visibility was limited to some twenty-five or thirty yards on the average, although there were occasional vistas perhaps three hundred yards long. There was a fair amount of long grass, about five feet high, wherever there was a clearing in the forest.

We had been about an hour on the spoor before we came near the big fellow, and it was not until he moved that I saw him. He had been plastering himself with red mud until he looked like a large anthill. He was sixty or seventy paces away and was just moving behind one of the clumps of undergrowth, which concealed him. With both barrels of the .600 loaded I advanced toward the bush and edged around the corner he had just passed. The clump was not quite so clearly defined as most of the others had been, and there were quite a number of thorny bushes straying out from it on my side. I wormed my way among these, and remember Joro's reaching past my shoulder to help free me from a thorny branch which had taken firm hold of my upper arm. That done, I looked about me and there was my bull about fifteen paces away and right in front of me. I could only see his backside, which had not had its share of red mud: it looked for all the world like that of an old man wearing a very baggy pair of gray pants with the seat hanging down around the back of his knees. There is nothing imposing about an elephant's stern, but I had no confidence in letting rip at it. However, I could not get along on his left because he was too close to the bush, and I did not fancy attempting to get around on his right as that would take me out into the open. There he would probably see me and move off before I could get a sure shot. It seemed best just to wait for him to turn. I had not yet learned how to attract an elephant's attention without scaring him, getting him to turn so as to expose the shot wanted. That was to come later. What little breeze there was today was entirely favorable, so it was merely a question of patience. I knew the beast would turn eventually—it was too early for his midday siesta. The only gamble was whether or not he would give me a fair chance at him. But there did not seem to be anything I could do about it. Luckily, I was so keen to see how he would react to the big heavy slug from the .600 that I had forgotten to be scared. And then, entirely fortuitously, I learned one of the ways in which an elephant can be turned: Because I had stopped immediately after passing through the thorn bushes, I had not left sufficient room for Joro to stand comfortably. (I ought to have taken one more pace forward.) And, in trying to free himself from the grip of an affectionate thorn branch, my companion stepped on a dry twig, which cracked sharply.

The bull's huge ears swung out till they stood at right angles to his head —he was listening. Then, slowly, ponderously, and in absolute silence, he came around. I was all set and ready for him. I had decided to take the brain shot, so when he exposed his broadside I had my sights lined up. I squeezed my front trigger. There came a thunderous, crashing roar like the last crack of doom: the rifle leaped out of my hands, and I was knocked flying backward into Joro and the thorn bushes. It was as though I had strayed onto the railroad tracks and been hit by a ninety-mile-an-hour express. The pair of us scrambled out of the bushes with eyes like saucers—at least Joro's were, and I don't mind betting mine were also— and looked at each other to see if we were still all in one piece. Then as one man we looked across to see what had happened to the elephant. He was taking no interest in the proceedings. Nevertheless, before attempting to approach I looked around to see where my rifle had gone. I could not find it at first. Then one of our trackers came up with it and told us it had come sailing over the bushes. They had not been able to see what had happened, and at first thought that the elephant must have got hold of it and thrown it away.

I did not have to open it to see that I had had a double discharge. Both barrels had gone off together. I reloaded the right barrel and made up my mind that in the future I would load it only. We then closed in to examine our elephant. That bull must have been literally blown off his feet. I had shot him on his right side and he was flat out on his left. Animals, particularly elephant, almost always fall on the side on which they have been hit; but as I say, this big fellow was down on the other side. He was as dead as a canned lobster, and all hands were satisfied that this was a sure-enough elephant gun.

The experience with the big gun did not worry me. It had not hurt me, and once I had explained to Joro why it had knocked us both down, he was satisfied. At first he had been a bit upset, figuring I could not continue using a weapon that sent us flying every time I fired it—though in view of the grand way it had flattened that big bull it would have been a pity if I had had to discard it so soon.

The headman's son hit the trail for home to tell his folks of the kill; but as it was still early I suggested we take a circular prowl around to see if we could not find any more Jumbo. We found plenty of spoor, but nothing fresh enough to justify following. However, late that evening, when we were taking things easy in our pleasant shady camp, we heard unmistakable elephant noises close by. There was a deep rumbling which, if you have ever heard it, you can never mistake—the intestinal rumbling of an elephant's stomach—followed by a shrill scream as some peevish cow chastised her youngster. I grabbed the .600, hurriedly wiped the oil out of it, and loaded the right barrel.

We found a party of cows and calves with a few immature bulls among them. There was nothing worth shooting. I stood watching them for a while as they fed. Presently Joro put his hand on my shoulder and pointed beyond the herd and slightly to the left. From where I stood I could not see what he had seen, so he drew me a little to one side and whispered that there were two or three bigger bulls beyond the herd standing by themselves under a shady tree. I gradually got to know that this is quite common, the old men liking to get away from the noisy cows and youngsters. Having tested the wind, we moved around the herd and commenced to close in on the three bulls. The approach was easy, and I took up a position by a convenient tree against which I could lean with my shoulder in order to ensure a steady shot and whence I had a clear view of the biggest of the three males. I had the usual two spare shells sticking out from between the fingers of my left hand where they would be immediately convenient for reloading. Had I had the use of both barrels I felt sure I could have got a right and left here; but I was afraid to load the left one. Leaning easily against the tree I now took steady aim for the big leader. He collapsed instantly as I fired, and I immediately reloaded. His two big companions had thrown up their trunks and swung around: one was facing slightly away from me, the other directly toward me, his ears out and his trunk over his head testing the wind. I shot him at the base of the throat, almost in the center of his great chest. His hindquarters gave way, followed almost immediately by his knees, and he remained in a kneeling position while I reloaded. The third big bull was swinging around in an undecided manner as though unable to make up his mind whether to run or not. I was hoping to get a shot at him also; but suddenly Joro drew my attention to the cows—I had completely forgotten them! They were clustered together, all facing toward us with their ears out; but there was one big old girl coming slowly toward us with her ears back. It looked for all the world as though she were tiptoeing into position behind us. I did not like the look of her at all, or the deliberate manner in which she was approaching. Had she had her ears out it might just have been curiosity; but those ears back gave her a very vicious appearance. Subsequent experience convinces me that she was, indeed, going to charge; but at the time I could only guess. She was about seventeen or eighteen paces away when I first saw her, but was now barely ten or eleven. It was too close to be pleasant. My companion whispered to me to shoot, and I considered it good advice. I let her have it between the eyes and she dropped instantly. That finished matters. The third bull decided he knew of a healthier spot and departed, the remainder of the herd going after him.

This was a great beginning, and I certainly was glad I had gone back that time to get a more suitable rifle than the little Martini.

We had an easy time during the next three or four days while the carcasses were being butchered and the ivory chopped out. We just loafed around in the shade, and yarned, and discussed life as viewed through African eyes. Civilization and the rest of the world seemed very far away, and I was quite satisfied that it should be so.

And then, late on the evening of the fourth day, after the last of the ivory had been brought in, came more disquieting news: some dog of a native policeman whom the new official had brought with him, a stranger around these parts and belonging to a different tribe, had been nosing around and had spotted the great quantities of meat everybody had. He had gone back and reported it to his boss, who thereupon had flown into a rage, vowed he would put a stop to this poaching, yelled for his *machila*,* and started out to scour his district. If he had a relay of *machila* boys, as he probably had, he could cover a very considerable amount of ground in a day. But he would stick to the *machila* paths—the forerunners of the motor roads that were to come—so that there was not much fear of his grabbing me provided I had warning of his approach. If he came on more freshly killed meat in the local kraals, though, he might be capable of roping in some of the owners of it and forcing them to tell him where they got it. As I was later to learn, once these "Outside" natives have thrown in their lot with you they will not betray you even to save their own hides; but naturally that does not apply to everybody in the kraals and villages, some of whom may never have seen you. Besides, if this fellow had a bad name it was quite possibly because he was given to roping in, not the men, but the women, and scaring them with threats of what would happen to them if they refused to talk. (The African does not like his womenfolk interfered with, and it was precisely such interference that had been responsible for most of the native uprisings that had taken place. I am glad to be able to say that the type of official employed by the Portuguese nowadays is of a very much better type than formerly. The advent of the automobile had a great deal to do with it.)

So, what with one thing and another, I decided to move farther out. I was certainly sorry to leave our pleasant little camp; but that is the way it goes. You will never make a success of your elephant hunting if you think

* A hammock slung on a pole. There is an awning over it to keep the sun off the lordly occupant, who sleeps while being carried at a run by four men.

only of camp comfort. Again there was no difficulty in finding willing volunteers to tote our small loads, and off we went. At our new camp I killed another three or four elephant and then moved on again.

I had by this time come about two thirds of the way along the third side of a big triangle and was again within about ten or a dozen miles of the border, and perhaps twenty or twenty-five from the *boma*. As was now my custom, I was camped in the bush and not in or near any kraal. I had killed a good bull a couple of days previously. There did not seem to be many elephant right here at this season, and I was determined to clear out as soon as the ivory was brought in and I had collected sufficient porters to bring it over the border. I had more or less forgotten the *boma* fellow, having been pretty constantly on the move and not having heard anything further about him. Then, on the night of the day prior to my departure, the porters having promised to be along at daybreak or a little after, a native policeman suddenly appeared. I grabbed the little Martini—I certainly wasn't leaving that behind, though I did not mind so much about the .600, but Joro snatched it up too—and got ready to make a break, naturally assuming that we had been surrounded. But the police boy, who I could see was out of breath and excited, said it was all right, that he was alone. So I sat down again, keeping the loaded carbine across my knees. The fellow—he was very young—told us that the foreign policeman had been nosing around pretty constantly, hoping to curry favor, and had heard that I was back again but was not quite sure where. However, the meat of this last elephant would undoubtedly give me away, and, indeed the *Chefe,* with his entire gang of cops, was expected around these parts next day. The police boy told us that he had a brother out this way and knew all about me, but had pleaded ignorance. He had slipped away and come to warn me. Was there anything else he could do?

I told him I should be mighty grateful if he would pass the word around the kraal where my promised porters were sleeping and tell them that they must not wait for daybreak but must be out here and ready to move off at crowpee. He promised to do that; and he kept his promise.

There was nothing I could give him by way of reward, and when I expressed my regret for this he replied that he was not looking for any reward. Thereupon he faded into the night. I am glad to remember that I met up with him long years afterward and was able to show my gratitude.

My porters arrived when it was still dark, with just the merest trace of gray showing through the trunks of the trees on the eastern horizon. Ten minutes later we were wending our way, with the ivory, through the forest.

3: WESTWARD AND A PARTING

I sold our ivory to the same trader who had bought the first lot and then looked around for a new battery of rifles. I had seen that my companion Joro's thoughts had been turning more and more toward his home. After all, he had been with me a long time now and had never previously been away except for short periods. He had made no suggestion himself. In spite of that—or possibly because of it—I felt that it was up to me to do the decent thing. But I said nothing about it until after I had bought the rifles and laid in a stock of ammunition for both weapons. Then I suggested that we head for his part of the country so that he could have a visit home. The way his face lit up showed me that I had done the right thing.

It was my intention to have a look at that bit of no man's land known as the Kaprivi Strip. It is shaped like an isosceles triangle with its base on the west coast and its apex running up to Barotseland. It divided Angola, Portuguese West Africa, from what used to be German Southwest and, at any rate in the days of which I write, really belonged to no one. At one time it had had the name of being an excellent place for poachers because of the numerous borders and frontiers that all met at its apex. Except that there were never so many elephant there, it was not unlike the Lado Enclave on the western border of Uganda in the days when it belonged to no one. The customary way of getting there was by ox wagon across the Kalahari Desert from some such place as Palapwe in Bechuanaland. I could not possibly rise to such an outfit. But I reckoned I could get there by canoeing up the Zambezi again and then cutting across a corner of either Barotseland or Angola. The only snag was that neither of us spoke any of the languages we would meet out there, knew nothing of what tribes there were or what chance we would have of being able to pick up porters to handle our ivory, and had no idea where we would find a market for such ivory as we got. Still, those were problems that could wait. And, like so many of the bridges that people worry themselves to death trying to cross before they reach them, we experienced no difficulty whatsoever when we actually came to set foot on them.

We were given a great reception when we arrived at my companion's home. His family had decided he must be dead, for it had been so long since they had seen him. (It had not been possible for me to write them any news because none of them could read, nor was there a post office anywhere around.) He had a fine time now telling them all his news and adventures. They were amazed at the extent of his wanderings, though they could not grasp the distances covered. He had bought all of them presents in Bulawayo when I told him we were coming—not one of them had been forgotten. His unheralded return, laden with parcels, was like a visit from Santa Claus, and I think he got as much pleasure out of distributing his gifts as the recipients did out of receiving them.

We stayed for nearly three months. His family just would not let him leave sooner, and it would not have been fair to ask him to. As for me, all places are home to me—wherever I happen to be, that is home for the time being. Naturally, we had no difficulty getting a canoe here, as well as a multitude of volunteers to paddle it, and we took a few of these fellows to carry our kit on our next expedition in the west.

We started hunting in Angola and met another poacher on the border, a Portuguese half-breed named Antonio who spoke a little French and German as well as Portuguese and a smattering of English. Joro—like all Africans, a superlative linguist, at least where African languages and dialects are concerned—and this fellow between them soon helped me to a working knowledge of the local dialects. Antonio had been poaching all his life and knew the best elephant districts on both sides of the border; furthermore, there was a friend of his to whom he introduced me who was running a trading store in which Antonio had an interest, and this man bought all my ivory, cheating me no more than was reasonable.

I don't seem to remember any outstanding incident that occurred during that expedition. The fairly easy conditions under which most of the elephant were found, and the thoroughly suitable choice of rifles I had, made things pretty straightforward. Since Antonio knew the ropes and we were far from civilization, I had no trouble with the authorities. So the best part of a year passed before we returned to my companion's home. This time I was not looking forward to it. I could clearly see that the eastern side of the continent was where I would be in the future. It would not be right to take Joro so far away with me for so long—possibly for ever. That he would come, I had no doubt; but—well, maybe I was just a fool. He was a wealthy man now, as wealth goes among Africans. We had shared everything right from the beginning, the easy times with the hard, the good days with the lean ones, so I had come to look upon him as my partner. And the word partner has but one definition for me, consequently I had set aside for him an equal share in whatever profits we had made. He didn't know that until we parted. Never once had money been mentioned between us; but he could now get himself a herd of cattle or goats, take several wives if he wanted them, and live as his fathers had lived since the world began. There was little likelihood of civilization's encroaching on his territory, at any rate not during his lifetime.

After my settlement with Joro and my farewells to his family I prepared to leave the next morning at daybreak. There was a canoe waiting. Joro came with me until we were in sight of the canoe, then he halted, we faced each other, and he said his farewells. He said them without words. He raised his hands, placed them on my shoulders, and looked deep into my eyes. My hands were on his shoulders and I looked back at him. For long and long we stood like that; and then without a backward glance he was gone. I never saw him again. I remember I blew my nose loudly and stumbled a bit as I made my way to the canoe. There seemed to be a slight mist in front of my eyes and I couldn't see too well.

Back again in Portuguese East I decided the wisest thing I could do was to enter the territory officially and make it my base. I would then be able to hunt the Portuguese elephant legally and have the three British frontiers—the Rhodesias and Nyasaland, to say nothing of Tanganyika if I made my way as far north as that—over which to poach if I were not satisfied with the number of elephant allowed on my license. There were no difficulties in entering Portuguese territory in those days, so I complied with all the necessary formalities and became a resident. This was certainly wise, for had I antagonized the Portuguese I would have been very much of an outlaw in that I never had permission to be in any of the surrounding British territories (and up to now had had no right to be in Portuguese territory either).

It was here in Tete on the Zambezi that I was given my first native name, Chimpondoro. The African is very observant and instantly spots any outstanding feature of a strange white man with whom he comes in contact. It is thereupon mentioned in conversation and those who hear generally realize how appropriate it is. It is used from then on when referring to the stranger either because his real name may not be known, or because it is often well to keep the exalted white from knowing he is the subject of conversation. *Pondoro* in the Chinyungwe dialect means "lion"; the prefix *Chi* refers to some attribute of the name to which it is attached. In this case the full name *Chimpondoro* (the "m" being inserted for euphony) means either "the lionlike one" or "the roaring of the lion." As the years rolled by the prefix dropped off and I became simply Pondoro. However, I did not acquire this distinction until I returned to Tete on this my second visit.

I met a most conscienceless poacher and gunrunner at this time: a big Dutchman, an Afrikaner, who did his best to get me to join him. He offered to pay all my expenses, supply me with what porters and kit I wanted, and whatever guns. I in return was to give him one tusk of every elephant I shot, keeping the other for myself. But I turned him down. He did no hunting himself, admitting he was afraid of elephant. Instead, he got hold of native hunters and gave them Mauser rifles, telling them to go shoot him so many elephant and use the remaining shells themselves. Then, when they brought him the tusks and the rifles, he would ask them if they would like to keep the rifles. Naturally they said yes. So he would dole them out more ammunition, tell them to shoot him so many more elephant, and they could keep the rifles. Thereafter, whenever they wanted more ammo, he would supply it in exchange for so many elephant. He had been carrying on this racket for years before the authorities got wind of it. He took flight eventually but they found some sixty-odd Mauser rifles scattered through the district: hidden in ant bear holes, in hollow trees, stuck up in the thatch of huts, and similar places; and they figured they had missed as many more.

I cleared out of that district, for I found there were altogether too many pricked and wounded elephant wandering around; in addition, all elephant were constantly on the alert owing to the extent to which they had been shot up by this army of partially trained hunters. That kind of poaching does not appeal to me at all. The Dutchman was just making a business of it. Money as such has never mattered too much to me: just so long as I can keep my spare ammunition bag well filled, and cover expenses, I am quite content.

But things began to go wrong now. I became restless and irritable. I could not settle down and stay put, even when there were plenty of elephant around. I had to keep going, I had to see what was on the farther side of those hills, I would leave the elephant here to go look for others. My men must have thought I was crazy, and I guess they were not far wrong. The fact of the matter is I was lonesome. I missed Joro. Several times I was tempted to go get him—maybe I was foolish not to, but I didn't. I started to drink too much, something I had never done. But then I had never felt lonesome before. I had not realized just how fond I had grown of that constant companion of mine. And then one day I was nearly killed by an elephant I wounded when half-tight—that shook me badly.

I decided that a complete change of scene was indicated. If I did not pull myself together, I would never make an elephant hunter—even if I survived. The best thing I could do was to get away for a spell. So I sold pretty nearly everything and sailed for Australia, where I stayed for some months.

Back once more in Portuguese East I found myself keener than ever on hunting. There were few of the better elephant territories in central, eastern, and southeast-central Africa that I did not visit during this period. I was constantly on the move, never remaining long in one part, which doubtless had much to do with the fact that I was never caught, for word of my activities could scarcely reach official ears before I was gone. It might be asked why I allowed local natives to take the elephant meat and distribute it far and wide when I knew it would sooner or later give me away. The reason is that in the first place it would be difficult to prevent them if one were shooting many elephant; but far more important is keeping their good will. A hunter certainly will not gain that if he refuses them meat. I am perfectly certain I would be behind bars if it were not for the good name I have among the numerous tribes in whose districts I have hunted. I knew three or four men who tried poaching and decided to stop the locals from taking meat. They would put a handful of white powder into a carcass and say it was poison, that anyone attempting to eat the meat would die in agony. The natives know that many men carry strychnine and arsenic with which to poison man-eaters and cattle-killers, hyenas, baboons, and similar varmints, and that these are both white powders. Therefore they were afraid to eat the meat. Quite possibly it was only salt the men used; but the effect was the same. And so was the result! None of these poachers lasted long. Two of them were caught, had their rifles confiscated, and were heavily fined, and at least one of the two had a lengthy prison sentence as well; the third managed to get clear but lost all his rifles and equipment; and I forget what happened to the fourth. So what did they gain? Moreover, if you are convicted of elephant poaching on a large scale, you will not be granted a hunting license for many years afterward, if ever.

It might legitimately be asked: How can I justify more than thirty years of fairly continuous poaching of elephant? The answer is that I personally consider the African infinitely more important in the general scheme of things than any elephant. I have always believed my poaching fully justified because of the benefit it conferred on the local natives, both directly and indirectly. I shall be saying more about this later, but would ask you to bear it in mind as you read on and not condemn me too soon.

I am now going to describe a raid into Southern Tanganyika, across the Rovuma, which can only be described as a piece of pure devilment. There were plenty of elephant on my side of the river. There was absolutely no necessity for me to cross into British territory. But I had a notion to indulge in the time-honored pastime of tweeking the lion's tail. Besides, the Elephant Control Scheme had been in force for several years in

Tanganyika, as a result of which vast numbers of elephant which previously had raided the crops to the north now came south over the Rovuma and raided to their hearts' content down there.

I had persuaded a friend, Sherif, an African-Arab and the world's champion smuggler, to bring his dhow into the mouth of the Rovuma to insure a clean getaway with my ivory—just in case. He had taken on board all the ivory I had collected over quite a considerable period on more or less legitimate hunting. Now, with his dhow tied up in a backwater and well camouflaged, he was to act as my base during the raid.

The British Elephant Control Scheme consisted of a few white hunters supervising an army of well-trained native hunters who did most of the actual work. Their job was to shoot any and all elephant that broke out of the huge elephant reserve to raid the natives' food and cotton crops. They operated from the north through the northwest to the west; but the Rovuma, the territorial frontier between Tanganyika and Portuguese East, also formed the southern boundary of the reserve. Since elephant learn quick where they may go in safety and where it is dangerous the British were soon congratulating themselves over the success of their control of the raiders. But all this simply meant that many hundreds if not thousands of elephant which formerly had raided to the north and around there now came south over the river and raided on our side. True, elephant always had crossed and recrossed the Rovuma; but their numbers were now considerably augmented. The Portuguese in those days were poor and had neither the men nor the money to organize a similar control scheme on their side of the border. And so the unfortunate natives on the Portuguese side had to suffer.

Since all natives who had previously lived in what was to become the reserve had been removed by the British when it was made a reserve, a poacher had to carry with him all the food that he and his men might require. And since porters must naturally eat their share of what they are carrying, my method was to have a string of porters bring all the food I and my "flying squad" would want for, say, ten days or so, dump it in a place I had chosen for a bivouac for the period in question, and return to base. After the stipulated time they would come back to where they had left us, bringing more food, and would take away all ivory shot during their absence. I would then move out another ten or fifteen or twenty miles to another center around which to shoot, and that is where the men would come with supplies next time. Depending on the conditions, it might be a week's or a month's supplies they brought; but when poaching in some pet reserve, I liked the men to return at not-too-distant intervals so as to make sure I would get a fair share of whatever ivory I shot. Otherwise I might have to leave in a hurry, abandoning all the fruits of perhaps a month's hunting. (Although as a matter of fact I have never yet had to do that.) My flying squad consisted of half-a-dozen specially picked men, all young, strong fellows, tough and fit and game for anything. I never loaded these men heavily, so we could and frequently did cover our thirty, thirty-five, and forty miles a day, sometimes for days and days on end.

Naturally, the *Seagull,* Sherif's dhow, was tied up on the Portuguese side of the river, and his men took my heroes and me across in the ship's boats under cover of the friendly night. I bagged my first two elephant, big bulls, scarcely more than an hour after daybreak. Having had a light feed—what might be called brunch—I was taking a prowl around to see something of the country when I heard an elephant's ears flop against his shoulders. We made quietly for the place from which the sound had come. What little breeze there was was favorable, so the approach was easy, and we soon saw two big fellows resting under a fine shady tree which stood by itself. They were standing cheek by jowl, facing in opposite directions, and were about thirty-five yards away when I first spotted them. I closed to within about twenty paces, moving up a bit to my right so I might get them broadside-on. I could see that if I dropped the nearer with a bullet in the brain I could expect to get my second barrel into the other one's shoulder or heart or lungs before he could slew around: because of the tree immediately beyond his head he would have to draw back a step before he could turn. I walked up to a convenient tree and leaned my shoulder against it as I raised my rifle.

The nearer bull dropped instantly to the shot and never budged again. His companion threw his trunk up over his head in alarm and drew back a step as I swung on him. Momentarily he paused, just as my sights were in the act of passing his ear hole. Instantly I checked and snapped off the shot. And this big fellow flopped in his tracks to lie with his forehead within about a foot of the first one's. (Why do so many writers speak of their elephant falling "with a crash like thunder" or "with a crash that shook the ground" or "like a ton of bricks"? Far more often than not you hear nothing at all when the elephant falls instantly to a brain shot. If you are very close you *may* hear a kind of soft soggy flop like a wet bag hitting the ground, and just occasionally, very occasionally, you may hear a dull thump if the head hits a rock. But there is nothing resembling thunder or tons of bricks! Certainly, if an elephant falls in thick cover you will hear the crash of breaking bush and sticks, and now and then a sharp splintering report of a young tree being broken by the fall; but there is nothing remotely like thunder about it.)

The following morning I bagged three bulls out of a fairly big troop; and that evening got another lone bull. The next day I bagged two: one in the morning and the other in the afternoon. Not a day went by there but I added to my bag. It was all perfectly straightforward hunting in by no means difficult country. We left the elephant lying where they fell, merely cutting off the tails in the customary manner to enable us to keep a certain count of them. Tusks can usually be pulled out by hand four or five days after death, and this is by far the best way of getting them out since there is then no fear of damaging them, which often happens when they are chopped out with axes. When our porters arrived we pushed on another ten to twelve miles and shot around there. Water had to be considered and was not always easy to find. But if you do not stay too long in one place and are not too particular, you can manage with a very small water hole or reservoir for rain water, such as a puddle, hole in a rock, or hollow tree. A few drowned bees and insects in it needn't worry you, and won't if you're thirsty.

One incident that occurred during this raid of mine is worth detailing because it illustrates one of the principal dangers connected with the hunting of mixed herds in close cover. I had been following the spoor of a family party of elephant into a patch of dense bush. It was, as I say, a mixed group, but there was one really good bull among them. I had a great deal of trouble getting into position. The troop had halted and some of the younger members persisted in wandering around, so there was considerable risk of their getting my wind and giving the alarm. Moreover, at least two of the cows had very young calves and would be dangerous to approach, for they would be likely to attack if they discovered me right alongside them. But I wanted that big fellow. The difficulty was to find him in the tangle of bush. I guessed he would be well away from the vicinity of the rest of them for the sake of peace and quiet; but I had to be careful lest I give my wind to the others. After about twenty anxious minutes, during which I was several times so close to elephant that I could have touched them with the outstretched muzzles of my rifle, I finally managed to get a clear view of the big bull. When I say "clear view" you must not picture him standing out in the open: "clear view" to me under such circumstances simply meant that I could distinguish that it was indeed the bull I wanted, and that there was a small gap in the bush and leaves perhaps six or eight inches in diameter through which I could slip my bullet into a vital spot. But while I was maneuvering into a position from which to take my shot I naturally lost touch with the other members of the herd. I could hear some of them: either the rumbling of their digestions, the flop of their ears, or the swish of branches and leaves as they fed; but I could not possibly place them all. The result of this was, as I was presently to discover, that one of the older cows had moved up silently beside me on the other side of a thick bush—or maybe she had been there right along without my being able to see her. At any rate, I brought the bull down with a bullet in the brain, and on the heels of my shot this old cow loosed a shrill screaming trumpet blast that quite literally made my hair stand on end. The sound seemed to come from right over my head. I looked up, and there, sure enough, were her tusks and trunk practically over my right shoulder. I wheeled half around, throwing my right leg well behind me to take my weight as I leaned backward, and blazed upward at the underside of the cow's face. I then threw myself bodily backward into the bush, fearing that the cow might fall on top of me. She dropped to her knees, and the density of the bush took my weight without letting me fall. Its resilience threw me back onto my feet again so that I could have kicked the old cow in the face as I passed her. But I wasn't thinking of kicks right then. My stouthearted gunbearer was holding my second rifle out to me even as I recovered my balance. I grabbed it, wheeled, and was just in time to slam another bullet into the cow's face as she scrambled to her feet and made a vicious lunge at me. There was no time to aim; besides, she was much too close for a brain shot. But the heavy bullet brought her down and I finished her off with my left barrel before she could do anything more. It was just about as close as you could wish.

Many a hunter has been killed or badly mauled by cows under exactly similar circumstances: I myself know four and have heard and read of others. It was the first time I remember being so attacked, but it was not the last. The lesson to be learned is that you have a much better chance of coming out of the encounter with a whole skin if you have armed yourself with a double rifle rather than a magazine. There is rarely time to reload from a magazine before the cow is upon you.

That was the only outstanding incident of the raid. I found that the elephant there were not on the alert and frequently just stood in complete bewilderment when I opened fire. I had the impression that they could not believe their eyes or ears when they heard the firing and saw their companions dropping—here, in the very heart of their sanctuary! It couldn't be true! I'm sure I could have killed double the number I actually shot; but although I have killed many elephant in my time, I am not a wanton slaughterer. I know I passed up many a shot I might have taken; with so many really big tuskers around I let the smaller and medium-sized ones alone, even though they were in many cases well worth shooting. And the cow mentioned was the only cow I shot, nor would I have killed her had she not forced me to.

It is possible that you who are reading, being an upright, law-abiding citizen, may feel outraged at my recollections of breaking into a jealously guarded game reserve and shooting the occupants. But then it is highly improbable that you have seen the effects of famine caused solely through the depredations of elephant and buffalo. I have. The famine itself is bad enough in all conscience; but don't forget the aftereffects. Those doctors who study such matters will tell you that the evil results of serious famine will be apparent, not only throughout the remainder of the sufferers' lives, but into the next generation of natives also. Nobody has a greater admiration than I have for the work done by the elephant control staffs of Uganda and Tanganyika. I have written several appreciative articles about them for British journals; but the point to be borne in mind is that elephant numbers are increasing to an enormous extent as a direct result of control. And those elephant don't remain peacefully in reserves all the year round. They break out and go raiding wherever they think they can get away with it. Nothing is ever mentioned about what happens when a reserve abuts on a territorial frontier in which there is no control, but I have seen what happens. And although I am mighty fond of those big gray ghosts of the forest, as I look at it man, be he black, white, brown, or brindled, is deserving of greater consideration than elephant.

4: SOME UNUSUAL EXPERIENCES WITH ELEPHANT

IN CAMP

ANGONILAND, PORTUGUESE EAST AFRICA

Curious set of coincidences today. My permit to kill five bulls arrived while I was actually killing them. I reached there only just in time to save a party from their attack—and it developed the individuals saved were old friends whom I hadn't seen for many years, and then it was on the other side of the world. Furthermore, I just happened to be armed with a powerful rifle when I most needed it, although I had recently been trying out light calibers. There! Can the fictionists beat that?

The above extract from one of my old diaries (by now I was keeping a notebook in which I jotted down happenings of interest) recalls an interesting day. In accordance with my now invariable custom I had taken out permits for Portuguese territory. Each of these allowed me to shoot five bull elephant and I could take out only one permit at a time. However, there was never any difficulty in getting another, so I just continued hunting and sending my runners in for fresh ones as I needed them. I had already exhausted two and had dispatched my men for a fourth while I still had two elephant left on the third.

This part of Angoniland consists of fairly abruptly undulating high veld with low hills here and there, the lot covered with light open forest and short grass. But there are open places called *dambos* in which the grass grows ten to twelve feet long. Because of the general openness of the forest I decided this was a splendid opportunity for trying out several medium- and small-bore rifles, which I had been using almost exclusively for the past couple of months or so. But on this particular day for some reason I took my double .577 along. I do not claim that I had a hunch—I don't know why I did it. But as it transpired it was a good thing I had the .577. I could never have done the work called for with any of the light Mausers with which I had been experimenting. I had to have power and plenty of it.

Having killed the two elephant remaining on my third permit, I ought, I suppose, to have waited for the new form to arrive before killing more; but I was confident it would come in due course, so after a day's rest I went out again. It was on this day I took the .577 along. It hadn't been out of its case for a couple of months.

I soon picked up the spoor of five bulls that had been nosing around a banana grove belonging to the kraal near which I was camped. The grove was now a shambles. The spoor showed that two of the elephant were snorters, the third a really good one, and the other two somewhat smaller but quite shootable if their ivory was all right. It can be cold up there on the high veld at night and for an hour or two after the sun is up, and my quarry were in no mood to halt. I followed them for several hours as they led me around in a great semicircle, back past my camp but about a mile from it. I was close behind them and several times climbed anthills to look ahead over the grass, which was fairly long most of the time. Each time I saw five great shapes moving slowly and silently along. I could not make out their legs in the grass, and they seemed to be floating rather than walking, quite effortlessly, like five large puffs of smoke. I kept on hoping they would halt, even for a few minutes, and give me a chance to get up alongside—I was seldom more than fifty to seventy yards behind them—but halt they would not.

And then suddenly I heard it—of all sounds probably the most unexpected—the sound of an automobile motor revving frantically in some intermediate gear. In those days there were no roads through that district and so, of course, no cars; but a road *had* been promised, and trees cut down the preceding year. When the rains began work was abandoned, so the grass had grown up again. Apparently, someone was now trying to drive on this rough grassy track. Immediately after the noise of the motor I heard another sound—and there is no mistaking it if you have ever heard it: the succession of deep throaty roars loosed by a charging bull elephant that really means business. I had been told that elephant were known to attack cars when they were unexpectedly encountered and if they were not accustomed to them, but I had never come across an authentic case of this. However, that elephant was certainly charging something. I had closed up till I was only twenty-five or thirty yards behind the hindermost bull and now rushed ahead hoping that I would be in time to stop the slaughter. Suddenly I found myself on what was to be the new road and saw the sterns of the five elephant. The two big leaders had their ears swung out, as bull elephant almost always carry them when charging, but the other three hadn't. It was apparent that only one or at the most two of them were actually charging, the others merely following to see the fun. The leaders were so big that I was able to aim over their companions for their spines just above the root of the tail, in order to anchor them. I threw up the .577 and took as quick a right and left as I could remember ever taking, even at birds. The biggest of the five, slightly in front of his companion, just halted and stood there with his hind legs wide apart. The other's hindquarters gave out and he squatted in the center of the road like a huge hog. The remaining three elephant at once swung around to face me. I had just completed reloading when the biggest of the three caught sight of me and promptly charged. I certainly didn't expect that. The two smaller ones came with him, but I don't think they had any evil intent—at any rate, they weren't roaring as he was. My heavy bullet took him between the eyes and he was dead before he hit the ground. The other two halted. One, with ears out and trunk up, faced me, the other swung around sideways in indecision. I shot the one facing me in the center of his great chest and quickly reloaded one barrel. As the last of them was broadside-on to me I took a brain shot and brought him down so that he lay almost on top of the other two. Again reloading I hastened up alongside the two leaders, as I did not know how permanently they were anchored. The biggest was still standing there quite quietly. He looked calmly at me when I came up alongside him about ten or twelve paces away. He seemed to be saying, "Okay, brother, you've won; get on with it." But the other was yelling furiously and struggling to get to his feet. The din was terrific. He made a savage lunge at me—I was almost within trunk reach—when I finished off his mate; and another shot gave him his quietus.

I then had time to look for the cause of all this commotion. It was in the shape of a sedan car only the upper portion of which was visible above the grass. The motor was stalled and the travelers were pretty well imprisoned in the thing because of the amount of baggage they had all over the place: jammed between mudguards and hood, all along the offside running board, and a mountain of it tied on behind. They had seen the leading bull's ears and head over the grass and wondered if they were dreaming. Their relief had been considerable when they saw him stop. They wondered why he did—the noise had been so great that they did not hear the rifle until almost the end, and the grass and the elephants' ears had prevented their seeing me. My arrival on the scene had been none too soon. The nearest elephant was only a dozen strides away from them.

The occupants of the car were old friends whom I had last seen in the north of faraway Eire: little Mrs. McAndrew, like a small brown bird with her bright black eyes; old Mac himself; and their daughter Shirley. They were on their way up to Nyasaland or Northern Rhodesia, I forget which, and I do not think they had any notion of how near they had been to not arriving. I certainly didn't tell them; but they had to spend a day or two in camp with me while the local natives cut a detour around the dead elephant to enable their car to proceed.

My new permit for five bulls was awaiting me when I got back to camp, my runners telling me they had arrived with it as they heard the shooting.

IN CAMP

MORAVIA, PORTUGUESE EAST AFRICA

38 elephant with 38 shots this morning. Sounds good; but it was a sorry business. Nobody regrets it more than I do. The darn fools had nobody to blame but themselves. It wasn't my fault; I only shot them to save the wretched critters from dying of thirst and starvation. Glad I had the little Rigby.

This refers to one of those unfortunate occurrences that sometimes take place—not very often, I'm glad to say. I have heard of only two or three similar cases.

I had been following a fairly large herd of about seventy or eighty. They led me along the flank of not very high hills covered with open timber and short grass with plenty of rocks and boulders. Visibility was good; the snag with this sort of country is the wind. It eddies around the hills and without warning will blow from the wrong direction, stampede your elephant, and then swing back again and blow steadily as before. It is the most infuriating thing. There are times when you believe the gusts are deliberate.

On the day in question I had sighted my elephant when he was about one hundred and fifty yards away and approached slowly through the trees looking for the best tuskers, which I expected to find up at the far end of the herd. But I could not see anything clearly. I was trying to decide whether or not to open fire on a couple of medium-sized bulls standing close together when one of my trackers touched my shoulder and pointed away up the side of the hill. I then saw that there was another herd there, one hundred and sixty to one hundred and seventy yards away. It was a much smaller herd, but I could see several good tuskers together on the right, indicating that the herd had approached from the left, as these were almost certainly the leaders. There was quite a strong breeze blowing along the side of the hill, and everything seemed all right. I at once abandoned the herd we had been following and made for this other. All went well until I raised my rifle to open fire. I killed the two best tuskers with a right and left; but even as I fired I felt a strong gust of wind on the back of my neck, and as the herd stampeded madly back the way they had come the wind came around still farther and blew strongly from me to them, hastening their steps. It was a wild, panic-stricken rush. Trees were broken and pushed down, the cows screamed and trumpeted as they guided their calves in front of them, and at least one big bull blew a blast that seemed to go on for a very long time. There was quite some noise from the other, larger, herd also, but nothing to the commotion these were making. I saw one bull get jammed between two trees that were closer together than he figured, but another came behind, either intentionally or otherwise, gave one mighty shove, and the two trees went over. The animals swept over the neck that joined this hill to the next, and down the far side. We came to where one of them had rushed too close to a tree so that its right tusk had cut a deep groove, seven or eight inches long, in the left-hand side of the trunk. It looked like the groove a bullet from a large-bore rifle would make. Just why I followed I cannot say. Usually it is mere waste of time to follow up a herd that has stampeded as this one had. But it was thanks to the fact that I did follow that I was able to see what happened to them. The country was considerably more open on the far side of the hills, and I was able to watch the terror-stricken beasts as they fled down the slope and then out across the open. There was a big flat expanse covered with too-green grass right ahead of them, and I remember mentioning to my gunbearer that it looked suspiciously like a swamp. Scarcely were the words out of my mouth when the herd dashed out across this expanse. They did not get far across it, but their momentum carried them all well out onto it. And then their speed suddenly dropped and we could see that they were in difficulties. Finally they all halted and just stood there. We followed them down and found that although some of the younger ones were still struggling frantically, the great majority had apparently realized the hopelessness of their predicament and resigned themselves to the end. Two or three of them had taken hold of one another and managed to turn around, or half around, but the others were all facing out into the swamp, hopelessly bogged. I had to get around an arm of the swamp to get into a position from which to shoot. I could clearly see that I would be able to bag most if not all of the shootable bulls, for even if they were able to get under way they would only be able to move slowly; but I hoped that the shooting would arouse the remainder from their apathy and in that way be the means of saving them. I certainly did not want to blot out the entire herd. But neither did I want to leave them there to die a lingering death.

I shot one of the bulls and reloaded slowly as I watched the effects of the shooting. All threw up their trunks in alarm and on the part of several there was a somewhat halfhearted attempt to pull their feet out of the mud; but most of them did not appear to be trying. At the second shot only some of the trunks went up. Some looked toward us, others didn't even bother to do that. It was gradually borne in on me that I would be compelled to kill the lot. I didn't like the idea at all; but what else could I do? However, I would not have to waste my costly large-bore shells on them; there was no need for that. Camp was not so very far away, and I had a neat little 7-millimeter Rigby-Mauser there that would do the job. Accordingly I sent off one of my men to get it and several boxes of shells. Besides, since shooting had not been able to move the elephant I wanted to see if they would try again to get out if I left them a while in peace. So I sat down under a shady tree and lit my pipe, leaving them entirely undisturbed. They did absolutely nothing. My man got back with the .275 sooner than I expected, accompanied by the rest of my men and the entire population of the district, straggling out after him to see what was happening. And so I had to get busy on one of the most unpleasant jobs I have ever been called upon to perform. There were thirty-four elephant, bulls, cows and calves, still alive. There were the two I had killed here in the swamp before sending for the little Mauser; then there were the two I had killed originally on the hillside. I would have been perfectly satisfied with another two or three bulls and instead I had to wipe out the entire herd. Nobody could have regretted it more than I did. I did not anticipate difficulty in explaining matters to the authorities. The Portuguese knew me by now and understood that I was a hunter of experience. They would realize that I would not go blotting out a bunch of cows and calves for fun or because I didn't know any better. After it was over I expressed suitable regret, explained the circumstances, and handed over all the small ivory—which would have been of little value to me anyway. I sent in for a suitable number of permits to enable me to keep the big tusks, and then brought them in.

You may ask why I bothered to say anything about the incident. The reason is that it would have been impossible to keep such an unprecedented slaughter secret. Literally hundreds of natives came from all over to get the meat, and there were long strings of them, men, women, and children, carrying it away on their heads for weeks afterward. I heard talk of that killing more than a hundred miles away. News of it would inevitably have reached the ears of officialdom, and I figured it was better to give them the true facts of the matter rather than let them hear distorted rumors. It was my obvious policy to keep in with the Portuguese, and I had— and have—a very good name among them. It would seem that they never associated me with my earliest poaching; or if they did they must have decided to let bygones be bygones.

As to how I got the ivory out: the swamp was not soft enough to be dangerous to men, who anyway could safeguard each other. A heavy African elephant, even a calf, is a different matter.

IN CAMP
TANGARAMBUZI, PORTUGUESE EAST AFRICA

Weird bag today: elephant and leopard with one shot!

From time to time men write of strange and unusual right-and-lefts: killing two animals of entirely different species with two quick consecutive shots. If men are writing from the four corners of the earth there are sometimes queer mixtures in their bags. I can remember one claiming a lion and a wart hog with a right-and-left; another a pheasant and a tiger; and a third a leopard and an antelope of some sort; yet another claimed a crocodile and a hyena—certainly an unusual mixture, that; and, of course, there are many, many claims of two different kinds of buck or antelope—I've had several of those myself. But I think you will agree that the mixture I refer to in that short note from an old diary is more than merely unusual—even if it had been a right-and-left. The fact that only one shot was fired lifts it still further out of the commonplace. I'll tell you about it here because I certainly look upon it as an unusual experience with elephant and therefore deserving of its place in this chapter.

I was hunting in the Chioko district south of the Zambezi, a country of very dense thornbush and a fiendish amount of utterly impenetrable stuff of the hawk's-bill variety with plenty of wait-a-bit thorn mixed with it. Mostly you can get around only by following the paths beaten out by the feet of the big gray beasts themselves. But you must not imagine that you can just stroll along because I use the word "paths"; "tracks" would be more accurate. These tracks are fairly clear to a height of about three and a half feet, but from there up they are draped with the overhang of the thorn, which runs about ten to fifteen feet high. The big elephant merely brush through this, but neither you nor your naked trackers and gun-bearers can. It means struggling along, all doubled up with your knees bumping your chin, for hours on end in a sweltering atmosphere. In the dry season there is no leaf on the thorn, and no cooling breeze can penetrate—but the sun can. It's fiendishly tiring work, but well worth while because the ivory you get in there is mostly heavy. To complete the picture, the district is hilly, with deep saucerlike depressions between and among the hills.

My men and I were taking a prowl through one of these deep valleys in the hope of picking up fresh spoor. Suddenly we heard an elephant yelling up on the side of the hills to our right. We at once made toward the sound. The yelling was repeated several times at intervals during the long and very difficult approach and seemed to be coming from the same spot. Since what breeze there is will usually drift uphill in such a place, the hot air rising out of the valley, we had to get at least on a level with the elephant or, better still (if possible) slightly above him. You can't pick and choose much in that sort of country; however, we found that there was a well-beaten elephant path running along the sides of the hills, and it seemed at about the right level. We hoped it would take us to where the elephant was, and followed it. Presently we came to a fork in the path, both branches being well worn. One arm ran more or less straight on ahead of us along the side of the hill, while the other swung out to our half-left and ran around the rim of the spur. We halted, listening for another yell from our quarry to tell us exactly where he was. Visibility here was limited to about fifteen paces on the average, which I considered good; elsewhere it had seldom been better than from twelve to twenty feet. We did not have to wait long before another yell shattered the silence. It came from away out on the point of the spur, so we moved quietly along the left fork. There was some thick bush out on the very point, but otherwise the spur was remarkably lightly covered—for this area. Guessing that the elephant must be in that thick clump, I left the path and moved across the more open patch to see what the bush looked like from the other side. Besides, from out here I could command both approaches to the clump. The ground appeared to fall away very abruptly from the rim, down into the valley we had just crossed. We reached the far side of the spur and, as I had expected, there was another elephant path leading away from the clump of bush. And there was the fresh spoor of a small party of ten or a dozen elephant, mostly cows and youngsters, on this path and leading away from that thick clump of bush. I could not see how we could have failed to see an elephant leaving after the last yell, so it seemed likely that at least one still remained. But there had been absolute silence for some minutes. I was just about to advance toward the bush, with my rifle very much ready for instant action, when there came a new shattering yell and a tremendous sweeping and crackling of bush. Although the breeze had been favorable, it certainly seemed that the elephant had somehow spotted us and was coming. I halted and waited, rifle half-raised, finger on front trigger. But nothing further happened. There was again dead silence. I crept forward very carefully and quietly to the bush. As I reached it there was still another yell that seemed to split the heavens, and I saw a trunk reach up, tear a branch off a tree, and hurl it down into the basin beyond the rim of the spur. I caught a fleeting glimpse of a tusk which told me that I had a good bull in front of me; but although I was not more than fifteen feet away from him I could not get a shot because he was stern-on to me though not directly so, and the bush almost entirely concealed him. Deliberating with myself for a moment as to whether I should wait here in the hope that he would move slightly and give me a better chance, or whether it would be wiser to slip back and move around to the other side of the bush where I could possibly get a broadside shot, he took the matter out of my hands by suddenly wheeling around until he was broadside-on to me and, with his trunk thrown back over his head, loosing another of those hair-raising yells. It was so unexpected—though just why it should have been I don't know—that I almost jumped out of my skin! However, I was sufficiently wide-awake to take instant advantage of the chance offered: it was improbable that I would get a better one. Standing on slightly higher ground than he was made it possible for me to get a side brain shot (had I been on the same level I would have been too close). When he wheeled around he must have shifted his near hind foot dangerously close to the brink and the ground must have given way just as I fired. Because, instead of falling toward me as I expected, he seemed to fall backward and away from me—and disappeared from view. One instant he had been there in front of me and the next he was gone: not a trace of him to be seen. I rushed to the very edge of the rim and looked down. There must have been a landslide here not so very long before, and a sheer drop of thirty-five to forty feet was immediately below me. My elephant was lying on his back with all four feet in the air in an attitude in which I don't suppose I'll ever see an elephant again. There wasn't a move out of him. My heroes were vastly amused at the sight of him, and although they had not seen it they rehearsed his fall over and over again as they mentally pictured its happening. (If there is one thing the African loves to see it is someone falling unexpectedly. I remember seeing a man fall straight down from the top of a tall palm tree which he had been tapping for palm wine. He hit the ground with a resounding thump and lay still. My men loosed one simultaneous yell of delight, although some of them ran up to see if they could help the fellow. But they were yelling and roaring with laughter as they did so, while others were rolling from side to side on the ground, gasping and groaning and holding their sides, breathless and speechless and in agony with utterly uncontrollable laughter. It wasn't callousness, or that they didn't feel sorry for the man, but that such a sight tickles their funny bones as nothing else can. As a matter of fact, the victim of the fall wasn't hurt in the slightest. After lying still for a moment or two he sat up, shook himself, looked somewhat dazedly around, gazed up at the top of the tree from which he'd fallen, and then joined in the laughter as he pictured the priceless sight he must have been.)

But it wasn't until the elephant carcass had been butchered by the local natives that we learned the extent of the bag with that shot. It was then they found the remains of what had been a leopard. The elephant had landed on top of him when he fell. Needless to say, the leopard was a pancake. Whether he had been there right along in spite of the noise the elephant had been making all morning, or whether he had bolted from some lying-up place when he heard the shot and just managed to pass under the elephant at the wrong moment, I cannot tell you.

5: MORE ELEPHANT STORIES

You don't have to be a crack shot to be a successful elephant hunter—a very mediocre marksman can still kill elephant. I do not pretend to be any Deadeye Dick or lay claim to any fancy degree of marksmanship; yet you will have noticed that I kill nearly all my elephant with a single shot apiece. That is not necessarily superlative skill. It is just that I do not get all steamed up: I do not attempt to squeeze the trigger until I am certain of at least anchoring my beast—no matter what it is—if not instantly killing it. Steadiness and patience are of much greater importance than actual marksmanship. After all, you must have noticed that most elephant are shot within twenty-five yards and that I refer to forty yards as a very long shot. So it is, at elephant. Accordingly, when you hear some fellow boasting about his skill and making it out to be a matter of many years' experience and practice, just bear the above facts in mind.

It is a curious thing how often one's bag is in odd numbers: fives and sevens and nines and so on. They are far more frequent than even numbers. I have noticed this right along, and what is more, I seem to remember that most other hunters have found the same thing. There doesn't seem to be any reason for it—it's just one of those things.

Every year immediately before the rains immense numbers of elephant come down from the north into the Zambezi valley. There they meet the comparatively few permanent residents of those districts but are unable to return until the various rivers they have to cross have dropped sufficiently. I have shot them in the Zambezi valley until I reckoned they were about due to make a break for the north. I would then hurry away, circle around, and await them up along the Nyasaland border. They have several big roads which they have been using since time immemorial, and I know these. I also know the best places along these roads in which to lie in wait for them—places where they like to halt and feed for a day or two. I have made those places more attractive for them by pouring bags of salt in heaps in chosen spots, for elephant, like almost all other animals, are very fond of salt. This has always paid handsomely.

In the Asenga country the grass is the trouble. There are oceans of ten- to twelve-foot elephant grass, and the herds seem to spend most of their time in it. I have heard it described as maddening. But there are swarms of elephant there in the right season.

When I got into the Asenga country the thought that instantly jumped into my mind was: Now if only I had a kind of house decorator's ladder, how easy it would be. Why I should have thought of that particular type of ladder I don't know—I've never been a house decorator myself, nor used such a ladder. But there it was. Moreover, there was plenty of bamboo growing in the district, so it was a fairly simple matter to make a usable ladder—though its not having any hinges made it a somewhat rickety affair. Still, with the two men who carried it steadying it when I climbed to the top, it was quite practical. I used it with great success. But I considered it preferable to use a small-bore rifle rather than one of my more powerful weapons because I was afraid the latter might send me flying from my perch on the top of the ladder if the fellows who were supposed to be steadying it got bored with the proceedings, as they almost inevitably would when the shooting had been going on for some time and they were unable to see what was happening; and also because I found that the elephant were not alarmed by the report of the small rifle to the extent they were by the heavier one. Sitting on top of the ladder with my shoulders just level with the tops of the grass I would wait for an elephant to raise his head sufficiently or move into a place where the grass had been trampled down a bit. Then it was merely a case of slipping the little slug into his brain. He would drop instantly and disappear in the grass—there wouldn't be a sound out of him. Consequently, his pals wouldn't know that anything had happened to him: because they couldn't see him fall on account of the grass, and because there was no commotion to alarm them, the whiplike crack of the small-bore being something they hadn't heard before. I have shot as many as seven like that without having to move my ladder; and then about half an hour later killed another five out of the same herd from a different position. The principal difficulty I experienced when using this method was to decide if an elephant were worth shooting or not. Frequently I would get only a fleeting glimpse of his tusks; sometimes I could not even get that.

Since the reader may have heard of the famous hunter W. D. M. ("Karamojo") Bell, I should like to mention here that he is invariably associated with this method of shooting, which he originated way up in the southern Sudan. At the time of which I write, however, I had never even heard of Karamojo Bell, much less of his methods.

A man's bag alone should not be taken as a criterion of his ability as a hunter. I have killed considerably more elephant than Bell killed, but I do not rate myself a better hunter on that score. Unless I'm mistaken, Bell hunted for fifteen or sixteen years. (He did no hunting during World War I and had only one safari after it.) I have been hunting twice as long as that but do not consider myself better just because of it. The steadiness, patience, nerve, and exquisite skill displayed by Bell in my opinion put him in a class by himself. Those who have not had much experience elephant hunting cannot be expected to appreciate what an astounding feat it was to kill eight hundred elephant with a .275 (7-millimeter) rifle. I am thoroughly qualified to appreciate it at its true worth, and in view of it I class Bell as the greatest elephant hunter of all time.

I picked up the spoor of a pretty big herd in Rhodesia and followed them over the Tanganyika border when they crossed. I caught up with them in one of those places you dream about with everything in your favor: there was a fair-sized clearing in the light open forest with a mud wallow in the middle of it and a couple of dusting places close by. Halfway between the fringe of the forest and the mud wallow was a small anthill with a couple of forked trees growing out of it. These afforded adequate cover for me and my gunbearer, for the trees broke up our outline—making us invisible provided we kept still—yet in no way interfered with our view of the herd or impeded quick handling and exchange of rifles. An ideal spot. The anthill was perhaps forty paces from the mud wallow and twenty to thirty paces from the two dusting places.

We sighted the herd when we were fully a hundred and fifty yards away. The elephant were thoroughly enjoying themselves: slapping dollops of mud onto their shoulders and backs with a satisfying *clop,* as happy as children making mud pies; others, having had their mud baths, were scraping the bare ground of the dusting places with one huge forefoot, then sucking up a trunkful of the dust and puffing it over heads, necks, shoulders, and behind huge ears, for all the world like women completing their toilet. One very big bull, which I guessed was the leader, had had his bath and shampoo and was now doing nothing under the trees. All this reminded me of a veritable "elephant playground" I had once found in a district to the north of the Zambezi. I had been hunting with but moderate success for some three or four weeks and was wondering to myself which of all the various districts known to me would be the best right now. I knew I ought to be doing better and would do better if I could just hit upon the right district. Having made up my mind, I decided to give this section one more day. I had noticed a large circular patch of extraordinarily dense bush with a good deal of heavy timber growing in it. Elephant paths led toward it, but so far I hadn't had occasion to examine it. Each time I passed that way I was following spoor which did not lead directly into it. I now decided to have a look at the place and see what it was like inside. But the local natives were horrified at the idea of entering. They declared the place was haunted—though they didn't know by what—and that anyway the elephant would certainly kill any human being who was foolish enough to enter. When I told them I had every intention of entering, they did everything in their power to try to dissuade me. They were really concerned about it. This one sent for that one, and he sent for someone else, until I had all the elders of the district around me. They told me what they thought were horrifying tales of the savagery of the elephant if their chosen playgrounds were ever violated by man. They assured me that elephant which might well be afraid of me and my rifles elsewhere would be very different animals if I attempted to look for them in their playground.

I didn't doubt there was a good deal of truth in what they said; but nevertheless I wasn't worried. The elephant could be as savage as they liked, but their savagery wouldn't be a match for my fine rifles—at least I hoped it wouldn't. It would all depend on the type of bush I found inside. If the place were, as the local men said, a kind of playground, then I had a hunch I would find it open once I succeeded in getting through the outer ring of bush.

But that same outer ring was an extremely nasty proposition when I came to tackle it. In all my wanderings only once or twice have I come across anything quite like it. I was following an elephant path which led directly toward it, but when I came to enter I found that the bush—not thorn—was as thick and dense as a box hedge which has been allowed to grow wild. It was utterly impenetrable except along the zigzag tracks made by the elephant themselves. The bush was about fifteen feet high, and I found that I would have to get down on hands and knees to get along the little tunnel which was all that could be seen of the "path" because the bush closed up entirely from a height of about three feet up. The big gray beasts could brush through this as easily as I could brush through a field of wheat; but a man could not. I had a look at one or two other entrances, but they were all the same.

When I signified that I was about to enter the local men again tried to dissuade me, and when they saw that I wasn't listening to them they flatly refused to take another step. They said they would wait under a shady tree, but that they never expected to see me again. I asked my two gunbearers if they were coming with me or if they would rather wait outside. Their snorts of disgust at the notion that they should wait in safety while I went forward alone were masterpieces. Nevertheless, it wouldn't do to be careless. These local men weren't cowardly and there was no doubt about their fear: I had a hunch it wasn't all bugaboo. Moreover, we'd look pretty foolish if we met a herd coming our way as we crawled along on hands and knees trying not to let the muzzles of the rifles pick up sand.

In fact, I didn't entirely like it. True, there wasn't much likelihood of our meeting elephant coming our way at that hour; but it was pure surmise on my part that we were going to find better going ahead. For all I knew to the contrary there might be only an occasional small clearing around some of the larger trees. But having once started it was obviously out of the question to turn back—I just had to see what was in front.

We crawled along, swearing and dripping with sweat from every pore, for what seemed like two or three ages. And then suddenly, and without the slightest warning, we found ourselves on the edge of what looked like an old English park that had gone to seed a bit. Only in place of the few scattered deer that you would have seen once upon a time in an English park, here elephant were scattered about. Just elephant and nothing else. The dense bush had ceased as abruptly as it had begun. It must have been about one hundred and fifty yards thick—though we had zigzagged much farther than that—and looked for all the world as though it had been planted around that park the way a hedge is planted around a garden. But this hedge had never known a gardener's shears or clippers.

There were great shady trees here and there and small clumps of evergreen bush, and away down in the center we later found a spring of cool water gushing out between two large boulders. It ran into a deep clear pool which the elephant used for drinking purposes, and then into a few shallow pools which they used for mud baths. There were dusting places close by and, as we afterward discovered, salt licks also. It was a delightful place, and completely private. The short green grass almost deserved the name "sward"—at least at first glance.

There were elephant drowsing under the trees, others drinking and blowing water over themselves, and cows washing down their youngsters; others again were slapping mud on themselves or powdering themselves with dust. All were perfectly happy and right out in the open. They obviously assumed they were quite safe in here. It seemed a shame to violate the peace of the place; yet one day's shooting wouldn't do much harm, and it might be many years before I again visited it.

There were not so many elephant, probably not more than forty to fifty, altogether. But it seemed as if there were many more because they were all over the place and right out in the open in a way you seldom see them nowadays except, perhaps, in some national park where they never hear a rifle speak. The glade seemed full of elephant. It was roughly circular and perhaps a quarter of a mile across.

We moved quietly around to our left, keeping close to the hedge, and so up along it to a spot where I could see two big tuskers under a shady tree. They were about seventy-five yards from the hedge, and there was a fair-sized anthill with a small bush growing out of the top of it roughly halfway between them and the hedge. I made for it. Taking up a position on top of the anthill, with the little bush to break up our outline, I opened fire. The two bulls collapsed in their tracks, and I reloaded the .400 myself instead of exchanging rifles, since no quick third shot was called for. The commotion that now ensued among the other elephant was truly remarkable; I have never seen anything quite like it. Some of them twisted and turned, this way and that, trying to spot the danger zone; others rushed here and there, trumpeting and screaming and adding to the general confusion. We stood quite still and watched them. There was one big old cow that appeared to be the leader of about a dozen other cows with a few half-grown calves among them and two or three immature bulls. I didn't at all like the purposeful manner in which she was looking for us. There was no indication of panic about her; on the contrary, she set out to find us in the most deliberate and reasoned way, her companions following her. These old cows are sometimes very dangerous. Since the licensee never shoots them, long years of immunity give them an utter contempt for man, and it is by no means uncommon for them to kill the wretched owners of the "lands" when they go raiding and those owners try to drive them away. This old girl led her party right up to the two dead bulls and sniffed over them. Getting a whiff of the freshly spilled blood she suddenly wheeled around and loosed a shrill trumpeting blast. The result was extraordinary: every elephant in the glade suddenly froze in its tracks. There wasn't a sound or a movement.

Then slowly and quietly the old cow began to circle, her trunk snaking about, trying to pick up our wind. I declare she appeared to be tiptoeing. For a moment her companions remained still, then commenced to follow her. They circled to within about twenty-five yards of us, and it was quite obvious that it was only a matter of time before the old cow got our wind. It was equally obvious that she would then charge. I really ought to have shot her then and there and been done with it; but I hated to fire if I could avoid it because there were several other shootable bulls in sight and I didn't want to stampede them if I could help it. But since a charge was so imminent, I might just as well have dropped her without waiting for it. Possibly I was interested in watching her methods.

Naturally I had kept turning to face the cow, meaning that my two gunbearers also had to move to be always in their correct positions; and just before she was due to get our wind, the old cow suddenly wheeled around and with a scream of rage came bald-headed for us. She must have seen some slight movement back over her shoulder in the way elephant can without your knowing they are looking at you at all—like hogs.

With her ears back she looked incredibly vicious. As she came, her party came too. I had no alternative but to drop her. My little Purdey brought her down without any fuss, and with one exception those with her halted. The exception proved to be another big old cow who, trumpeting shrilly, endeavored to press home the charge. However, my left barrel took her between the eyes. Exchanging rifles, I waited. For what seemed a very long time the other members of the troop just stood about, ears cocked and trunks up, unable to make up their minds what to do. I did not want to turn my back and walk away, for that might well have provoked another charge, and I certainly didn't want to waste any more ammunition on them. But these two shots had started the ball rolling again among the other elephant in the glade. They trumpeted and yelled and rushed around but didn't seem to get anywhere. No attempt was made by any of them to clear out of the glade, though there was nothing to prevent their going. Never have I seen elephant so excited. At long last the troop of cows in front of me wheeled and dashed off for perhaps one hundred yards or so, and then halted again.

I once more took over the little .400, since it looked as though anything could happen here. There was a good bull standing all by himself about one hundred and twenty yards away, and a convenient tree within some thirty to thirty-five paces of him. I decided to make for it. We had to cross the open to get there and would be pretty nearly in the middle of the glade when we did so. I got the tree between him and myself and signed to my men to walk in single file behind me. We had no difficulty in getting to the tree without the big fellow's seeing us. However, I noticed that at least two other tuskers had spotted us, though they did not seem to realize what we were. They had seen something moving, something that wasn't an elephant, and their suspicions were aroused. One of them started slowly toward us with his ears out but his trunk down; the other stood there, ears cocked and trunk up, staring hard and trying to make out what it was. There were about eighty or ninety yards between them: one of them out on our right about seventy-five paces away, and the other beyond the one we were stalking, and also some seventy-five yards away. I slipped up behind the tree, edged around it, and let drive. My bull dropped dead without ever knowing that a rifle had been fired. With the other two bulls so threatening, I immediately exchanged rifles. The one on my right rolled up his trunk and came on the heels of the shot. But his rush appeared to be somewhat halfhearted. He wasn't roaring, and he didn't seem to be coming at full speed. The other certainly meant business. However, he didn't start quite so soon. In fact, he didn't start until he saw the other one coming. He made up for lost time then; but I decided to take the one on my right first as I felt pretty certain that the carcass of the first bull, almost directly in his path, would prove disconcerting. Whether the one on my right was really charging or merely bluffing, I cannot say. Anyhow, I dared not take a chance—besides, he was well worth shooting. My bullet took him, too, between the eyes and, without waiting to see the result, I instantly swung on the second. As I did so he reached the body of the earlier kill and immediately lost all interest in me. His trunk, which he had rolled up under his chin, he flung up over his head. He made a frantic effort to slew around. As he must have been coming at around twenty-five miles an hour he had to heel well over to make the sharp turn he wanted. My left barrel took him through the shoulder before he had completed the turn and literally blasted him off his feet—there was no question about his charging. He had loosed the charging bull elephant's characteristic series of short roars—a tremendous volume of sound—up to the time he encountered the first dead elephant; the other hadn't made a sound of any sort.

I again exchanged rifles, for there was no telling what was going to happen now. The various other elephant in the glade seemed to go crazy, stark staring mad when they heard this shooting and heard the roars of the charging bull. One big fellow with only one tusk stood there blowing a long-sustained blast through his trunk. The others dashed madly around in the most senseless manner. One party came rushing straight toward us as though they intended to run us down. There didn't seem to be a really shootable beast among them, so I let them come on until they were about thirty to forty yards away in the hope that they would pass. When it looked as though they were really coming over us, I raised the rifle with the intention of dropping the two leaders, because that would probably cause the rest to halt or swing outward. But it was not necessary to shoot. As my finger tightened on the trigger, of their own accord they pulled up and stood there staring at us. And then just as suddenly they wheeled around and dashed away again. My two men and I looked at each other with raised eyebrows, shrugged a shoulder, and grinned. We had had many strange experiences together, but today's performance beat anything we had ever seen.

I decided I would like to add that big old single-tusker to the bag. If I could get him I would be willing to call it a day. He was about one hundred and twenty paces away standing broadside-on to me. It was an incredibly long shot at elephant; but I could get a beautifully steady shot from where I stood, and since there were several other beasts that would make a closer approach to the single-tusker difficult, I decided to have a try at him. My bullet got him through the shoulder and there was no need for a second. The other elephant in the immediate vicinity cleared, thereby enabling us to wander around and collect the tails of the slain. But those elephant farther off wouldn't go. They stood watching us as we went from one carcass to another. Every now and then one of them would take a step or two toward us but would not attempt to interfere with us. They had quieted after the shot that killed the last, the old single-tusker; but it was most unusual for them just to stand around like that in the open and not make the slightest attempt to clear out of the vicinity. There were some of them within sixty to seventy yards of us the whole time, until we came to make our way out of the glade. I acted as rearguard then, and just before I started to crawl I looked back and saw the elephant still standing where we had left them.

As we emerged from the hedge the local natives, who had been sitting under a shady tree listening to the shooting and trumpeting, came racing up to hear our news. They could scarcely believe their eyes when they saw we were all in one piece and had actually to handle the tails of the dead elephant before they could be convinced they were real and not figments of the imagination. Of course, they assured one another, I must possess some powerful spell, magic, medicine. How otherwise could I have emerged alive? And not only with a whole skin, but with elephant also! The thing was almost unbelievable—entirely unbelievable if it hadn't been for those freshly severed tails. They looked with genuine awe and admiration and respect at my two staunch gunbearers and pondered on the strength of my "medicine" that was sufficient to cover all three of us. This morning's work would be something to talk over for the next quarter-century.

I had heard and read of these occasional playgrounds, but mostly they had been referred to in fiction and I hadn't known what basis they had in fact. I can assure you that such places do exist, though they aren't very numerous. It is quite otherwise with the great elephant cemetery or graveyard that was so widely believed in in days gone by—"the place where the elephant go to die." That myth originated with those old-timers of one hundred years ago, who stated that they had never seen a dead elephant other than one that had died of wounds. Moreover, it appeared appropriate to Africa, the Dark Continent, the Land of Mystery, to suggest that there must be a favored place away in the very heart of the Congo or some such spot where all aged elephant go to die. It gripped the imagination, and fictionists took it up and wrote their yarns around it. Those without experience accepted it without question, and even to the present day you will find many who believe wholeheartedly in it. There is no such place.

A note in my diary reads, "I liked the calm, imperturbable way he took his licking. I have always admired a good loser. Good luck to him; and good hunting." These sentences bring back memories that are both pleasant and amusing. I was again raiding the big southern reserve in Tanganyika. This was a much larger raid than any of the others, and I had collected a very respectable pile of fine ivory. Most of this I had sent out, and it was now reposing safely in the hold of my friend Sherif's dhow. But I had quite a considerable string of porters with me, all carrying tusks, as I was making my way out intending to call it a day. I had been nearly three months in the reserve this time and had bagged more than ninety good bulls. (This had no appreciable effect on the total number of elephant in the reserve. There were literally many thousands of them. One very keen and accurate observer had estimated that there were *at least* eight thousand elephant in the Lindi province alone; and he knew little or nothing about the thousands that had quit raiding northward and now did all their marauding across the Rovuma to the south.) And then on this occasion, with all that ivory, I came face to face with another hunter. In that trackless immensity our ways had to converge! He also had a string of porters behind him, some of them carrying ivory. I halted and waited for him to approach. He was a white man and out there in the middle of nowhere gave an impression of immaculateness. Doubtless this was because he was freshly shaved and wore a rimless monocle screwed into one eye—he was the only man I have ever met who could wear a monocle without looking like an utter ass. Whatever else I may have looked like, bearded and brown all over, I certainly did not look like any kind of white man. I saw the fellow eying me up and down as he approached, his monocle glinting and flashing in the sun. He was of medium height, slim and dapper, lean and hard. I liked the look of him. He strode up to where I was standing in the shade and addressed me in Kiswahili. Wanted to know who I was and what the hell I was doing in the reserve, how long I had been in here, and if this was all the ivory I had. Without answering any of his questions I asked him who the hell *he* was and what the hell *he* thought he was doing here. At that he commenced to bawl me out, doubtless figuring that a white man would have no difficulty in bluffing a mere brownskin. He said that he was a game ranger and was arresting me then and there, confiscating all my rifles and, of course, my ivory.

Well, he might have been a ranger—but if so what was he doing with a string of porters carrying ivory? Nobody could get permission to shoot in the reserve. I therefore decided to call his bluff. (Anyway, bluff or no bluff, I hadn't the slightest intention of being arrested by anybody.) So I produced the Smith & Wesson .38 Special from the sensible type of open-topped holster in which it invariably reposed just back of my hip, and loosed a shot over his head, both to show him that it was loaded and that I wasn't falling for his bluff. And I told him that if he tried to be funny he would get the next one on his belt buckle. He had an automatic in one of those holsters with a buttoned-down flap and had no hope of getting it into action. I then invited him to be seated in the shade. I got hold of all his rifles and dismantled them, but did not mix up the bits and pieces—I put them separately. His name was on some of his things, the Baron Manfred von Richter, and I guessed he was just another poacher like myself but on a somewhat smaller scale. I had no hesitation in taking his ivory as I knew very well he would have done the same to me had he been able; but I left him all his guns and rifles and, of course, all his porters. As we play this game, you must never leave another hunter in the bush without arms and servants. If his guns are very much better than yours, you may swap with him—he will then be no worse off than you were before; but you must not leave him unarmed or without porters.

The man's bearing and manner were admirable. Nary a whine or a squeak out of him. He saw I had beaten him and took it. He even seemed faintly amused. I told him I would have to borrow some of his porters to carry all the ivory, as my fellows were laden, but if he would come to the nearest water hole and remain there I would send them back as soon as they had dumped their loads where I wanted them. So we did just that. And then, by another strange turn of the wheel of fate, damned if I didn't meet up with this same bold bad baron years afterward during World War II. His astonishment was boundless when he found that I was a British Intelligence Officer then. He told me he had never suspected that I was a white at all and had now and then felt a sense of inferiority when he looked back on the time he had been bested by, as he thought, a brownskin. He also assured me that he was no Nazi, even though he had been fighting on the German side.

There is a story current about a man who wired a game warden, telling him he had mortally wounded an elephant which had escaped into the reserve and asking for permission to follow and collect the ivory. After a good deal of hemming and hawing permission was granted, and this hero went into the reserve and had the time of his life. I hear there is a warrant still out for his arrest and that it will be served if the fellow ever again ventures to set foot in Tanganyika. I should like to state here and now that I was *not* the villain of this piece. I've never had permission to shoot in Tanganyika or in any other British territory. I've never asked anybody's permission to enter any reserve or territory—when I wanted to enter I just entered, but I did so by the back door and left the same way.

It might be asked just why I have been killing elephant for the greater part of my life. The answer is that it is my sole means of livelihood. As mentioned before, I always wanted to be an elephant hunter, but I get no pleasure out of killing just for the sake of killing. Besides, as was also stated earlier, I feel justified in killing marauders because of the damage they do. Except in those parts of Africa where the governments run control schemes there has been practically no elephant hunting for many years because of the poor price of ivory and the toughness of the life—men have found that they can earn more money very much more easily in other ways. This means that the elephant have been breeding away to their hearts' content and raiding the crops with impunity. I am only too willing to help the natives by shooting marauding elephant and buffalo and man-eating lion and similar varmints.

As to my habits: it may be foolish, but I hold to the custom of pensioning off old and faithful servants. Furthermore, it is my boast that I have never had one of my men even injured, much less killed, in all the years of my wanderings in the wilds. Compare that with the accounts of other hunters who are constantly telling how their gunbearer was killed by elephant, buffalo, or lion, and how some of their porters were carried off by man-eaters.

I did have a stranger grabbed by a man-eater from my camp one time, but never one of my own men. And even at that, I managed to rescue that stranger before he was seriously injured. (This was before the days of penicillin. I can not be held responsible for the fact that the fool doctor allowed the unfortunate man to die of blood poisoning instead of immediately amputating his leg.)

But if I ever did have one of my own men lose his life while in my service, I would most certainly make myself responsible for his family.

I spent one year in that magnificent elephant country in the north of the Belgian Congo, east French Equatorial, and southern Sudan. Need I add that I had no right to be there? I had thought of entering French territory openly but had heard that the big unlimited licenses they used to issue for the equivalent of £100 sterling were a thing of the past; while the Belgians had long followed the British lead of allowing only two elephant a year to be shot by any one hunter. It's a fantastic restriction where elephant are as numerous as they are there; but that's the way it goes. So I decided to slip in in my usual way without saying a word to anybody. There are immense seasonal migrations of elephant across the international river dividing the Congo from French territory every year. (The river's name varies along different stretches of its length: in its upper reaches it is known as the Boma; then, after its junction with the Uélé, it becomes the Ubangi.) The rainy seasons are just the opposite of what they are south of the Equator, and the herds leave the dripping Congo forests for the open, pleasanter country in French territory until the annual grass fires there drive them back across the river into the Congo again. There is always ample feeding for them and plenty of the varied diets they love. This, I'm sure, must be the reason for the fine tusks they grow. I saw more heavy tuskers up there than in any other part of Africa. Another thing I noticed was the frequent concourses of bull elephant up along the Sudan frontier. Here in the open grasslands it would seem that the bulls were holding some sort of congress or stag party. Nary a cow or a youngster to be seen: just mature bulls, with some mighty fellows among them. It was a glorious sight for the ivory hunter.

As might be expected, with an international river running through the center of such a fine elephant district, there was a good deal of poaching going on. But the poachers were a miserable lot and did no actual hunting themselves. They parked themselves in comfortable camps and traded ivory from the local natives for caps and powder for their old muzzle-loaders or shells for the few who owned breech-loaders. I didn't meet another poacher who hunted and shot his own elephant. I was invited on more than one of these parties but wouldn't consider it at any price. The poachers were of all nationalities: French, Belgian, Portuguese, South African Dutch, and Greeks predominating, but there were at least two Britishers. About the only good word I can find to say for them is that if I had any difficulty in disposing of my ivory elsewhere, I could always sell it to them.

The Azandi, a very fine tribe of elephant hunters who have lived in this country and been accustomed to elephant ever since the world began, showed me something I'd never seen before and which I've never heard mentioned by any other hunter, not even those who have hunted in these parts: how to drive elephant to any given spot so that they may be shot by a waiting gun. (Since the above was written I have received from the hunter Bell a copy of his fascinating new book, *Karamojo Safari,* and see that he mentions having elephant driven out of an extinct volcanic crater; but he admits that he doesn't know what method his old hunter employed.) I had often thought that it would be a fine thing if elephant could be driven out of some difficult place into another from which a fair shot might be had, but had never seen how it could be done. Then one day my Zandi tracker (Zandi or Mzandi is the singular of Azandi) suggested I take up a suitable position in a certain tree we were passing. It had a broad and comfortable fork some ten to twelve feet from the ground and another a mite smaller about five feet above it—a "bolt hole" for me in case things went wrong, since the second limb would have been above the reach of any elephant. I was told if I would just sit there and wait the elephant would be driven straight toward me.

Now, I don't care for sitting up in trees to shoot. I don't like the feeling of being anchored, I like freedom of movement so that I have a better chance of getting the shot I want. I therefore told the men I would wait at the foot of the tree instead of up in its branches. Oh, but they had never heard of such a thing, every other hunter for whom they had driven elephant had been only too pleased to be up in a tree, in fact had insisted they find him a suitable tree before commencing the drive. I didn't care a hoot what other "hunters" had wanted; I wasn't climbing into any tree. Let them get on with the drive—I was anxious to see how they did it. I'd look after myself. When they saw I was adamant, off they went, telling me not to expect anything for at least half an hour but to be on the lookout after that.

We were in very heavy forest, great tall trees everywhere, the branches of which met overhead. There was comparatively little undergrowth, just clumps here and there and, of course, no grass. Visibility was reasonably good though somewhat dim. There was absolute silence—not a sound. I don't know quite what I expected. I certainly didn't expect the men to drive the elephant by banging drums and tin cans and whooping and yelling as they would if they were driving a lion. It seemed totally inappropriate; besides, they had no drums with them. It wouldn't be of much use stampeding the elephant in a terror-stricken rush past the tree: the idea was to give me a shot, and nobody knew better than the Azandi that elephant must be shot carefully in the right spot—a very different thing from loosing an ounce and a half of shot after a wild duck.

My gunbearer (who of course had remained with me) and I had a smoke and then sat at the foot of the great tree and chatted quietly of this and that. How long we sat there I don't know, but it must have been almost an hour. Then, away down one of the long vistas in the forest, fully two hundred and fifty yards away or more, I saw something move—something big and black with a glint of white. I instantly stopped talking, pointed, and whispered to my companion to draw his attention to it. But he also had seen something, although he wasn't quite sure what, and had been about to mention it to me. So we sat there without moving, our eyes everywhere. Almost immediately I saw other big black shapes moving slowly toward us between the trunks of the mighty trees, most of which had no branches for a long way up. In the dim shadows of this great forest the elephant looked very black, and their tusks showed up remarkably white. More and more shapes appeared; and then it looked as though they were all going to swing over to our left. I was about to get to my feet and make over that way when I saw the leaders swing back again and once more head steadily and directly toward us. On they came, slowly but steadily. When they were about one hundred yards away I saw a slim naked black figure sprint for a tree away out on our right, on the herd's left. No sooner had he reached it and, like a cat, swarmed up it for about ten feet, than the leaders of the herd began to move over that way. And then I heard a peculiar *clap, clap, clapping* coming from over there. It was not loud, but clear and very distinct. The elephant also heard it and swung away from it to continue straight toward us. Another naked black figure sprinted out from somewhere behind the herd, on our left, and also swarmed up a tree. Then again came that *clap, clap, clapping,* this time from both sides. The elephant looked in both directions and continued their steady progress toward the chosen tree to which they were being so cunningly driven. It was clear they knew there was something in the wind but couldn't make out what it was—that clapping had them guessing. And so they came drifting quite slowly right into the muzzles of my rifle. It was as neat a piece of work as I had ever seen. The elephant weren't alarmed, just a mite puzzled and uneasy. I waited until they were about thirty paces away and then stepped out from behind the tree which had concealed me ever since they were within a hundred yards.

I was using a pair of double rifles and took a quick right-and-left at the two leading bulls, killing them both, then grabbed my second rifle and got in another right-and-left at the shoulders of another two as the herd wheeled around to rush off to my left. Again exchanging rifles I was just in time to take a heart and lung shot at a big old bull that had allowed himself to become something of a straggler. Because of the angle-off I wasn't too sure of that shot, so I gave him the left barrel also, holding a mite farther forward. He ran about fifty yards and then collapsed.

I congratulated the men on the success of the drive, but they didn't seem to think they'd done anything very remarkable. There's no question that the Azandi know more about elephant and their ways than any other tribe in Africa and are more accustomed to them. And I was greatly interested to hear that Chinkhombero, the legendary mighty multiple-tusked Father of all Elephant, was well known to them. This monster is spoken of throughout all Central Africa frequented by elephant. I had originally heard of him way down in the Zambezi country, and on one occasion followed him for more than a thousand miles without getting a shot. And, as I say, it was most interesting to hear the same legends being told about him up here, in spite of the different languages spoken by the tribes.

I put this elephant driving to good account not long afterward. An old friend of mine, a man who called himself Lincoln Cadillac, drifted across from the French Cameroons where he had been gold-prospecting and joined me for a crack at the elephant. Although a hunter and a good one, Cadillac was first and foremost a prospector. He looked to the elephant to provide him with a grubstake only when things hadn't been panning out too well. He was one of the very few white men I have ever met who would "do to take along." Usually I do not care to have another white around when I'm hunting seriously; but Cadillac was utterly reliable. I *knew* he wouldn't do some damn-fool thing at the wrong moment; I *knew* he wouldn't grumble and bellyache if the wind proved contrary or the grub or tobacco fell into the river; I *knew* he'd place his shots as carefully as I did myself and not make us waste endless time and energy following wounded beasts that ought to have been killed clean; and I knew that he wouldn't be slamming his bullets into the same animal I was shooting. Our teamwork was good, and we could each see which was the other's obvious shot—and let him take it.

I had shot five good tuskers in the more open country on the French side of the river. There had been a big concourse there, all bulls—I estimated that there had been all of two hundred of them. The long grass had been considerably trampled down, and from the top of my ladder I was able to watch them as they stampeded. They ran northward for about a mile and then swung around toward the northwest and seemed to be making for some not very high hills some twelve to fifteen miles away. I asked the local natives what the chances were of catching them if we made straight for the hills, did the elephant ever stay around there? They assured me that they did, that it was a favorite place for them—so much so that a certain valley or basin with many attractive features for human habitation was left exclusively to the elephant. Two or three families had tried to settle there but were eaten out of house and home and pretty nearly scared out of their lives. They quit, and the elephant had been left undisturbed ever since.

I packed up and trekked across, arriving about an hour or so before sundown. I camped in a nice shady spot close beside a small creek of clear cool water that ran out from a gap in the hills. On the far side of the creek I could see the spoor of the herd I had shot up. They had gone in through the gap, and there was no sign of their coming out again. Some locals who had turned up told me that there was no other entrance to the circular basinlike valley and that it was quite customary for a herd to remain there for two, three, or more days. Two rather small herds had gone in a day or so before and must still be there.

After a pot of tea I strolled along to the entrance and had a look at the basin. The hills which formed it came around like a horseshoe, and I was standing as it were between the prongs of the shoe. The valley was about three quarters of a mile in diameter, and the creek beside which I was camped ran through the center of it. It was more or less flat and there was plenty of long grass and buffalo bean, indicating very fertile soil. There were heavy trees scattered about, and here and there were clumps of them close together with considerable undergrowth and trailing vines and creepers all over them. On account of all this, visibility wasn't too good; but some of the grass had been trampled down, giving long vistas in some places. Away down two of these vistas I could see elephant. If two other herds were in there as well as the big lot that had entered today, there must be quite some elephant in there right now, I thought. For ten or fifteen minutes I stood smoking my pipe and deciding on a plan for the morrow. If I went in and shattered the peace of their valley with a burst of gunfire they would all make for the only outlet. I might get several; but I could scarcely hope for a very big bag. And then my experience in the heavy forest on the Belgian side of the river came back to me: How about driving these fellows? Could they be driven in this sort of country? It would be easy enough to send a couple of men around with my revolver and tell them to blaze off a few shots over their heads; but that would stampede the elephant. I didn't want that. I asked the Zandi men I had with me if they thought they could persuade these elephant to drift along slowly toward me if I took up a position near the gap next morning. They replied that it wasn't the kind of country in which they were accustomed to drive elephant, but at least they were willing to try. They were optimistic of success if only because there was but one outlet. So we returned to camp, and I was delighted to find my friend Cadillac just arriving. I told him if his luck were in and all went well he would get his grubstake next morning.

No elephant came out during the night, so next morning Cadillac and I took up our positions, one on either side of the gap, perhaps one hundred and fifty yards apart. There was no danger in this, because we would be taking shoulder shots and therefore there would be no chance of bullets driving clean through and possibly hitting someone standing opposite. Moreover, neither of us would be getting all steamed up and blazing off wildly and perhaps missing our elephant. I certainly wouldn't have allowed an inexperienced man to stand directly opposite me like that with a powerful rifle; but I knew my man on this occasion and had no qualms.

It would have been nice to stand on the inner side of the gap so that when the first three or four elephant had been dropped their carcasses would cause the remainder to wheel around and stampede back into the basin; but I was afraid for our beaters. Had there been more big trees around, well and good; but the trees were few and far between, while there were better than three hundred bull elephant in the three herds. (Actually, we finally estimated that there must have been more than three hundred and fifty elephant altogether.) Consequently we stood just outside the gap, which would allow the elephant to swing out both ways in order to avoid the bodies of the slain. I gave the beaters my revolver and Cadillac did likewise, so that if the elephant showed any inclination to dash back into the basin—as they almost certainly would when we opened fire—the men could fire a few shots, which would probably send them on again.

We were each armed with a very similar pair of double .465-bore rifles. After about an hour the first of the elephant began to put in an appearance. They were drifting along quite slowly, seeming to be in no way alarmed. And, oh boy, had they tusks! There were others behind them, and then more and more. I waited until they were opposite, glanced across at Cadillac, saw he was ready, and then opened fire. Cadillac's first shot roared out on the heels of mine. His second synchronized with my second, the two reports merging into one. Four mighty tuskers came down, and we grabbed our second rifles. It had been so totally unexpected that the remainder of the elephant stood for a moment in consternation. Again our rifles synchronized; and then two more shots followed close on the heels of each other—and another four great bulls were down. The herd wheeled around in panic and endeavored to get back into the basin; but the press of animals in the comparatively narrow gap caused them to jam. Again exchanging rifles, I waited. Presently a mild fusillade of revolver shots came from way beyond the herd. The elephant jammed in the gap surged backward and forward, those beyond trying to force their way to get away from the revolvers, while those on our side were shoving and pushing in frantic haste to get back into the valley. However, the press of animals on the far side was the greater, and gradually overcame those on our side. They came around and started slowly toward us again. They moved quite slowly and cautiously as though they did not fancy the notion at all. We waited until they were almost past and then opened fire again. As we did I just caught the cracking of the revolvers again. Those Azandi heroes were really doing their stuff. As the leading elephant came down those that were following split their ranks and rushed past on both sides of the fallen. Although I fired and exchanged rifles as fast as possible, I could not cope with them all. They flowed past like a mighty torrent. And above the general din I could hear Cadillac's rifles ringing out regularly. I fired and fired, again and again, my gunbearer reloading as he had never reloaded before. My one regret was that I didn't have a set of three double rifles that day with two men reloading for me. I could have used them and kept them busy.

Gradually the rush petered out. The barrels of both my rifles were too hot to grasp tightly although the sun was scarcely more than an hour above the horizon. There were dead elephants scattered all over the place, and a few, a very few, that required a second shot to finish them. But they were all down and neither of us had lost any wounded ones.

How big are elephant? I remember a huge one I once shot. I had no tape, but I measured him as best I could with strips of bark knotted together and then measured that against the barrels of my rifle, the length of which I knew. I made the height from the sole of the foot to the withers twelve feet one inch. (A fairly accurate estimate of an elephant's height can be obtained by measuring the circumference of his forefoot. The height, in inches, is almost exactly twice the circumference of the forefoot, in inches. So you can imagine the size of this fellow's pad marks —that was why I had followed him that day, a long way, to shoot him.) This height is interesting because there are men who declare that *no* elephant over twelve feet at the shoulder exist; while others are equally certain that elephant over twelve feet at the shoulder *do* exist. Personally, I have never doubted it. A good average African bull elephant runs a mite more than eleven feet at the shoulder; but I have seen bulls that quite literally towered above their companions. Now to appear so much taller than good bulls would not be a matter of an inch or two when heights of around eleven feet are being considered. A foot or eighteen inches would be more like it. I am by no means the only hunter who has remarked on this. There was another fellow who shot a big bull in this same district and declared that the most careful measurement showed the height of his big fellow to be exactly twelve feet. I noticed in a photograph he showed me that the beast appeared to be carrying disappointingly small tusks. This one of mine also seemed a mite light forward —very short indeed in view of his great size. But the tusks made up for their shortness by being exceptionally thick. They were almost perfectly straight and their girth continued nearly to the tips, where they abruptly terminated in quite sharp points. After they were out I was quite flabbergasted at their weight. They had no hollow—just a saucerlike concavity—being solid ivory throughout. Although scarcely four feet long they weighed sixty-nine and seventy-two pounds respectively. That is very good for these latitudes.

This elephant must have been very, very old, because the hollows in the tusks only close up with age. I have shot hundred-pounders with pretty deep hollows in their tusks. Another indication of age is the maintenance of girth. Young herd bulls with tusks perhaps six or seven feet long look fine in the bush, but they are very deceptive because their tusks taper throughout their length and probably weigh no more than thirty to thirty-three pounds apiece in spite of their length.

Water is a real problem at some seasons, but by no means an insuperable one. I am in the habit of carrying with me a few ten-gallon drums in which to store flour, sugar, rice, and what-have-you in any base camp I build, because of the rats; and these drums naturally make excellent receptacles for water elsewhere. In dry times every available man carries water except my gunbearer, cook, and the young boy who helps him. Big trees here and there will indicate that there is probably water not so very far below the surface; but some such trees are baobabs. These weird vegetable monstrosities are plentiful and many of them hold water in their hollow trunks for long spells after the rains. It can be seen where elephant rear up against them, keeping their hind legs on the ground, and reach as far as they can with their trunks, down into the "tank" as the level of the water drops. Earlier in the year these reservoirs can keep hunters going, since men can draw water from them long after elephant are unable to get down far enough. But toward the end of the dry season the water evaporates from all but the biggest of the trees.

You probably bought this book because you wanted to read something about present-day elephant hunting, and I've tried to tell you about it. But I don't want to give a wrong impression. If you've read as far as this you will be likely to have the notion that elephant hunting consists of camping in some pleasant shady spot and then wandering out and knocking over half-a-dozen elephant more or less whenever you feel like it. Nothing could be farther from the truth. If I had attempted to give you a day-by-day account of any ordinary hunt (not one like that described in the preceding pages) you would have flung this book out the window long ago. The hunter does an immense amount of tramping around for every elephant he shoots. He may trudge through the bush quite literally for weeks without getting a shot. But if I filled every other chapter with descriptions of that sort of thing it would be too wearisome for the reader. Therefore, I have been picking out the red-letter days in my career.

When I speak about trudging around for weeks without getting a shot, I don't mean trekking from one district to another, or tramping around a district in which there are no elephant because you've come at the wrong season. I say you can and sometimes will be hunting daily with elephant all around you and yet may be unable to get a shot. I have vivid recollections of one such occasion when I hunted for fully six weeks without firing my rifle, though I encountered elephant almost every day and frequently had them so close that I could have touched them with the outstretched muzzles of my rifle. But the bush was so bad that I couldn't see a vital spot into which to slip my bullet. And then don't forget that no matter how great your experience you have no control over the wind. You may have made a faultless stalk lasting an hour or more, taken every possible precaution not to scare your quarry, and then when you are at last in a position from which to take the shot, without the slightest warning a little draft of wind comes on the back of your neck—and your elephant have disappeared like a puff of smoke.

One day during that bad period to which I have just referred a big herd of elephant played hide-and-seek with me for a solid three hours in very heavy forest. They knew that forest better than I did and realized they were safe so long as they stayed in it. Try what I would, I could not drive them out of it. And then I suddenly became aware of the fact that there was not one, but two, herds in it. And I declare those two herds communicated with each other, told each other I was there, *and exactly where I was*. Finally, I'm convinced, they became as tired of this fruitless game of hide-and-seek as I was and deliberately tried to scare me out of it. This is what happened: After fully three hours of this extremely nerve-racking game with elephant moving silently about within a matter of a few feet of me and I unable to see them, my gunbearer and I sat down for a short rest at the foot of a tall tree. The dense undergrowth hung over and around us so that it was possible to see only by lying down and looking along the ground. That enabled me to observe the elephants' feet. As we wondered if it were worth while trying again, I took another look and found that I could see elephant feet in every direction whichever way I looked. They were all around us. The second herd had closed up and filled the gap there had been along which I was thinking of going. There was no breath of air stirring. The scent of man must have mounted straight up the trunk of the tree under which we were sitting. The elephants' feet were without exception facing toward us in the center of the circle, and even as I watched them they started slowly to converge on us. Ever so slowly and silently the ring was drawn in. There was something unpleasantly cold-blooded about it. We could do absolutely nothing to escape. There was no tiny gap anywhere in that ring of feet through which we might have risked creeping—what spaces there were between the pairs of feet were completely blocked by bush. From all around the circle came a soft *poo-poo-poo-poo-poo*. That was the elephant talking to one another. It was so soft that it was scarcely audible; but I had heard it many times before. There isn't the slightest doubt in my mind that each and every elephant knew exactly where we were squatting at the foot of that tree. At first the ring had been some ten or twelve yards from us, but it gradually closed in until it was not more than that many feet away—in other words, the elephant were practically within trunk reach. The overhanging bush prevented their seeing us, and prevented our seeing anything of them except their feet and the tip of an occasional trunk. I had told my lad in a whisper what to do when we saw the ring closing in and warned him not to shoot unless absolutely necessary. I honestly didn't believe that the elephant would deliberately attack us; but anything might happen if a shot were fired. So we held on and waited. I don't think I would be far wrong if I say we held our breath also.

I cannot tell you how long we squatted there like that. During such tense moments time, as we figure it, ceases to exist. It might have been five minutes, it might have been five centuries. But four or five minutes under such conditions is a whale of a time! Finally, when the tension had become almost unbearable, I very slowly and quietly stooped down for another look under the bush. And then I rubbed my eyes and looked again—there wasn't an elephant's foot to be seen anywhere! That big mob of elephant had simply evaporated without making a sound of any sort in the extraordinary way elephant do. Nothing will convince me that the whole performance was not deliberately and carefully calculated to show me how useless it was hunting them in here. They won. It was quite apparent that I was merely wasting my time. If they could play with me like that and get away with it, I would do better to drift along elsewhere.

Whenever elephant hunters foregather and the conversation turns, as it inevitably will, to rifles, sooner or later someone will mention the great Karamojo Bell's name and refer to his phenomenal success with his beloved little 7-millimeter Rigby-Mauser. (Bell's total bag amounted to 1,011 elephant, 800 of which he killed with the 7-millimeter and some 200 with the .303 British.) So I do not consider that this first section of the book would be complete without some discussion of this great hunter of the first decade and a half of the present century.

Time and again I have heard men declare that what one man can do can be done again: that Bell may have had, indeed must have had, physique and stamina above the average; nevertheless he was human and if he could slay large numbers of elephant and make a handsome fortune for himself with a small-bore rifle why shouldn't the speaker be able to do it also, provided he could get himself an unrestricted permit? I repeat, I have heard this said on numerous occasions; and although Bell's original book, *The Wanderings of an Elephant Hunter,* has long been out of print, his recently published *Karamojo Safari* is being widely read, and I haven't the least doubt that many readers of it are asking the same question as that quoted above. In fact, I have myself received more than one inquiry in this connection. And the answer, of course, is easy: *If* the inquirer could put the clock back half a century or so, if he were as keen as Bell and as fit, and, most important, an equally fine marksman, then, if he hunted the same districts as Bell hunted and could win for himself the confidence and friendship and help of the local natives to the extent that Bell did, why, there is no very good reason why he shouldn't do as well as Bell did. But that "if" is a mighty big one.

You do not find mobs of old bull elephant right out in the open nowadays feeding and enjoying mud baths in broad daylight as Bell found them—remember, he was the very first man with a rifle among those elephant, and it was mighty seldom he lost a pricked or wounded elephant. It is true that he did occasionally hunt and kill in heavy forest, but it was lone bulls or pairs of bulls he was following. Not once does he mention tackling mixed herds with nervous cows and their young calves under such conditions. And although it is customary to speak of those elderly bulls as "having tempers in inverse ratio to the length of their tusks," and even Bell himself does so, with all due respect to the man I have always ranked as the greatest elephant hunter of all time, that is hyperbole. My experience has been that the aged, whether elephant or man, are not looking for trouble: all they seek is peace and quiet. There is comparatively little danger in hunting lone bulls or pairs of bulls provided you go about it the right way. Why, in my younger days I was advised to let the herds alone and hunt only lone bulls. (That I did not follow the advice is another story.) When Bell shot mixed herds, he did so in open-grass country where he could see if a cow's charge was meant or merely bluff.

It cannot be seriously disputed that Bell's skill with the rifle was far above that of the average hunter. He admits that his marksmanship was of an "automatic accuracy" in those days, and that when he was shooting at fast-moving birds or elephant "the conscious section of mind allowed the rifle a certain amount of lead, but the instant the projectile was started on its way the subconscious section took charge, corrected the rifle, almost invariably in a forward direction, and a clean kill would result. It was only when the subconscious aimer was not functioning that a miss would result. . . . I caught but a fleeting glimpse of a disappearing stern. I succeeded in introducing a nicely judged bullet which, but for the above-mentioned subconscious aimer, would have passed harmlessly beneath the bounding rascal [lion]. The correction in this case was high, with the result that he was caught on the spine just abaft the shoulders while on the rise."

Well, I don't know how many hunters or sportsmen can claim such adventitious aid to their marksmanship. I wish I could! Bell, I consider, was one of those outstanding marksmen only one or two of which appear in a generation. The late Annie Oakley was just about at the peak of her career when Bell was starting out on his, and had he been a man of different caliber and concentrated on trick shooting instead of on elephant, he might well have become a serious rival to Little Sure-Shot herself.

But the point I wish to make is that when tackling mixed herds in dense bush, as one has to nowadays if one wishes the bag to grow, circumstances can and sometimes do arise in which the greatest marksman who ever lived could not be sure of extricating himself if armed with a small-bore rifle. These occasions are not frequent but they must not be overlooked or forgotten: I have experienced them myself on several safaris and both know personally and have heard and read of several other hunters also experiencing them. Those who were armed with small-bores were either killed or badly mauled. Remember, it's not necessarily the elephant at which you're firing that constitutes the danger: the real danger may suddenly appear from some entirely unexpected direction and be right beside you before you have the remotest notion of its existence. It may have been there right along on the other side of a thick bush within trunk reach of you without your knowing.

There is another very important point to remember, and that is that the greatest marksman will occasionally misplace his shot. It may not occur very often, but where elephant in thick cover and small-bore rifles are concerned, it doesn't have to occur more than once!

Bell describes a hunt in West Africa. Not having hunted since before the war, he admits that he was a bit out of practice. Carrying a .318, he followed a big bull into some dense bush. He was close behind. Without warning the bull suddenly swapped ends and came rushing back over his tracks. The range was very close. Bell snapped a shot at him but missed the brain. He says that he just had time to jump aside and put another shot into the elephant's heart as the brute rushed over the very spot he had been standing on a moment before. The muzzle of his rifle was within inches of the elephant's side as he fired.

Now Bell was much too fine a marksman to miss an African elephant's head at ten yards' range; yet the elephant took not the slightest notice of the shot—a heavy bullet would have brought him to his knees. Then Bell's luck stood him in good stead by permitting this to take place in a type of bush which allowed him to jump to one side out of the elephant's way. But I know places, and he knows places, where it would be a physical impossibility to jump aside; and if one just throws oneself blindly into the bush, I know places, and I don't doubt Bell knows similar ones, in which the resilience of the bush would merely throw you back under the elephant's feet. It's a moot point whether being trampled underfoot by an elephant would be preferable to impalement on a tusk! I have no hankering to experience either.

Since I have repeatedly urged both orally and in print that no light bullet can possibly stun an African elephant if it misses the brain even by but a small amount (owing to the honeycomb formation of his skull, which dissipates the bullets' punch), and that only a heavy slug can hit a sufficiently powerful blow to have it transmitted to the brain, the question is certain to be asked: How do I account for the indubitable fact that Bell stunned many elephant with both 7-millimeter and .303 rifles? And as any truly experienced hunter can tell instantly that Bell belongs to that select few—and all too few they are—who have put on paper their African hunting experiences and told us the truth and nothing but the truth, without allowing their imaginations to run away with them to the extent of inserting fictional adventures and observations for the benefit of the thrill-lovers, there can be no doubt whatever of the accuracy of his descriptions. For instance, there was the occasion when he dropped a mighty tusker and climbed up on his back for reconnaissance while his man cut off the tail. Bell then jumped down and went on to kill a number of other tuskers, but after he had left that first big one recovered consciousness, got to his feet, and cleared off minus his tail without anyone's being the wiser until they failed to find him next day, although the mark where he fell was plainly to be seen. There can be no question that that elephant was truly stunned, knocked out—yet the rifle was a 7-millimeter and the bullet only weighed 173 grains.

My answer is that Bell did *not* miss the brain, the elephant was *not* stunned by "having the bullet pass close to the brain," as Bell says. I contend that the bullet struck or entered one of the subsidiary areas of the brain but just lacked the necessary momentum to carry it on into one of the more vital regions. If this is admitted there would be no question of the shock's being transmitted to the brain for the excellent reason that it would have been administered to the actual brain itself, where a very slight tap would be sufficient to stun even an African elephant.

From time to time you will hear or read of some man who has spent most if not all of his life in the wilds and who acquires, or more accurately develops, a peculiar sixth sense which warns him of imminent danger. I say "develops" because I see no good reason to suppose that this instinct does not lie dormant in all of us. I have heard fools scoff at the notion that anybody possesses such an extra sense. It goes without saying that they were not hunters—by which I mean real hunters as opposed to mere game shooters.

Jim Corbett of *Man-Eaters of Kumaon* fame speaks of this premonition more than others and would seem to have derived more benefit from it than anyone else I know. Corbett, of course, had the inestimable advantage of being born and bred in the Indian jungles and presumably being blessed with wise parents who didn't try to dissuade him from wandering around those jungles quite alone from the time he was a small boy. This naturally enabled him to develop his natural hunter's instincts to an unusual degree. Nevertheless, any keen hunter who spends his life or a good deal of it in the bush where dangerous game are to be found can also develop this sense. I speak from my own experience. I flatter myself that I am a natural hunter if only because I've wanted to be an elephant hunter ever since I can remember. It was my chosen profession and from the time I was a child I have made it a hobby to perfect the traits which are essential to the genuine hunter, scout, and bushman. As a Boy Scout I studied all those small points which in the aggregate constitute bushcraft. And I noticed quite early in my career as a hunter that there were times when I felt uneasy and disliked the notion of entering some patch of bush. At first I put it down to stupid, needless nervousness, but after an experience or two showed me that my hunch had been entirely justified, that the danger was there and very real, I began to take more notice of such occurrences. I don't think it is possible to develop this instinct consciously—that is, with one's objective mind; it can only develop itself. But it can, I'm convinced, be most definitely encouraged, if only by not ignoring it. I haven't expressed that too well. Let me put it differently: this instinct, or sixth sense, does not require developing; your powers of receptivity need developing, and the surest way to do that is by never, never refusing to acknowledge that intuitive urge. You must accept it without question or hesitation, and most certainly without attempting to balance it against your extremely finite reasoning power. Any mystic will readily understand.

As the years went by, to my great joy and delight I found that my instinct in this direction was becoming more and more certain, until today I place the utmost confidence in it. Let me give you an instance from my own experience to show how it works.

Some years ago I was following three big bull elephant in forest with dense undergrowth. The ground was covered with little round loose stones and pebbles which made it extremely difficult for even my unshod trackers and gunbearer to move quietly. The breeze was fitful and uncertain. Since for the last hour or thereabouts we had seldom been more than fifty or sixty yards behind the elephant, there can be no doubt that they had had a whiff of us from time to time: not enough to stampede them, but just enough to let them know we were coming. And then we came to where the bush disappeared and the forest thinned out as the ground sloped down to a dry watercourse. At the edge of the dip I halted to view the ground in front.

The spoor of the three bulls led straight down and across the dry creek bed, and I could see where it continued up the opposite rise through a narrow clear place between the forest on the right and a large isolated patch of heavy bush with tall trees growing in it to the left. There was open ground covered with short grass to the left of this clump and also beyond it right up to the brow of the opposite rise where the forest commenced again. We could see two fine tuskers just entering the forest opposite. They were walking quite slowly. Now there was no reason under the sun to suppose that the third one had not already entered the forest immediately in front of them, for they were in single file. They hadn't been shot at, I hadn't wounded and lost any elephant in this district, there was no other hunter working there. Yet I knew, I knew beyond possibility of doubt, that that missing third elephant was waiting for us in, or more probably just beyond, that isolated clump of heavy bush. I could picture him as having turned off the spoor, moved some ten or a dozen yards to his left, and then turned around so as to face the spoor along which he expected us to come.

I whispered to my trackers to leave the spoor and make over diagonally so as to pass to the left of the clump. It was the first time I had been out with these men and they didn't know me. They disagreed with me and assured me that the third elephant had already entered the forest. But I wouldn't have it—I *knew* he was ambushing us. We started in the manner I had indicated, but our little argument had occupied some minutes and the elephant must have lost patience and decided to come and see what had happened to us and whether we were really following. Without any warning he appeared from behind the clump of bush. Had it not been for that most positive premonition of imminent danger waiting, we would have found ourselves charged unexpectedly at a mere dozen yards.

I could give many similar examples but perhaps I have said enough to show that this sense for danger is very real if only one will encourage it and *listen to and act upon it always.*

I sometimes wonder if imagination has anything to do with it. I don't mean that one merely imagines the whole thing, but that the possession of a vivid imagination helps in the developing of this intuition, or sixth sense. I'm inclined to think it probably does. My reason is that one would naturally suppose the African native, living as he does so close to nature, his entire life spent surrounded by dangerous and potentially dangerous game, would have this extra sense developed to a remarkable degree. But to my surprise I have not found it so—witness those two trackers—most excellent trackers, who had done little else all their lives and they were middle-aged men—who had no notion whatsoever that that third elephant had decided to ambush us, and at the least must have thought me a nervous fool for refusing to follow along the spoor—until the elephant put in an appearance! (My reputation received a very considerable boost as a result of that morning.) But the general run of African is not particularly imaginative where game is concerned. In that respect he is not unlike the game itself: as soon as danger departs in fact, it also departs from his thoughts until next time; he doesn't dwell upon it or permit the possibility of a recurrence to prey upon his mind. In which respect, where man-eaters, etc., are concerned, he is certainly wise —as are the animals. For if game and birds were constantly worrying about predatory beasts, furred or feathered, they would all have died as nervous wrecks long ago. And in many places much the same applies to the natives.

This being a chapter of odds and ends I'd like to slip in a word on the subject of safety precautions. But since the word I have is a word of warning, let me hasten to state that I am all in favor of instructing every child, boy and girl, in the use of firearms and in the safe handling of them. But what I want to say is that safety precautions should not be carried to such lengths that they defeat their object and become a positive danger. That is precisely what they can become and what they have been known to become on many occasions.

Take for example that incident related by Jim Corbett in one of his books: an acquaintance wounded a tiger one evening and after following the blood spoor for a while had to quit when the light failed. The following morning the sportsman went out to pick up the spoor where he'd left it the previous evening. He was accompanied by the local shikari, who was leading and carrying the sportsman's *empty* rifle, and various other helpers. When still half a mile or so from where they had quit the previous evening the shikari almost stumbled over the wounded tiger, which clawed him down and killed him.

Now I ask you, what kind of absurdly exaggerated safety precautions are they which cost a man his life? But it would seem that in India at any rate, and to a somewhat lesser extent in Africa, it's quite customary for men to omit to load their rifles until just before they expect to need them.

If a man can't trust himself to carry a loaded rifle out of camp without risk of shooting somebody, then he has no business ever handling a rifle at all and should take up golf or tennis instead.

I am so often asked exactly how many elephant I've shot that I'll try to answer it again here. Let me say at once that my answer can be only approximate. As mentioned before, I kept no notes for years after starting and didn't even then keep note of all the elephant shot. I have never been particularly concerned with the actual bag and admit that I surprised myself when, in response to numerous requests, I made an effort to arrive at the total. The big bags are mostly noted in my journal or diaries, but there are many, many lone elephant, or rather just one elephant shot out of a herd, of which no particular mention was set down, since there was nothing remarkable about the hunt. It has been the thrills and excitements of the hunt, and the knowledge that I was helping my friends the Africans by shooting marauders—and the satisfaction I derived from diddling authority—that has been the main attraction for me. However, I have a pretty accurate idea of the number of elephant shot with different rifles and calibers, and by comparing that with the approximate number I know I've shot legally on license, and the very approximate number I've poached, I can give a rough idea of the total bag. Let it be clearly understood that I count only those elephant I have actually shot myself. I never employed a native hunter to shoot for me, as practically all the old-timers did (with the exception of Bell), and naturally I don't include any of those shot by Cadillac whenever he was with me. Moreover, I count only the really shootable bulls out of the thirty-eight I killed that day when they ran into a swamp, which I've described in another chapter.

As near as I can figure it, I have killed about three hundred elephant on license and am quite sure I am on the conservative side when I say I have poached four for every one shot legally. That may sound a great many; but when you spread it over thirty-three years you will find it works out at barely one elephant a week. Even that would be a lot to the occasional hunter; but then you must remember that I live all the year around in the elephant bush.

I might mention here a point concerning which those critics who delight in describing me and others like me as wanton slaughterers, blind with bloodlust, seem to be in entire ignorance. And that is, that the shooting of the old males of any species is the surest way to bring about an immediate increase in the birth rate of that particular species. At first glance you may find that a little difficult to believe, but give it a little thought and you will see why it is so. The old males of most species are polygamous and like to gather around them a large harem, thereby keeping the younger males away from the females. If you shoot the old fellow, his harem will be broken up and the younger males will each take one or two of the females and their greater procreative powers will result in more intensive breeding. There was ample proof of this when the railroad was being constructed from Mombasa to Nairobi in Kenya. As the construction advanced across the great open Athi plains on which the game simply swarmed, sportsmen came from all over the world to hunt. Immense numbers of lion were shot, many bags running into double figures, and those who hadn't studied such matters too closely feared that they would be exterminated. But to the men's astonishment it was seen that the lion numbers rapidly went up. The reason was that sportsmen wanted the best manes as trophies, and since these are usually carried by the older lions it was mostly they that were shot.

Another little point perhaps not widely known is that in the case of elephant it is the bull that comes in season (*musth,* as they call it in India), not the cow. It stands to reason that a young bull will come in season more frequently than a much older animal. Game departments are so jealous of their jobs that they are inclined to overlook such matters—even if they realize them. Moreover, in my experience, clean killing of some of their number will not cause game to evacuate a district, even if the killing is quite heavy. It's the constant wounding and battering around they receive at the hands of inexperienced and excitable sportsmen that drive game to seek pastures new. And this applies to any African game, including elephant and rhino.

There cannot be the slightest question that there are too many elephant in Africa at the present time. They have been breeding to their hearts' content since the early thirties when the price of ivory dropped to next to nothing, and, then, during World War II and for several years after no suitable ammunition was available with which to shoot them. But it must never be forgotten that the African has also been breeding, and his numbers are also increasing at a great rate. And the African is of greater importance than any elephant.

You may remember the great Wall Street crash back in the early thirties, the reverberations of which were felt even in Central Africa. I was one of those who felt them, and there was a fairly lean spell. A consignment of elephant ammunition I had ordered from the United Kingdom got misdirected after landing at the coast and didn't reach me until it was more than twelve months overdue. No such ammunition was to be obtained locally. The result was that I was completely stranded, with nary a shell capable of killing the big fellows and no money with which to order another shipment from Britain. It didn't look so good.

I put in some deep thought and then went around to a grand old fellow who always had a lot of junk in his place which he wouldn't sell. He and I were good friends, and I knew he'd help me out if he could. I persuaded him to root out all the old firearms he possessed. You never saw such a collection! They ran the gamut from flintlocks to walking-stick guns; and they included one monstrosity about five and a half feet long, stocked to the muzzle, with a bore diameter of about an inch and a half, and weighing about forty pounds. It was intended to be fired off a tripod. It was no use to me; but there was another which looked as though it might do.

It was a single-barrel, smooth-bore, cap-lock gun of good grade for its day and looked as though it had had very little use or handling. I calculated it had probably been built about a hundred years previously. Except that it was a single and Oswell's was a double, it looked very much the same as that grand smooth 10-bore Purdey had built for Cotton Oswell about 1830, which gave him such great service throughout his career. This gun wasn't a Purdey; but as I say it was of good grade. It was regulated for six drams of black powder, so I guessed it was also a 10-bore. The owner refused to sell it but was quite willing to lend it to me —although he tried to back out when he heard I intended to go elephant hunting with it. I must be plain crazy even to think of it: he wasn't going to be responsible for my death, and so on. However, when I assured him that I had no intention of hunting by day he reluctantly acquiesced.

I managed to get some solid hardened spherical lead balls for it in South Africa, some Curtis & Harvey black powder, and some caps. So equipped I sallied forth to do battle with the big fellows. Although the old gun seemed to be in quite good condition, I was afraid to load it right away with the full six drams of powder. I started with four drams and then worked up through four and one-half to five, and after that five and one-half. For these tests I tied the old bundook to a tree, pointing at another tree, and fired it by remote control by means of a long cord, I being safely behind yet another tree. Since all went well, I then loaded the full six drams. The gun didn't turn a hair, so neither did I.

Now I'd had sufficient experience among elephant to know that it would be sheer madness to hunt them by day in thick cover with such inadequate armament. In bygone days when the elephant were still unsophisticated and spent all their time in the open, well and good: they were hunted and shot from the saddle and if one of them turned nasty all the hunter had to do was to sink his spurs in. His horse would have no difficulty in showing an elephant a clean pair of heels. But conditions are very different nowadays. No, what I figured to do was to make for a dry locality known to me, where there were some fine big tuskers, and sit up for them over the scarce water holes on moonlit nights. There, if I were armed with a rifle, I knew that from time to time I might be tempted to take a brain shot, which would kill the elephant in his tracks; with the muzzle-loader I could take only broadside lung shots. And this would be all to the good because if I killed an elephant right at the water hole, that water hole would be ruined for months, maybe for years, as far as elephant were concerned. They'd give it a wide berth in the future. But if I just drove the ball into an animal's lungs, he would run for anything up to half a mile before falling.

It has been my experience that an elephant shot through the heart or lungs will always clear off after his trunk—that is, in the direction in which he is facing. He may slew round a mite and head directly away from you after running a short distance, but I have never known a bull to charge on receiving such a shot. A cow, yes; it's by no means unknown for a cow to whip around instantly on feeling the lead and make a most determined charge, but not a bull. I had no interest in cows; it was the big tuskers I wanted. So you see I wasn't really taking such serious risks as it may have seemed.

The area I was making for was divided by two fair-sized rivers and a smaller one, but they all three ran only during the rains. At the time I got there they were dry, though you could always get water by digging. There were a few scattered native kraals along the course of each river. I camped down near one of these, for I knew there was a good and more or less permanent drinking place for game about three miles upstream. I'd seen the pad marks of a mighty bull elephant there several times in the past, and the local natives told me he used the water hole regularly twice a week throughout the dry season. He had done so for many years. There were also at least two rhino and a party of elephant cows and calves that also used it.

I had arrived in the evening after a very long hot trek, so I decided to do nothing more that day. Next morning I went out to view the drinking place and see what animals were using it. The river here was about forty to fifty feet wide and, as it was throughout most of its length, sandy. But there was a rock bar here running out from the north bank and extending about halfway across the river. When the stream ran it scooped sand out from above the bar so that when it ceased to run it left a fairly deep pool against the north bank. Trees and bush grew out of the bank and overhung the pool, which kept the water reasonably cool. A small native footpath crossed the river bed—the river was dry now—just above the pool.

I found clear evidence of a small troop of elephant consisting of two cows and three calves which evidently visited the water nightly—it would seem that the youngsters must have at least one drink in the twenty-four hours. There was also the spoor of two rhino, and they also appeared to be nightly visitors. Rhino are very regular in their habits. A big lion had had a drink there as well, possibly shortly before dawn. At any rate he had been the last arrival. And then I found what I was looking for: the pad marks of a really big elephant. But it was clear that he hadn't been here for two or three days. His tracks had been almost entirely obliterated by subsequent visitors. However, I found one beautiful circular imprint of a giant forefoot. The lion had trodden right in the center of it, but that didn't in any way spoil it. It indicated a monster. And it wasn't one of those tuskless brutes either: the local natives knew this big fellow, had known him for years, and assured me he had fine teeth. Well, if he had teeth at all they would be good ones—his pad measured just on twenty-two inches across, not from front to rear. Good enough. The moon would be full tonight, and he should be due again if he came every third night or thereabouts.

I looked along the path that crossed the river bed and found that all the elephant came along it from the south. The rhino sometimes used it but also came up the river bed from the east (the river right here ran almost due east). The lion had come down the river bed from the west and having had his drink had taken the path to the north. The elephant and rhino did not seem to use the north side of the river at all: their tracks showed that they invariably returned to the south.

There was nothing more to be done here, so we returned to camp. That evening, about an hour before sundown, my gunbearer and I returned to the drinking place, but without walking up the river bed. We used the north bank instead so that the scent of man would not be too apparent. We scooped ourselves a shallow, saucerlike depression in the clean sand about fifteen paces above the footpath and close against the south bank of the river bed where a couple of tall trees leaned slightly over the river and would throw a deep shadow over us when the moon was well up. Since my quarry habitually came along the path from the south, this should give me an easy and certain shot for his lungs when he stepped out onto the river bed—a clear broadside shot at not more than fifteen paces. Provided the old gun didn't misfire, I could reckon that elephant as mine—if he came. There was practically no breeze, but what little there was was blowing up the river from the southeast.

I climbed up the south bank, which was only about half as high as the north bank, to have a look around, but there was nothing to be seen. As the sun dropped behind the horizon I rejoined my companion. We had brought a blanket with us, both for comfort and to prevent the gun's getting full of sand if I had occasion to lay it down. We spread this in the saucer and I kicked off my shoes and sat down cross-legged, a position I can hold for hours if necessary without movement. I gave my lad a smoke and lit one myself also, since we mightn't get another for a long while. It doesn't take long in the tropics for darkness to fall once the sun's down. But since it was the night of the full moon, the big moon balanced the sun as it were and showed up over the eastern horizon as the sun dropped behind the western. So there was no real darkness.

I told my companion he could sleep whenever he felt like it. At first he lay down, resting on one elbow, but presently he made himself more comfortable and soon his quiet breathing told me he was deep in the Land of Nod.

About an hour and a half after sundown I heard an elephant scream and guessed the cows and calves were coming. Except for that one scream there wasn't a sound, even when they appeared like great black shadows drifting down the path from the south. When they reached the dry sand of the river bed I could then hear the sand squeaking under their feet as they made their way toward the pool. Here they blew water over themselves, and the cows washed down their youngsters. The third calf was quite well grown and fully capable of washing himself. After that they all drank from the small pits they'd dug in the sand a short distance from the pool on previous visits. In a sandy river bed elephant seldom drink from a pool, much preferring the clean water that filters into the pits they dig. In due course they turned away from the water and made their way up along the path down which they had come. I was sitting quite motionless, and although the moon was still too low for the tree overhead to put me in shadow, I'm certain they never saw me.

Not long after they'd gone a rhino came up along the river bed from downstream. He thoroughly enjoyed his drink, snorting and blowing, and then ambled off down the river again. Scarcely was he out of sight when another rhino arrived, coming down the path the elephant had used. The first one had had quite good horns, but they weren't in the same league as these. I was tempted; but the temptation wasn't difficult to put aside. I had long ago learned my lesson: the ivory hunter must concentrate on elephant and elephant only when there are any around. He mustn't fire a shot at any lesser animal for fear of scaring the big beasts. How was I to know that the giant tusker wasn't within a mere hundred yards or so? If he heard a shot he'd go for his life and I'd probably never see him. Besides, I knew my rhino. I knew that in addition to the drink shortly after sundown they would always come for another before dawn and before heading for the place where they would lie up for the day, from three to five miles from the water. Accordingly, I would almost certainly get another chance at this fellow before morning; and if I didn't —he'd be here again tomorrow night. He, or rather she, had her drink and then went off down the river bed in the direction taken by the other one.

An hour or so later I heard the singsong roar of a lion behind me. I had been sitting facing the path along which I expected the big tusker to come, so that when I heard the lion roar upstream it put him behind me. The roars came slowly closer and closer. It was apparent that the animal was coming down along the river bed for a drink just as he'd done before dawn. I could see about a hundred and fifty yards upstream, and when he came into view I turned so as to face across the river. He loosed a tremendous roar when he was about a hundred yards away. My companion awoke, but I put my hand on his upper arm and squeezed it gently in reassurance. He was a well-trained lad and just rolled over slowly and quietly so as to look upstream. The lion came on until he was about twenty-five yards away. He then halted and I could hear the intake of his breath as he filled his lungs for another voluminous roar. I was sitting quite still and by now in shadow, and I'm certain he never spotted us until this moment. I think my companion must have made some slight movement which caught the lion's eye. He choked the roar off and instead gave a little gasp. He stared and stared at us as though he were unable to believe his eyes. When at last he realized it was indeed man he was looking at, he loosed a deep purr, not a growl, and sprang up the north bank. Here he moved slowly along, eying us all the time, until he was on the path that led down to the water. Before descending it he again halted and subjected us to another prolonged stare. Then, apparently satisfied that we didn't intend to interfere with him, he came down the path and made for the water without another glance in our direction.

My companion went back to sleep, and I sat on.

It must have been an hour later, or maybe an hour and a half, when without the slightest warning—not that I had expected any warning—a vast shape materialized out of the night on my half-right front (I was again facing the path). The moon wasn't quite overhead yet, so that the shape was silhouetted against the white sand. It seemed to float through the night, the big white African moon showing up the mighty tusks.

Holding back the trigger of the gun, so there would be no warning clicks, I drew the hammer to full cock. With a slow, steady, almost imperceptible movement I brought the gun up and then, as the big bull reached the river bed and turned ever so slightly to his right front to make for the water, I squeezed the trigger. An orange-red flame leaped from the muzzle, a billowing cloud of light gray smoke, which, however, wasn't as dense as you might have thought owing to the dryness of the atmosphere, and the old bundook roared its song.

The elephant lurched forward, flung his trunk up and back over his head, and surged forward into a run. Straight across the river bed he went and up the path to the north.

The shot wakened my companion. I stood up to reload the gun and we both listened for further sounds. Presently, from about three hundred yards to the north, there came a deep groan. I knew that sound. When an elephant comes down after a lung shot he frequently gives vent to that deep far-carrying groan. I have never known him to loose it until after he has fallen. He may or may not then get to his feet again, but provided he isn't disturbed he probably won't move from that spot and will presently fall again (if he is up) for the last time. I had been perfectly confident of my shot; but that groan assured me I would find the big fellow there next morning.

Having had a smoke, I suggested to my companion that he take next watch. I didn't expect anything else to arrive until close to daybreak, but I certainly hoped those rhino would then put in another appearance. I slept soundly until I felt my companion's hand squeeze my shoulder. I looked up to see him peering down at me. As soon as he saw that my eyes were open, he turned his head and looked beyond the water hole. I did likewise and saw a rhino coming up the river bed. I sat up and got hold of the gun. The moon was well over to the west by now, but we were still in deep shadow. The rock bar would have made it difficult for anything but baboons or monkeys to get a drink from the downstream end of the water hole, so I knew the rhino would have to turn and expose his broadside. In due course he did so, and again the old gun roared.

The rhino loosed a snort of surprise, bounced up and down once or twice, then whipped around and went dashing back downstream. The range would have been close to twenty paces, but I felt sure that the six drams of powder would be able to drive the ball deep enough to kill. I again stood up to reload and then had another smoke, as there was no likelihood of the other rhino's showing up immediately after the shot. If she had been close she would doubtless have gone for her life and I wouldn't see her again tonight. If she were so far out that she didn't hear or couldn't place the shot, then we would have ample time to enjoy our smoke before she arrived.

I told my companion he could have another forty winks if he liked. I had had about four hours and was greatly refreshed and wide-awake. But for a long time nothing happened. In fact, it wasn't until long after the morning star had risen and was climbing high in the eastern sky, and I knew that daybreak couldn't be far off, that the second rhino at last arrived. She hurried down the same path she had used before as though she knew she had been dawdling, and I shot her exactly as I had shot the elephant. She loosed a muffled scream of surprise and pain and went haring off down the river bed in the direction taken by the first rhino.

As there was little hope of anything else arriving that I would want to shoot, I told my lad he could collect a few dry sticks and brew us a pot of coffee. Day was breaking before the coffee was ready. As soon as we had swallowed it we went out to look for our elephant. Sure enough, he was flat out just where that deep groan had come from. After admiring his great tusks, we cut off the tail in the customary manner, as proof of possession, and then went back to the river to look for the rhino.

We found them lying on the sand within about sixty yards of each other and perhaps a hundred and fifty yards downstream from the water hole, around a bend which had prevented their being seen from it.

This was a splendid beginning, but really no more than I had expected. I killed another fine tusker four or five days later at a different water hole; and altogether during the two and a half months I used that old gun I bagged thirteen good bull elephant and eight rhino. Since the small number of suitable balls I was able to get for it were then exhausted, I had to quit. I didn't have a single misfire and didn't lose a single wounded animal.

Men with their modern breech-loaders and repeaters are all too much inclined to sneer at the muzzle-loader. But a good muzzle-loader, properly handled, is a very deadly and effective weapon—provided its limitations are fully realized.

6: THE GREAT TANA RAID

I'm not being too specific about the date of this adventure—it's still too recent. And I doubt that there has ever been a bigger, more highly organized, or more successful poaching raid anywhere. Furthermore, the beauty of it was that, as far as I was concerned, it all came about quite accidentally.

I was supposed to be en route to faraway Eire and had boarded a steamer making for Europe via Suez. But I never reached Eire. We put into Dar es Salaam, that pleasant place (as its name signifies), and I went ashore and wandered around the Arab section where I had many friends and acquaintances. I was hoping to get news of my old friend Sherif, the smuggler, and great was my delight when I found the rascal in a small Arab eating house run by a Somali who was known to me. He greeted me jovially and roared for the proprietor to bring something special. In due course a most delectable meal was served: the flesh of a young goat curried and cooked in ghee, with onions and garlic and numerous spices; snow-white rice and saffron-tinted rice cooked as it is cooked only east of Suez; delicious little patties of finely minced lamb, curried and spiced and seasoned with ground-up red chilis until it made my beard curl, wrapped in paper-thin pastry; and countless little side dishes of hard-boiled fowls' eggs chopped up with raw native cucumbers, little sweet native tomatoes cooked with ground peanuts and seasoned with red peppers, green peas mixed with carrots and covered with a smooth white sauce, slices of ripe mangoes and pawpaws, oranges and lemons and grapes and pineapples; and all served together to be eaten at the same time. In due course we sat back, easing our cracking belts and wistfully eying the remains of the feast. Sweet Turkish coffee was then brought, and I passed around my fat Turkish cigarettes. When the coffee was finished the proprietor, Saidi, who had personally supervised the service of the meal, joined us with his hookah, to which he had fitted two new amber mouthpieces for Sherif's and my benefit. And so, a decent interval of time having passed, as we sucked in the fragrant smoke through the bubbling rose water in the belly of the hookah Sherif asked me whither I was bound. I told him and then asked what he was up to. And what he had to tell me made me prick up my ears.

It seemed he had arranged to meet one Mir Hafiz Ullah Khan, a fine Pathan who was known to me, and a man called Hidayetulla whom I did not know but who was, I had heard, a good buyer of rhino horn. Sherif was to pick up these heroes in Lamu, one of the oldest Arab townships on the island of the same name, on the East African coast, and take them along to a certain quiet spot on what was then the Italian Somaliland coast. It appeared that Mir Hafiz was all man and wasn't satisfied merely to stick around Lamu and buy poached rhino horn—he wanted to go poach it himself. From what I knew of the Mir I could well believe that. I had also heard that it was quite a regular thing for Somali and Jubaland tribesmen to sweep down across the Juba desert on poaching raids into Kenya, British East Africa. They killed rhino for the horn, which is greatly prized throughout the East for its aphrodisiac properties. But those poachers did practically all their work with powerful bows and poisoned arrows. This poison, which I have used myself, kills in a remarkably short space of time when fresh. But it *must* be fresh.

Now I had long promised myself that I would join one of these poaching parties, though naturally I was thinking in terms of rifles—good as the bows and arrows were, they weren't in the same country block as a rifle in the hands of a man who knew how to use it.

Sherif must have seen the faraway look in my eyes because his own were twinkling at me when I turned to him and he realized that I had risen to the bait.

"Do you have to go to Europe just now, my friend?" he asked. "The Khan has a very high opinion of you, and I know he would be overjoyed if you could be persuaded to join him on this safari. He was asking about you the last time I saw him. Well?"

I grinned at him. "Can you send your dinghy across tonight to get my kit off the steamer?"

That is how the thing started.

Sherif and I had a glorious sail up the coast and found the other members of the party impatiently awaiting us at Lamu. Mir Hafiz Ullah Khan was a magnificent specimen of a fighting man and adventurer: six feet of lean, hard, tough manhood. His companion, Hidayetulla, was short, squat, burly, immensely broad, and looked as though he had the strength of an Alaskan brown bear. He was armed with a Manton double .470 which he wielded as easily as the average man would a 20-bore shotgun. The Khan had a Holland double .465. So had I; and also my little Purdey .450/.400, which I intended to use, taking the .465 along as a spare.

Leaving Lamu we had another fine sail up the coast before Sherif brought us one dark night into a quiet and sheltered little cove rather less than a million miles north of Kismayu. There wasn't a cape or a point, a bay or a cove, a rock or a shoal or a reef from south of Ibo to Suez that was not known to Sherif. We had had several conferences concerning the proposed safari and decided now to do things in a much bigger way than had originally been intended. We would part from Sherif here, and arranged to meet him some five to seven months hence in a certain quiet spot known to him and to me on Formosa Bay, away to the south. We fixed ourselves up with camels and moved inland. Here we had to undertake a considerable amount of staff work, for there were many arrangements to be made beforehand if all was to work smoothly when we got into action. The main difficulty was one of distances and the fact that we would be unable to use the camels throughout because of the thorn. The scheme I proposed made it necessary to send reliable men ahead right away on fast camels to arrange for a number of pack mules if they were available, or donkeys if they were not, to await us at a certain water hole in the northwest frontier province of Kenya. In due course we would sweep over the Juba River and across the Karoli section of the Juba Desert. We would poach the rhino along the Uaso Nyiro to where it runs to earth in the Lorian Swamp. Rhino were our main object, but there was no reason why we shouldn't collect ivory also. We ought to get plenty with the aid of ladders in the Lorian. We would exchange our camels for the mokes and cut across to the Tana—along the Tana the thorn would play havoc with the camels' feet so they would return while we went on with the hooved animals. But apart from those we needed to carry grub and ivory and horn, I wanted another lot to drift along behind us and if necessary act as decoys.

So far as I knew, all previous poaching parties which had come as far as the Uaso Nyiro had returned thence. I had never heard of any attempting the long run down along the Tana to the coast; though from time to time they raided in from the coast, it was only locally. However, I had great hopes of this long run. I knew there were plenty of rhino, and more heavily tusked elephant are shot in Tanaland than in any other part of British Africa. But it's mighty tough going. It's no good just following the river, whether it be the Uaso Nyiro or the Tana. The rhino are to be found from three to five miles from the river in each case, coming in just evenings for a drink, while the elephant will rarely be within less than ten miles of the river and may be fifteen to twenty or thirty miles from it.

I had met a fine Somali, whom I shall call Hamisi, an accomplished hunter and poacher who had never handled anything but a rifle from his youth up, who had begged me to take him with me. And so what I proposed was that Hamisi and I take the south side of the river, hunting from three to five miles apart and more or less parallel with the river, while the two Pathans take the north side of the same river and, in the same way, hunt some miles apart parallel with us. We would all have half-a-dozen young strong porters with us carrying water and grub and such ivory and horn as we shot. The main body of the safari would follow along the river and we would all come in from time to time to connect with them. In that way we could renew supplies, hand over all horn and ivory, exchange porters, and, if all four of us hunters happened to come in together, we could have a day's rest and exchange notes and news. Besides, the men with the pack trains would be wanting meat from time to time. My idea in having the second train following a day's march behind, and accompanied by two intelligent fellows mounted on fast mules, was that in the event of the British game department's officials' getting after us, the spare pack train, with nothing but grass in the packs, would swing away to the north and head out into the desert as though fleeing from the wrath to come. If the spoor of the real pack train was blotted out for a short distance, it was a hundred to one that the ranger would miss it and make after the fleeing burros. The scouts on the mules would gallop along to tell us what was happening and give us any warning that was needed should our decoys fail in their object—though I felt pretty confident that we would be able to trick any ranger who might appear on our trail. After all, these fellows we had with us were all hand-picked men who had had plenty of experience poaching. Game rangers in Africa spend most of their time in offices, and when they go out they drive and have almost forgotten how to walk. Hunting for months in dry-bush zones and thorn deserts needs a tough man. No matter how keen a ranger might be, he couldn't hope to be as tough as we were because we would have had months of it before he heard of us at all. I fully realized that word of our activities would get around sooner or later but I expected to be well away before authority was close enough to worry about. We would be constantly on the go: we would not be sitting down for ten days or a fortnight every few weeks. I couldn't see any present-day ranger catching us. And even if they did get the drop on us—well, we were four, weren't we? We were all wanderers, gypsies, adventurers: none of us had any hankering to find ourselves locked up within four walls. I had a hunch it would take more than one East African game ranger to rope us in—a man, like as not, who imagined he would only have to show us some tin badge to have us promptly hand over our guns and rifles!

I have mentioned earlier my grief when trying to get around Africa with pack burros; but at that time I hadn't had any experience with Somali animals. The pack mokes and mules the Somali supplied us with were splendid. Many of the burros, like Zanzibar donkeys, were almost as big as mules, and all were willing workers. We had no trouble with them whatsoever. And the same applied to the camels we used for the first part of the safari. If you take a look at the map you may reckon we had an insuperable job making all the necessary arrangements beforehand; but it really wasn't so difficult. I had lived sufficiently long in the East not to be too concerned with exact time—it's only a fool who is, when trying to get things done there. We merely told those concerned what we wanted and left it to them. They could make their own arrangements; and darned well they must have made them because we had no hitch throughout the whole safari. If we had tried to attend to all the petty little details and have everything just so before starting, seeing to and supervising all matters ourselves, why, we should probably still be there as aged men vainly trying to get things squared up for the start.

Having given our advance party adequate time, allowing for all contingencies, in which to round up our pack trains, we mounted our camels, crossed the Juba River, and struck out across the desert to the southwest. When we reached the previously arranged rendezvous we exchanged the camels for the mules and mokes and made for the Uaso Nyiro. Here Hamisi and I crossed over and, as I did not expect to find many elephant yet, we arranged that he should hunt about four or five miles from the river and I about another mile farther out. He was the proud possessor of a quite illicitly owned .404 Jeffery-Mauser. If Hamisi hadn't been a good Mohammedan I guess he would have worshiped that rifle.

The inexperienced or uninitiated who have visited the Uaso Nyiro and hunted within a mile or so of the river might well get the impression that there are few rhino around those parts; but stroll along about four to six miles from the river and more or less parallel with it and you may encounter twelve to fifteen rhino or more a day. However, I'm not going to say a great deal about rhino here; I shall have more to say about them by-and-by. This section of the book is intended to deal principally with elephant. We didn't get any elephant here, so I'll push along to the Lorian Swamp—I don't mean to imply that there were no elephant along the Uaso Nyiro, but we had agreed that it wouldn't do for any of us to pick up elephant spoor and just follow it indefinitely (it's so difficult to drop a good spoor when you are on it). Consequently, we would shoot only those elephant we actually encountered or found after following spoor for not more than an hour. Otherwise our safari would inevitably become disorganized. There were plenty of rhino waiting for us, and we were to consider them our main object.

The hunting along the Uaso Nyiro was comparatively easy when compared to what lay ahead of us; and it was a good thing that it was, because it enabled all members of the safari to learn the ropes and general procedure. In the Lorian we found the ladders I had had made of inestimable value. The grass ran about ten feet high and was very tough. It would have been almost impossible to make anything of a bag without the ladders. This was an entirely new game for both the Pathans. Hidayetulla had shot tiger in India and had been across a couple of times to Africa to buy rhino horn, but had never previously hunted in Africa; the Khan had done a fair amount of hunting in India and had had a couple of short safaris in Africa during which he had killed one elephant, a couple of buffalo, several lion, as well as two or three rhino; but he had shot his rhino on the open plains. Naturally, I had had many talks with them all and had given them the benefit of my experience and as many tips as I could think of. They both became excellent hunters; but the Khan was the better of the two. He had a cooler head, was less excitable than his companion. Of course, on a safari such as this, lasting more than half a year, they had an unequaled opportunity to acquire experience and could not have had a better introduction to real African hunting. And they took the fullest advantage of it.

In the long grass of the Lorian we would go out together and I would make a reconnaissance from the top of my ladder to see exactly where the elephant were. We would then close in and all mount ladders after I had pointed out where each was to go. I would wait for them to get into position. At length I would open fire. Sometimes after the first shot, sometimes not until I had fired several times, the remaining elephant would stampede. And inevitably they would approach one of the other ladders. Swinging away from that rifle, they would approach another. And so it went until we figured we had killed all the shootable bulls. There was plenty of excitement floating around and not a little danger. It's not too easy to kill an elephant coming straight toward you when you are on top of a ladder—at least when he's stampeding and not charging. A stampeding elephant in long grass and high bush usually carries his trunk up over his head or out in front of him. If you are on the ground you can shoot him in the chest, but you can't do that if you are ten feet above the ground.

On one occasion I was watching after the elephant had run from me toward Hidayetulla. He managed to twist himself into a most uncomfortable position from which to shoot; I could see that from where I was. He fired, and next instant all I could see of him was the soles of his feet as he disappeared backward into the grass. The recoil of the rifle had knocked him off his perch because of the awkward position from which he'd fired. But the shot had turned the elephant so that he wasn't run down. Otherwise that might well have been the end of his career—the elephant would have been unable to see him on account of the grass and would likely have trampled him underfoot without knowing they had done so.

Hamisi was excellent. I never saw him become the least bit excited. Calm, cool, and entirely without fear, he was a patient and deliberate shot. A natural-born hunter. His .404 fitted him as though it had been built into his hands.

Some of the ivory we shot here, and most of what we shot along the Tana, was too big for the pack mokes; but I had anticipated that and had lack saws with which to cut it into more suitable size for packing. I had found this an excellent thing with porters. Big tusks make a very awkward load for man or beast, whether carried separately or tied to a long stick and carried by two men. If you cut them into more suitable lengths and weights you will get along much better. (I well remember how grateful my men were when I first produced the hack saws.)

While we were hunting in the Lorian our mule-mounted scouts were ranging far and wide to spot the approach of any other safaris. But none was reported. Having skimmed the cream from this district, we now push d south by west to the Tana. Almost at once we commenced to get big elephant. They were generally lone bulls, though occasionally they were in pairs. To cover the greatest amount of ground, Hamisi would start hunting some five miles from the river and then zigzag over perhaps a coup'e of miles as he made his way along roughly parallel with the river. I would push out four or five miles beyond him and follow a zigzag course out there. Hamisi's zigzags would not take him toward the river but out toward me; while mine would take me toward him. The two Baluchis were doing the same thing as far as possible on the other side of the river. In that way we should be hunting pretty thoroughly a strip close to five miles wide between five and ten miles from the river on each side. Naturally, we could not expect to cover *all* the ground; but we should be able to spot all fresh spoor anywhere in those strips, and any rhino or elephant that escaped us could consider himself mighty lucky.

As we worked down into Tanaland proper it became really tough hunting and I felt that we deserved every rhino and elephant we shot. We certainly worked for them. There was nothing of the champagne safari about this kind of hunting. This was no millionaire's luxury outing with iceboxes and long cold drinks and radio and airplanes for spotting the game, and a walk of seldom more than a quarter of a mile to get your shot. This was the real thing. But believe me, the rewards were truly princely when the god of hunters figured that a reward had been earned. Almost without exception every tusk had to be cut for easy packing. And, as is so often the case with these big bulls way out in this sort of tough bush country, the elephant were never on the alert and so were easily approached if you could spot them without bumping your nose into them. Though even that wasn't so bad, because they were often found in the shade of some tree they had known about and used so often that there would be a clear space around it. Needless to say, the shooting was all at very close range. The longest shot I fired on this safari after we hit the Tana was about thirty-five paces. And there was only one of these; the vast majority were well under twenty paces. The average was probably somewhere between twelve and fifteen strides. And much the same applied to rhino. If anything, the rhino were shot at even closer range— some of them at a very few feet. Owing to the type of bush, the elephant could be seen more easily than the rhino, which were better concealed because they were not so tall. Although some of the rhino charged unexpectedly, getting our wind when we passed them without knowing there was a rhino there, we did not find them so very aggressive. They were too far from everywhere and any sort of molestation—the country was too tough for most modern hunters with white skins, and we were beyond the range of the Wakamba with their poisoned arrows. But the bush was so thick and thorny that a rhino would be almost on you before you could see him at all, so it was most necessary for a hunter to *carry his own rifle*. No leaving the rifle to a gunbearer here! It was fiendishly hot and tiring country to hunt, and you had to be constantly on the alert because a rhino might be encountered at any moment of the day.

As in the long grass, I found the ladder a great help here also and had advised my companions to take theirs with them, and *use* them. There were sections where they were useless, but there were many occasions when they enabled me to spot my rhino—or elephant—while still a long way from him and decide on the best approach. Moreover, by mounting the ladder at not-too-infrequent intervals, I could spot the various trees and patches of shade and make for them. During the hot midday hours both elephant and rhino would seek whatever shady spots they could find. The hunting often consisted of wandering from one patch of shade to another with the virtual certainty that if rhino or elephant were in the immediate vicinity they would most likely be here. On a number of occasions I was able to shoot my beast from the top of the ladder, over the intervening bush, while it would have been impossible to make a silent approach on foot to get a clear shot. I have not heard of any other hunter using a ladder in this way other than in grass.

The first big tusker I encountered here along the Tana gave me the longest shot I had to take on the safari. The bush, as is the case almost everywhere in Africa, varied from extreme density to places which by comparison were quite open. I had struck one of these sparse patches and spotted a mighty tusker standing close to a tree near the center of the open section. Although, as I say, he was near the tree, he must have been about fifteen yards away from it—without doubt he would have used it later when the sun rose higher. But as yet it was scarcely midmorning and the big fellow was just doing nothing. It was impossible to get within thirty-five yards of him owing to the mass of dead and partially burned scrub, sticks, and canelike grass between him and me. Nothing bigger than a cane rat could have moved quietly through that. In any case, there was no real need to get closer. The elephant was side-on to me and offering an easy shot. There was a convenient sapling, about as thick as my wrist, close by. I steadied myself against that as I aimed for the brain. It's really surprising how little is needed to steady you: that sapling was flexible, yet it served its purpose admirably. Is this steadying psychological? I'm quite sure psychology plays a very real part in it, the knowledge that there is something to steady you being frequently of greater assistance than the actual help rendered. Be that as it may, I killed this monster without any trouble, my bullet finding his brain and bringing him down instantly where he stood. We then circled around until we found the track he had used to get through the mass of dead stuff to where he lay. We had had a lot of talk about this business of shooting elephant because of the time it usually takes to get out the ivory. Originally my companions had intended to shoot only rhino; it was I who had suggested taking ivory also. Since, especially in the case of big elephant, it is generally necessary to cut off the head of a fresh kill before you can get both tusks out, I had suggested we amputate the lips as high up as possible and then get busy with the hack saws. It would mean wasting a certain amount of ivory, but far less than you might imagine. Naturally, you take the whole tusk when possible; but on a prolonged safari like this, where the elephant were mostly large and single, it wouldn't do to hold up the entire safari for the sake of two or four tusks. Having considered this when we first decided on our operations, we all had hack saws with us. This magnificent fellow's teeth were all of six feet long even after being cut off. For ease in carrying I had to cut them in half. I figure from this that these teeth must have been over eight feet long and probably weighed around one hundred twenty pounds apiece. (By the way, elephant tusks are not really teeth at all; when I speak of "teeth" I am merely using the customary colloquialism.)

The elephant weren't numerous; but then we hadn't expected them to be. The rhino made up for it. I was greatly and most pleasurably surprised at their numbers. They were almost always alone, though there were a few in pairs: male and female or, more often, cow with more or less well-grown calf. But the bulls seemed to be considerably in the majority. I speak, of course, of those I personally encountered. Our two Pathan friends were not particularly concerned with the sex of the rhino they shot so long as the horns were good; but Hamisi, having had so much more experience in African hunting, did take note. Besides, you can usually tell the cow's horns from the bull's—they are longer and thinner. And I gathered from Hamisi and the beasts he shot that the cows and calves did not push out quite so far into the bush as the bulls. This, of course, was what one might have expected.

We didn't return to the river nightly—it would have been sheer waste of energy and time. We would bivouac wherever we happened to be each night, then, after two or three nights, would make toward the river to get more water. Every night we slept in a different place, because each day we hunted in an easterly direction. The breeze, such as it was, was mostly in our favor. During the midday hours it would drop considerably and become a mite fitful, but that didn't worry us because the heat was so great that we usually took an hour or two's rest then in the best bit of shade we could find. Lean and hard and tough, it's remarkable how you can train yourself to go for long spells without water, even in such heat. The more you drink, the more you want and the more you suffer if you don't get it. Much the same applies to food: the man who habitually overeats will suffer and weaken more and sooner from hunger than he who eats seldom and sparingly.

It was a full six weeks before the four of us met at the river. And then Hamisi and I did have a laugh! The two Pathans were literally in rags and tatters. Even their puggrees (turban cloths) were ripped and torn and slashed by the thorn. Long years of hunting in dense bush have in large measure trained me to make my way through it as the African does, without leaving it festooned with my hide and flesh. Hamisi wore far more in the way of clothing than I did, but he had the true African knack of sliding through apparently impenetrable stuff without getting himself hung up on it.

Mir Khan enjoyed the joke at his own expense, and he told me that whenever he and Hidayetulla had met at the river and seen the ragged condition to which they were being reduced by the thorn, they had chuckled to think of me in all my nakedness trying to get through it, and wondered how long it would be before I took to wearing clothes. They expected to see little but my bare skeleton walking around by the time we met—reckoned I would have left every scrap of flesh I possessed behind me, ornamenting the thorn. But as a matter of fact it's going without clothes that teaches you how to get through thorn, both silently and expeditiously. In addition, when you have no clothes on you don't suffer from the heat to anything like the extent you do if you are fully clothed. This is because even your own movements cause a slight draft, when there is no breeze stirring, and that slight draft causes evaporation to start on whatever perspiration there is and so immediately commences to cool you. You don't get the benefit of that if you are wearing clothes, no matter how light and open those clothes may be. Then if it rains you have nothing to worry about; it's most refreshing, and when it's over you have no wet and clammy things sticking to you and possibly chafing you. You are dry in a few minutes.

Needless to say all four of us were delighted at our success so far. But I had to remind my companions that this was but the beginning, that we could look forward to even greater success as we worked our way down toward the coast. I warned them also that we could look forward to even tougher conditions when we entered the coastal belt. My prophecies were not unjustified. Right here we were practically on the equator, about halfway between the 39th and 40th parallels of East Longitude. Presently the river would take a turn toward the southeast and then run almost due south along the 40th parallel. From the time we were roughly halfway between the 1st and 2nd parallels of South Latitude we would be getting into more and more fertile soil. The dry scrub thorn would gradually give place to heavy forest with incredibly dense and tall undergrowth for some miles back from the river. After crossing the 2nd parallel I was convinced that we would do better to hunt closer to the river than we had been doing. There was so much cover and fine shade and so much feeding that I was certain neither elephant nor rhino would wander so far after watering. Accordingly, after we worked our way down there, we closed in and hunted the strip lying between three and five miles from the river on each side. Whether or not I was correct in my assumption I cannot say, but if there were more elephant and rhino farther out than there were in this strip then they certainly must have been abundant. I ı m quite satisfied in my own mind that we did the correct thing in working the strip closer to the river. Only once did I shoot more than two e. ephant in a day (that was when I shot one in the morning and then two in the afternoon) and sometimes I would go several days without an elephant in the bag; but I was rarely without a rhino and usually there we. e several. Of course, I encountered many, many more rhino than I sho . Time and again there would just be a snort and a crash in the bush close by to tell that there had been a rhino there. I never attempted to follow up such animals: it would have been mere waste of time, much better to go on the hope for better luck next time.

We were not quite halfway to the coast, roughly where the 1st parallel of South Latitude cuts the 40th of East Longitude, when the first news of possible trouble reached us. Hamisi and I had reached the river and were wondering if the other two would put in an appearance this day. They were due to do so, and we hoped they would. Having had a thoroughly enjoyable bath in the river—keeping a wary eye out for crocodiles, the bane and curse of all African rivers—we were lounging in the shade and chatting of this and that. Suddenly there came the pounding of hooves, and one of our mule-mounted scouts came galloping up from the rear. He hauled his mount to a sliding stop close by, threw himself from the saddle almost before the beast had stopped, and came running to where we were sitting.

"They're coming, *Bwana*," he gasped in Kiswahili. He was short of breath from excitement. "There are two white men and I'm sure they're officials. They have natives in some kind of uniform like police, and they must be game scouts. All are armed except the servants and those driving the asses. The whites are mounted."

"Are they close?"

"No, *Bwana*. They are more than a full day's march behind our rearguard, who, as you know, are a full day's march behind you. I saw them myself—they had camped down. I left my companion to watch them and galloped along here to tell you, warning our rearguard as you told me to. I passed the two Indians about a mile back; they are coming here."

(He was referring to our two Pathan friends. To the African anyone who hails from across the Indian Ocean is an Indian. Pathans, of course, are not really Indians.)

"You have done well, son," I commended him. "Rest yourself and your mule now. Presently, when we have had a talk with our friends, you will return with orders."

So it had come at last. Had we merely been trekking we could easily have outdistanced or lost our pursuers, but we still had a whole lot of fine country to hunt. I didn't take to the notion of skipping it just because of a couple of officials. Besides, there was our rearguard. They might as well do something for their keep. It was precisely for this that they were there.

When the Khan and his companion arrived they at once asked me to decide what steps we should take. I had the whole thing clear enough in my own mind—had considered just such a possibility long ago when we were first planning the raid, so it did not take long to make things clear to them. What I suggested was that the mounted scout return and tell our rearguard to swing away to the north after wiping out our spoor for a reasonable distance. He would then go on and tell his companion, who was keeping our pursuers under observation, that he was to *let them see him following on the spoor of the rearguard* where it had turned off. If that would not entice them to follow I didn't know of anything that would. Our mounted scout would lie concealed where he could see what happened when the pursuers reached the turnoff, and come along and tell us. The other mounted scout was to keep with the rearguard—by now red herrings—for a day or two until he was sure the officials were following. He could then cut through the bush back to the river and follow us. We could use him; having done his stuff he would be wasted with the decoys. We ourselves would remain where we were, and have our customary day's rest, but would be ready to move off at a moment's notice. Our mounted scout would be able to give us ample warning if the rangers refused to be decoyed out into the desert. If all went well I could see no very good reason why we shouldn't be able to continue hunting right down to the coast as originally planned.

It might be asked: Had we not considered the possibility of the rangers' catching up with our decoys, realizing they had been diddled, and then haring after us determined to extract vengeance for such a slight to their dignity? Well, we did consider it, but I immediately brushed it aside. My experience with cops—both the regular police and such quasi-police as game rangers, revenue officers, customs men and coast guards—has been that if they fail in their first attempt they just give up. Have you ever heard of the police putting a second man up for trial if the first suspected murderer actually brought to trial is found not guilty? It would seem that, having roped in one fellow and made a sufficient case against him to bring him to trial, they have expended all their energy for that particular murder. And so it seems to be with these other fellows. I was confident that when they eventually caught our decoys—if they ever did catch them—and found nothing but bundles of grass on the burros, they would swear like hell and return to their headquarters without making the slightest attempt to follow us again. They would excuse themselves and their failure by saying that the real offenders must be far away by now and they would have no hope of overtaking them. It wouldn't occur to them that there might be a white man leading the raiders, and since they aren't accustomed to audacity from brown or black skins in Africa, it wouldn't enter their heads that we might be continuing our nefarious practices in spite of them. These petty officials have an overweening sense of their own importance and would doubtless salve any murmurings of conscience with the remark that it was unreasonable to expect Europeans to be able to catch desert-bred "wogs" in such country, and that at any rate they had done their duty by putting a stop to the poaching. And they would kid themselves that they had actually stopped it and would have no difficulty in finding specious excuses to cover their ineptitude.

So it was that we were able to continue our safari as planned, unmolested. Hamisi actually ran out of shells for his .404 when we still had some weeks' hunting before us—so greatly had the reality exceeded his fondest expectations. To his unbounded joy I lent him my .465. I am not in the habit of lending rifles but had had ample opportunity to see what a first-class hunter he was and the truly loving care he took of his own rifle. When he returned my .465 to me at the end of the safari I would never have known it had been fired. Mir Hafiz Ullah Khan also ran out of ammunition, and I was able to give him some of my .465s. Hidayetulla finished up with only three shells left for his .470. I do not permit myself to run short of ammunition. It happened to me once in my early days, and I have taken very good care that it has never happened again.

Finally the day came when we sighted the Indian Ocean once more, and gave our rifles their final cleaning, oiling, and greasing before packing them away in their cases. I dare not tell you the extent of our bag. If a copy of this book ever found its way out to East Africa—as it almost certainly will—the entire game department might come down with apoplexy and I'd be blamed for it! Not so very long afterward, when I happened to be in Kenya and was talking to a certain official of the game department, the question of poaching was mentioned. The official's florid face turned an expensive purple as he spluttered and fumed into his gin and water over the recollection of this particular raid. I clucked and tut-tutted in sympathy and condemned the audacity of the rascals. Blackguardly! Outrageous! Dastardly! I gave them every adjective I could lay my tongue to.

2

MIXED BAG

7: RHINO

The rhino—we never give him his full name out here—is the only animal in Africa likely to make an unprovoked attack: always excepting the occasional rogue hippo that delights in upsetting canoes. Even at that, nine out of every ten rhino charges are blind rushes with more bluff than evil intent. The rhino is afflicted with poor eyesight and an inquisitive disposition, and these two attributes don't mix well. On the great open plains of British East Africa the rhino stampedes, startled, from one part of the long straggling safari which is characteristic of those parts and blunders into another part. Thinking he is being surrounded he converts his stampede into a blind charge on the assumption that attack—or bluff —is his best defense. He is not difficult to dodge in the open, since he usually just continues at full speed in the direction in which he is facing. But if you fire a shot and fail to kill or drop him he will often circle around, pick up your wind, and come again. However, he's not hard to turn. Almost any bullet on the end of his nose will suffice.

In thick bush the situation is rather different. If the thorn is of the hawk's-bill or wait-a-bit variety it may be a physical impossibility to get out of his way, especially since you may not be able to see him until his head breaks through the bush right beside you, perhaps a mere three feet away. You must just stand your ground and shoot the brute. That's all right if you are hunting rhino, but you will curse him if you are following elephant spoor. If the elephant hear the shot they will go for their lives. Many a time have I sworn at rhino under these conditions when hunting in certain districts. But when I took to hunting the beasts in a different area on the other side of the river, which no other hunter had ever worked (the local natives told me) and in which the rhino were very numerous, I spent about three months a year there for four consecutive years and never had a rhino do more than make faces at me. Yet I shot about two hundred of them. The point is that I lost no wounded—all those I shot I killed, the others I didn't molest. Do you have the picture? On the south side of the river there had been considerable hunting for many years, and the rhino there had been wounded and chevied around until they became bad-tempered; but my rhino had never been interfered with. The local natives were eternally wandering around looking for wild honey and trees to fell and hollow out into dugout canoes; yet in spite of all the inquiries I made I did not hear of a single one of them ever being attacked by a rhino. As I have remarked before, clean killing doesn't worry the game; it's incessant wounding and battering that clears game out of a district or, in the case of rhino and similar animals, makes them dangerous to man.

During the course of my great poaching raid along the Tana River my three companions and I encountered a great many rhino, but we were charged on remarkably few occasions. There were times when we passed close by some rhino that was probably sleeping on the other side of a thick bush; when he got our wind he not unnaturally made a blind rush straight for us. But many that were surprised in that same manner did not attack: there would be a snort and a crash in the bush and we would hear the sounds getting farther and farther away as the beast put as much distance as possible between us and him in the shortest possible space of time. (And a rhino will go through stuff that even a stampeding elephant wouldn't face at full speed—from twenty to twenty-five miles an hour— as though it were wet paper.) So you see, the ordinary rhino scarcely deserves his evil reputation.

The small rhino in the far north of the northwest frontier province have a very bad name for pugnaciousness. I have not had sufficient experience with them to express an opinion; but Blaney Percival, for many years game warden of Kenya and a keen observer who kept copious notes, has stated that he found them very much more dangerous and aggressive than rhino in other parts of the territory. However, he appeared to overlook the small point that these rhino are not infrequently poached by raiders from what was then Italian Somaliland and that such poachers nearly all used poisoned arrows. As in the case of the Wakamba, these folks don't make their own poison but have to buy or trade it from the Wanderobo. The result is that the poison isn't always as fresh as it ought to be. When fresh it kills in a very short space of time—the animal runs, stops, sways, and falls—but if it is not fresh it probably won't kill. Instead, the wound will fester. Percival knew that such poaching took place but possibly he didn't realize to what extent, and therefore how great an effect there would be on the game.

An idea of the numbers of rhino in those parts may be gained when I tell you that throughout our better than half-a-year safari there was scarcely a day when we didn't encounter some except when we were cutting across from the Lorian to the Tana and, of course, when we were actually in the Lorian, which is mostly swamp. My companions made no attempt to keep count of the rhino they encountered, other than those they actually shot and those that charged them. Even then, if they failed to kill the rhino that charged, they would sometimes forget about him when, later, they were charged again. (I would like it to be clearly understood that I use the word "charge" here for lack of a better term—I don't wish to give a false impression because I am not writing for the lovers of thrills at the expense of the true facts.) It would usually be the last attack that would remain in their minds and that they would describe when we met for a day's rest. But judging from my own experience and that of Hamisi, and as well as I could get it from the two Pathans, we each encountered from seven to twenty-seven rhino a day; and, of course, there were many others thereabouts which we didn't encounter. This means that the rhino of those parts can be reckoned in the thousands. The conditions are so tough that they are practically never hunted except by poachers. In many parts along the Tana I don't suppose they had ever been hunted before our raid; and I'm quite sure they haven't been hunted since.

Some of the blank stretches we struck were doubtless due to distance from favored watering places. In his day habits the rhino seems a surly misanthrope who wants no company but his own; but just see him at night around a watering place! It appears that a rhino must have his "sundowner," and must have it as soon as possible after sundown. He wakes up during the late afternoon or early evening, depending on how far he has to go, and almost at once starts making his way toward the water, feeding as he goes. If he has dawdled and finds the sun dropping he will break into a trot and keep that up until he reaches his destination. Here, especially on moonlit nights, he seems to go completely crazy when he meets with others of his species. The animals squeal and snort and gambol around, boosting each other like young pigs. Their agility is amazing. It's an incredible sight. Sheer lightness of heart would seem the only explanation. Percival describes this very well in one of his books. He watches a rhino come to a water hole a hundred yards away and says that in a couple of hours there were about a dozen of the brutes there. Shortly afterward two of them appeared to go mad, marching up and down as though they were holding the river against all comers. They made so much noise that Percival at last fired a shot into the air to quiet them.

Pack animals—especially males—don't like the smell of rhino. A rhino passing close upwind will usually stampede them. Which reminds me that horses can't abide the smell of giraffe, and mules don't like them either. But to return to rhino: the animals are most regular in their habits, feeding and watering in familiar places and even returning to the same spots to dung. They will be found under the same trees and bushes at the same hours each day, and use the same paths to and from watering. This last is a detail you would do well to remember. Never pitch camp on or close to a rhino path. I've never done so myself but know others who did and sorely regretted it. I mention Percival again. He tells us how around nine-thirty one night he was sitting writing in his diary. Upon finishing he left the companion with whom he was sharing his tent and went out to look at the traps he had set for small mammals wanted by a certain naturalist he knew. There was bright moonlight, so he did not take a lamp. When he was about fifty yards from his tent he heard from upwind something which he describes as sounding "like a motorcar gone mad" and saw a cloud of white dust coming toward the tents. The cloud passed close to where he stood so he could see it was raised by a rhino and her half-grown calf. In the next moment there was a crash, a squeal, and another crash followed by a chorus of yells. He hastened back to camp and found his companion creeping out from under the wreck of their tent, asking if it had been a whirlwind. Having destroyed the first tent the rhino had then made for the second, in which Percival's servants were sleeping. The camp was completely wrecked—torn tents and smashed gear scattered all over the countryside. There was even a muddy rhino footprint on Percival's pillow. It was a good thing he hadn't yet turned in. And, since there had been eight natives sleeping in the other tent, it was remarkable that no one was seriously injured. Percival adds, "By sheer luck this was the only night during that trip on which we had not tied up the horses in front of the tent, otherwise there can be little doubt one or more of them would have been killed."

There is little sport attached to shooting rhino on the open plains. Provided the wind is right, all you have to do is walk to within easy range and fire. But in bush country it is real sport. Spooring from the water is seldom difficult, owing to the rhino's constant use of the same path, and if you arrive at his feeding grounds and lying-up places when the sun is well up you will usually find him flat out to it. If it is a hot district he'll be panting and foaming at the mouth. The rhino is about the only animal I know that relaxes as completely as a hog. When he's asleep he's dead to the world. Still, he's a denizen of the wild and it doesn't take much to awaken him. I remember once during the Tana raid I spotted a rhino asleep from the top of my ladder. I had first seen his tree from about a third of a mile away and had gradually approached, taking a reconnaissance from the top of the ladder from time to time to see that I was closing in from the right direction. Finally I mounted the ladder when I was about ten yards away for a last look around before attempting an approach on foot. But I couldn't see how I was going to move closer without giving my wind to anything under the tree, as the bush was very dense between me and it and going around to the far side where things appeared to be somewhat more open would put me upwind. As I stood there on the ladder I realized that the black bulk under the tree was my rhino, asleep. Since the straggling top of the thorn between me and him prevented my getting a clear view of him, I beckoned to my gunbearer, an excellent youth called Nasibbin-Risik, an Arab-Swahili cross and a good one. He quietly mounted the opposite side of the ladder so that I could whisper into his ear. Only a word was necessary because I'd had many talks with him around the campfire at night or when resting at midday, had told him what I might be wanting him to do from time to time, and had shown him how to do it. Consequently there was no long conversation now. He nodded, grinned, and descended the ladder. He then stooped, picked up a couple of stones, and gently tapped them together. Nothing happened, so I nodded, and again he tapped the stones, a bit more loudly. That was all that was necessary. The rhino had heard him and raised his head to sniff the breeze. Had it been a metallic sound, like that of the butt of my rifle clashing against the butt of my revolver, it would have had a very different effect. Any metallic sound is quite foreign to the bush and therefore spells danger to the game, but the click of two stones might be caused by another animal also looking for a patch of shade. So my rhino wasn't particularly worried. When he lifted his head he gave me the shot I wanted, and I slipped my bullet into the base of his skull just where the neck joins it. It killed him instantly. But on the heels of the shot there came a snort and a scrambling rush through the bush on my right. It was a second rhino, of whose existence I had been totally unaware. The bush was very dense and I could see nothing but I yelled to Nasib to get around the ladder and out of the way. Had I been standing at the foot of the ladder I would have been unable to see the rhino's head until it broke through the bush within less than three feet of me. From the top of the ladder things were rather better, though if I failed to bring him down he would inevitably whip the ladder from under me. I don't think he was charging, but the result would have been the same as if he had been. From my position on top of the ladder all I could do was use the rifle like a revolver, letting it hang down at arm's length and firing at an angle of about fifty degrees from the horizontal. As the rhino's head broke through the bush I drove my bullet down through the top of it. He crashed to his nose and his momentum skidded him forward until his face was right alongside the foot of the ladder. Just for interest, and to give my heroes something definite to talk about, I showed them how it was barely possible to slip a matchbox sideways between the rhino's cheek and the foot of the ladder.

They were greatly delighted over the whole performance: they had never seen a man use a rifle that way before—could I not kill rhino with my revolver if I could provoke them into charging? And I had to extract a shell from my revolver and put it alongside one from the rifle to show them why that notion wouldn't work. But this didn't worry them. They were willing to bet no other hunters had ever shot a rhino with one hand that way, and wouldn't, either. There was, of course, the usual friendly rivalry between the gunbearers and servants generally as to whose *bwana* was the best hunter and the most skillful. They would have bets on it and actually ran what amounted to a sweepstake on the final totals. Even if we didn't bother to keep tally on our individual bags, our men did.

This little incident may serve to emphasize once again the great advantage of using a rifle you can really handle under all conditions. The .465 can be and has been built as light as and even lighter than the .400, but it's a whole lot more powerful and I wonder what would happen if a man tried to shoot it with one hand like a revolver. It stands to reason that at that reduced weight its recoil would be vastly more pronounced than that of the .400. I have many times had occasion to fire rifles in the .450 to .470 group without putting the butt to my shoulder, but holding the weapon in both hands; and the recoil, though severe, was not unmanageable. But that is a very different thing from firing it with one hand only. Still, you aren't likely to be wanting to do so very often.

Whenever I think of rhino I want to philosophize. Every rhino I've ever shot has been poached. Do game departments not realize that by heavily restricting the shooting of any species with a commercial value they are merely encouraging poachers? (Rhino are shot for their horns, Asiatics believing that they make a powerful aphrodisiac.) If a thing is illegal its value naturally goes up. If rhino were in danger of extermination the restrictions would be quite understandable, and I can certainly appreciate the laws of Kenya which prohibit the shooting of game from automobiles. These "sportsmen," so-called, who used to drive out from Nairobi, the capital, in their cars and shoot the game, almost wiped out the rhino of the Athi plains. Even an incorrigible poacher like myself can look only with scorn and contempt upon that sort of "hunting" and applaud the regulations which put a stop to it. Yet it's amusing that some of those selfsame individuals who to my certain knowledge took part in that slaughter blackguard me and others like me as "wanton slaughterers"! At least we hunt our quarry on foot under the most difficult conditions and stand up to the charge when it comes. We don't take unfair advantage by remaining in the safety of a wire-enclosed automobile.

Much the same applies to those self-styled sportsmen, principally from India but also from Africa, who have never in their lives shot a lion or tiger face to face on foot but only from the safety of a tree or enclosed car or, in India, from the back of a trained elephant. I am fully aware that there are parts of India—the tough grass jungles of the Terai, for instance—where a man on foot would be helpless and would rarely get a shot at all at a tiger. There are many other parts, however, where tiger could well be hunted on foot if the hunter had the necessary nerve; but it's so easy to arrange for beats and drives with the assistance of a couple of tame elephant that that is the method usually employed.

There are also many men in Africa who have photographed and shot lion from the safety of an enclosed car and who would not dream of going after them on foot. These characters, too, are loud in demanding that poachers be laid by the heels and flung into prison for long spells. It's perfectly reasonable, as I say, to restrict the shooting of any particular species that is in danger of being wiped out, like those heavily shot rhino within easy motoring distance of Nairobi; but why restrict the shooting of the great numbers of rhino along the Uaso Nyiro and Tana rivers? It's not as though many of the modern generation in Africa will be wanting to go shoot them, anyway.

I don't and I never shall subscribe to the belief that any government in Africa "owns" the game, the wild animals, and that government and government only has the right to make a profit from it. In the same way I can't recognize the "ownership" of any territory in Africa by a European country. It was acquired by force—with breech-loading rifles—from the original owners, and although it may be given fancy names such as "empire-building" and so on, I prefer plain language. In plain language it was nothing but theft. Because the theft took place some time ago doesn't make it legal. And that is one reason why I wander whithersoever I list and shoot whatsoever I want, without asking permission.

The rhino in thick bush is a truly sporting antagonist, and the hunting of him under these conditions truly a man's game.

Rifles? If I couldn't afford a powerful double rifle for rhino in close cover, I would very much prefer a powerful single-loader to any magazine because it's just as short and compact as a double and has a similar type of safety.

Where to hit him? As with all other game, slam your bullet through the shoulder if you can and the rhino is yours. This shot brings him down with spinal concussion, and if your bullet is any good it will then drive in among the big main arteries located at the top of the heart and kill the animal within little more than a minute. *He will not get to his feet again.* The shoulder is the biggest, steadiest, and most vulnerable target on *any* animal: go for it. In very thick bush, of course, you can rarely choose your shot. Under such conditions I think most rhino are killed with head shots. There isn't much to tell you about them.

Another very good shot for rhino is the frontal chest shot, whether you are directly in front of him or on his half-right or half-left. If you are not directly in front you will not, of course, put your bullet into the center of his chest, but somewhere between the point of his shoulder and the center of his chest, depending exactly on where you are standing. Don't be afraid to aim well up on these chest shots. Most men aim too low, whether it's elephant, rhino, or buffalo they're shooting. The most vital parts of the heart are the upper regions where the big main arteries are located; the bottom of the heart is not nearly so deadly.

Daly says that when he was out with an American sportsman one time he saw him put both barrels of a .470 into a charging rhino without stopping him. Daly killed the rhino with a brain shot. When they examined the rhino later, they found that the first barrel had split the bottom of the heart, while the second had drilled through the hump. Had that first shot been six inches higher it would have killed instantly. Next day they were out again and had to face another charging rhino. This time the American, who was obviously a hunter, remembered and placed his first barrel well up, bursting the top of the heart. Death was instantaneous. I can fully corroborate that. Practically all writers describing the heart shot at elephant, rhino, and buffalo advise the bullet's being placed too low— especially in the case of buffalo. This can definitely be dangerous. I've seen a charging lion come on with the bottom of his heart split open and a large hole through it caused by a soft-nose-split bullet. He was mortally wounded, of course; but it won't be of much satisfaction to kill your beast at the charge if he succeeds in running you down before he dies. Many instances can be given of game's being shot through the heart and still coming on. This inevitably upsets the inexperienced sportsman and tends to make him fire his second shot wildly. It is naturally unsettling to see a savage beast taking no notice whatever of a shot you feel certain was centrally placed.

I've already mentioned that a shot almost anywhere at all in the face will usually turn a rhino: many men not too sure of themselves slam their first shot into his nose below the base of the front horn, and then give him their second barrel through the shoulder as he rushes past. In very dense bush where you won't be able to see him until he's within a matter of feet you won't have much time in which to make up your mind where to hit him. I suppose most rhino shot under such conditions receive the bullet in from and slightly above the eye. That should find the brain. If it doesn't, it will either drop him or turn him and a second shot will finish him in either event.

Taken all around, a rhino is not difficult to kill with modern rifles. It's the hunting of him when in thick cover that's so difficult, dangerous, and gloriously exciting. Your satisfaction when you kill clean is considerable and well deserved. Therein lies the attraction. The hunter who consistently hunts dangerous game soon loses interest in the killing of animals that can't hit back.

Rhino are by far the best well-diggers I know. They go at it like a terrier digging for a rat, the sand flying out between their hind legs. Other species will patiently wait for the rhino to finish before approaching for a drink. I've even seen elephant waiting—they are also good diggers, but much slower. I've seen some places where the elephant knew perfectly well they couldn't dig a well deep enough for water to seep into without the sand's caving in, and so they just drove their trunks down, boring, as it were, rather than well-sinking, until they had to kneel down to reach the water. There was merely a round hole exactly the diameter of the upper reaches of the trunk. Having filled the trunk, they drew it up and squirted the water down their throats in the usual way, and then inserted the trunk into the hole again. And so on until their thirst was quenched. No other animal could have got a drink there.

For that matter neither could we, because it looked a most unlikely place in which to dig, and I shouldn't have attempted it if I hadn't seen the elephant. This, incidentally, gives you an excellent idea of the elephant's ability to scent water. Such water may be three and a half feet below the surface—yet the elephant will go straight to that spot and bore down to it, not trying anywhere else.

8: HIPPO

Hippo—we never give him his full name, either—hippo are usually classed among the dangerous game, although there is little danger attached to the manner in which they are most often shot. But they can be infernally dangerous if you are canoeing. The ordinary hippo will give you the right of way and merely blow and eye you in mild curiosity as you pass; but there is no telling when you are going to meet a rogue that will take fiendish delight in upsetting your canoe and maybe taking a bite out of it bigger than the typewriter I'm using to write this book. Even if he doesn't bite you or one of your men, the danger is that there is usually a big man-eating croc waiting his chance just downstream from where all this takes place. There isn't the slightest doubt in my mind that these crocs get to know when there's a bad hippo around and take the fullest advantage when he tips over a canoe and sets the people in it afloat. True, he isn't always on the job, and I have certainly been lucky; but all too frequently he *is* on the job—and you have no hope at all if one of those big brutes gets hold of you.

I have twice had hippo upset my canoe without the slightest provocation or warning and have been attacked on several other occasions. I have also read about hippos' attacking boats and canoes, coming for them on the surface open-jawed, their mouths yawning, pink caverns. Well, that certainly hasn't been my experience. A hippo coming that way would be easy money. Every time I have been attacked the brute has come under water and hurled himself up when he figured he was directly under the canoe. On the two occasions when his judgment was good the first intimation we had that anything was happening was when we suddenly felt the canoe lift up by the bows and found ourselves in the water before we had time to do anything. The hippo then turned around and either bit a great chunk out of the ironwood canoe—so hard that you couldn't drive a nail into it—or, as on the second occasion, reared up until half his body was out of the water and then came smashing down with his forefeet onto the bows, splintering the canoe into kindling. We all struck out for the bank, which fortunately wasn't far away, but guns, rifles, kit, and equipment went to the bottom of the river and doubtless are still there. On other occasions I've seen the hippo while still some distance away and when he submerged I quickly changed the position of the canoe so that he would miss it if he didn't come up again for reconnaissance. I have never had a hippo charge me on the surface if there was sufficient water to cover his back.

Your chance is when he comes up for reconnaissance—just a quick look-see to make sure he has got his direction right. Whether you kill or not, have your paddlers instructed beforehand to change the position of the canoe instantly when you fire. It will be a head shot and you can almost always tell if you have found the brain: if the hippo submerges without a ripple you can bet on it that you have killed him. But if he goes under with a considerable splash you can be equally certain that you have missed the brain. In which case, look out! There are times when a head shot which misses the brain seems to make a mess of the hippo's sense of balance. He will lurch and slew around half in and half out of the water and keep rolling over and over. Sometimes he will be on his side; on other occasions he will be throwing himself backward so that his stumpy legs and belly will be all that you can see. He seems to be quite unable to keep on a level keel. This may go on for up to half an hour. It's not unlike a whale's death throes. But although it sometimes amounts to the hippo's death throes also, more often than not it's just that he's punch-drunk. He'll keep circling around until you get a chance to finish him off. And that's not always too easy, because he causes a considerable commotion in the water and your canoe will be bouncing about—which doesn't make for good shooting. Succeeding shots will have no effect unless they reach the vitals.

There was possibly some excuse for the first hippo that upset me. I was canoeing down the river and we were just letting the current take us along while we had a bit of a rest. We were passing a backwater in complete silence when the canoe suddenly rose into the air. As we subsequently discovered, it was a hippo cow that had recently dropped a calf up the backwater and was without doubt on guard at the entrance in case a big croc took a notion to drift up to where she had left the youngster. The whole thing was so utterly unexpected that there was no chance to grab anything. This was when I lost my grand wee gold-inlaid Martini-Henry. When I realized that it was gone beyond all hope of recovery, did I curse that damned cow! After that I vowed I would never again travel with all my eggs in one basket—though as it happened there came times when I couldn't help it.

On the second occasion it was an old bull that did the damage. I had been warned about him and told to watch out when passing a certain deep pool that he usually favored. But on the occasion in question he wasn't in that pool: I had pulled in to the bank before we reached it and stalked along, rifle in hand, in hopes of getting a shot at him before we brought the canoe past. When I could see no sign of him I returned to the canoe. We paddled along past the pool and were just abreast of a couple of small rocky islets with deep water around them—a positive breeding ground for big crocs—when the canoe suddenly soared heavenward and we were all in the water. The brute must have been in between the two islets and had seen us coming. I managed to grab a rifle on this occasion, a double .470, and brought it ashore with me onto one of the islets. The bull reared right up and—as I said above—smashed the canoe to smithereens with his forefeet. He took no further interest in it then, but just snorted and blew among the wreckage, greatly pleased with himself. When I was satisfied that all my men were safe, and had shaken the water out of the rifle, I killed the brute from a range of about fifteen yards. He was so proud of himself that I don't believe he saw us at all there on the little islet. Again I had lost everything except, this time, the one rifle, and the revolver and knife I was wearing, plus a spare ammunition bag my gunbearer managed to grab.

I'm not very fond of hippo now.

Normally hippo, like other wild animals, won't attack unless you're close; but I was very nearly caught one time by a rogue charging from all of a hundred and twenty to a hundred and thirty yards away. I'd spotted his head when he was fully a hundred and fifty yards away, I being downstream of him, and had instructed my paddlers to cut across the stream right away. We were traveling in a big freight canoe, a three-tonner, and had barely three and a half inches of freeboard—there are no Plimsoll marks out here! I'd run out of fuel for my outboard, but had eight paddlers and a steersman. I figured it was quite safe to cross now, as the rogue was too far away for charging, and therefore took little notice when I saw him submerge. My men were all young, strong, muscular fellows and easily drove the big heavily laden canoe across the strong current. I was sitting amidship with a loaded rifle across my knees. The hippo had been upstream to my right. Without the slightest warning there was suddenly a tremendous commotion about a dozen yards upstream of us, and that hippo shot vertically out of the water until fully half his body was exposed. He smacked down again, causing a considerable wave which came slopping aboard us, and for a moment I feared we were going to be swamped. Naturally expecting him to attack again from the same side, I slued around and raised my rifle as I waited for him to show himself. My men paddled furiously. But it appeared that the hippo had thrown his head backward when he jumped up, that time, so he failed to see us; or possibly he had misjudged our position. Anyway, he passed completely under us and again hurled himself out of the water, now downstream of us. Once more I frantically twisted around in order to keep facing him— but he had fallen back under the surface before I was ready to shoot. He had been facing downstream that second time, with his back toward us, so he certainly failed to see us. Our position was none too enviable. The heavy canoe wasn't easily maneuvered and, as I have mentioned, was heavily laden; this was a particularly bad place for man-eating crocs; the nearer bank was all of a quarter-mile away, while the farther one wasn't less than a mile and a half away. However, we struck the main channel, which was perhaps fifteen or twenty feet deep, and that was too deep for the hippo's acrobatics (see below). He looked after us for a while as though debating with himself whether or not he had a chance of catching us. Finally he decided against it. I killed him ten days later. Had that fellow come for us on the surface he would have been easily killed.

Hippo don't swim: they walk along the bottom. This explains how they manage to remain motionless and facing upstream when they are in a strong current. Their hind legs are on the bottom and they have reared up and are leaning against the press of the current. When they submerge you will see that the back of the head goes under first, the nostrils being last to disappear, thus clearly showing that they have just allowed themselves, or rather their foreparts, to drop. It also shows why they don't care about remaining in water more than ten or twelve feet deep or thereabouts. But indeed it is inconceivable that those stumpy little legs could possibly drive that great clumsy barrel-like body through the water at high speed by swimming. If they attempted it there would naturally be a considerable commotion in the water; and there's no such disturbance when hippo are moving around. I'm not suggesting that they *can't* swim —of course they can swim—but their usual method of locomotion is by walking along the bottom. It is evident that they can, in submarine parlance, give themselves positive or negative buoyancy at will. In a lake or pool deep enough to cover them you will often see a back bob up and remain on the surface for some time as its owner enjoys the warm sun. When the big rivers fill up each year during the rains, the hippo mostly forsake them for the pools and lagoons which then appear some little distance from the river and which seem to indicate the old course of the river in days gone by. Those that remain in the river won't be in the same pools they frequent during the dry season, but will now take up residence on submerged sandbanks and islands. If they wish to cross a broad river when it is in flood, they will struggle up against the current some considerable distance so that when they make their crossing the current will carry them back to roughly where they originally wanted to cross.

During this season, with all the small streams and creeks bank-high, hippo wander many miles from the big rivers and lakes and way up various of these tributaries. They think nothing of traveling anywhere up to three miles at night to raid the growing crops. You can have some excitement hunting them at night when they are on these marauding expeditions; but you really need a moon.

The usual method of shooting hippo—just potting at their heads from the safety of the bank—is a poor business when viewed as sport. (Hippo are shot not only because they endanger native fishermen, especially if there are crocs around, but also for their meat and fat.) About the only thing you can say for it is that it calls for a fair degree of marksmanship, for the target is not large. If the hippo have been shot to any extent it also calls for a great deal of patience: if they know you are there you might well believe they have gone. For a long, long time there will be no sign of them at all. Knowing that a hippo will usually come up to breathe after five minutes or less—generally in about three minutes—you have some justification for your belief if you don't know the ropes and the minutes run on past the quarter hour into the twenties. But the hippo are still there. If there are a few water-lily leaves or lotus plants about you can bet your life there is a hippo's nose under each one of them. Without the slightest ripple that might catch your eye, unless you are actually watching for it, each hippo will push just his nostrils up under that lily pad or lotus leaf to get a breath of air. After any time up to half an hour one of them will finally stick his head up for a quick look-see. That's your chance. The top of his head, and only the top, will be exposed for a brief instant, and you've got to be ready for it. Open sights are just about useless for this kind of snap shooting—they will inevitably tire your eyes long before the hippo gives you your chance. Aperture or peep sights are infinitely better; but when you're dwelling on your aim like this for twenty to thirty minutes, or longer, a low-powered, low-mounted telescope sight and light trigger release can spell the difference between success and failure. There is nothing here to blur or tire your eyes. But if you are very close to your hippo, as I was only yesterday, don't forget to remove your scope. I'll tell you what happened, to make clear the reason for that advice.

I had sneaked up along the edge of the sudd* on Lake Namaramba until I was able to work the canoe behind a little outjut barely twelve to fifteen feet from where I could see the nostrils of five hippo being lifted above the surface every now and again for a breath. From time to time one of them, a big cow, would lift her eyes also for a quick look around. (There was a big bull among them but he wouldn't play ball.) I had the scope on my rifle, and it just didn't occur to me to remove it, though no man could possibly *need* a scope sight by day at a range of feet. It wasn't until after I'd fired and realized I hadn't killed that cow that my thoughtlessness and stupidity came home to me. When the cow raised her head, quite horizontally, my flat-topped aiming post was centrally in her left eye. I squeezed, completely forgetting that at such point-blank range the line of aim through even so low mounted a scope as mine was neverthe-

---

* Sudd, as you may know, is a kind of reed—papyrus or something like it—that grows in a minimum of soil, the roots becoming entangled with one another. It is light and buoyant. When rivers and lakes that contain it become flooded, as they do every year, sometimes small and sometimes huge islands of the stuff float away, and on the upper Nile, for example, seriously interfere with the navigation of river steamers.

less appreciably higher than the flight of the bullet over that short distance. The result was that, instead of taking her fairly in the eye, I hit her below it—too low for the small brain. And then the fun started! The other hippo cleared; but the wounded cow hurled herself out of the water until only her hind legs were in it. She flopped over on her back and then started rolling and wallowing, almost entirely on her back with her little stubby legs flailing the water and the air, around and around in drunken circles. As soon as I saw she was too punch-drunk even to think of attacking, I slid off the scope and handed it to my lad Aly to hold. I then stood there in the bows of the dugout canoe, rifle ready, hoping for a chance to slam another bullet into her to finish matters. But she didn't give me even the faintest chance. She eventually managed to get herself under the sudd, and there seemed to recover somewhat. She remained still, but we could hear her labored breathing.

I had seen another hippo approaching from a direction opposite to that in which the remainder of the troop had fled. He was curious to know what all the commotion was about. That suited me fine, as I wanted two of the animals. I mounted the scope again, sat down, and waited for him to close in. But I didn't want him too close, as I had immediately realized why I'd failed to kill the cow. Accordingly, when he was about fifty yards away I fired. He was killed instantly—just as that first one should have been.

I then set to to see how I was going to kill that wounded cow. I doubted if my canoe men would be able to pole our fairly heavy craft across the sudd, even though it wasn't as dense as it might have been. But just then a stouthearted fisherman came to our assistance in his light canoe. Without waiting to be told, he immediately started driving his small craft along through and over the sudd to where he could clearly hear the hippo breathing. He indicated presently that he had located her and that there was a track through the sudd, doubtless made by the hippo themselves, along which he reckoned we could get our dugout. We got pretty close, but not close enough. So I signed to the fisherman to give the hippo a prod with his twenty-foot pole. He did so and she moved close up alongside my canoe, but facing in the opposite direction. Her head was directly alongside me as I stood in the bow of the canoe, but I couldn't see her. I had her muzzle located, because I could hear her breathing, but the sudd completely concealed her head. So I again signed to the fisherman, who had followed her, to give her another prod, but only a gentle one, since I didn't want her moved. I hoped that she might raise her head slightly so that I could get a better idea of just where her ears were. The fisherman complied, and the cow obligingly raised her head. I still couldn't see it, but figured I could estimate closely enough just where to slam in a bullet.

If I failed to find the brain, at least it would almost certainly drive her out from under the sudd (she was close to the edge); otherwise she would get far away under it and I would lose her.

I drove a bullet into the sudd covering her head but underestimated the length of the skull. As I later discovered, my slug took her directly between the eyes. And since I was shooting straight down on her—the muzzle of my rifle was only about three or four feet from her—my bullet passed downward just in front of the brainpan.

Once again the same circus started. She hurled herself up and backward, draped in the sudd like a mermaid. I was glad she didn't topple over our way. Her gyrations this time were much more acrobatic than previously. She kept throwing herself out of the water, backward, until only her hind feet were in it. This took her just out of the sudd into the clear water, and there she continued the performance. I had only one shell left, as I told my men, and I certainly wasn't going to waste it on a chancy shot. Nowadays out here shells are pretty well worth their weight in ruby-studded radium. I'd killed all my previous hippo with one shot; yet here was this old cow with two in her already, and it was virtually certain that she'd be wanting another. There must be no doubt about this one. I wanted that cow, and I meant to get her. If I failed to kill her outright now, she would get back in under the sudd and, alive or dead, I would almost certainly lose her.

For a considerable time I stood there watching her, my rifle half raised, finger on trigger, waiting, waiting for the shot I wanted. At last I got it. When she was about fifteen feet away she threw herself straight up with her back toward us. There was a long-drawn *Ohoooh* from the gallery. They knew as well as I did that this was the moment—it might never be repeated. My eyes were on the base of her skull, my rifle came up like a shotgun—I never thought about the sights, much less used them. As the butt came home on my shoulder I squeezed. Everybody heard the smack of the bullet. There was a simultaneous yell of delight and pent-up excitement from my boatmen, from Aly, from that stouthearted fisherman who had been nonchalantly standing on one leg in his little canoe (it was too narrow to kneel down in) leaning on his twenty-foot pole as unconcernedly as an ebony statue; but the relief from tension was too much for even his imperturbability. All the men knew, just as certainly as I did, that that bullet had gone home in the right place.

Heads now appeared above the sudd in all directions as other fishermen closed in. They had been watching things from a safe distance. But do you get the lesson I've been trying to drive home? If I had had the sense to remove my scope sight for that first shot, those other two would never have been necessary.

If I seem to have made something of a song and dance about this shooting, it's because I've seen men completely miss just such point-blank shots as that final one. They allowed the tension and excitement to take control and just fired blindly. I remember one, trying to take an almost identical shot, who only just missed drilling a hole through the bow of his canoe! I wasn't excited. My mood was one of cold determination. Actually, there was little danger, except of the cow's throwing herself over on top of us. She was much too punch-drunk to realize we were right beside her.

Another method of bagging hippo is to find where they leave the water and take your position there, on the downwind side of their track, just after sundown. Having given the mosquitoes a treat you may get your shot from a range of eight or ten yards as the hippo come ashore.

Yet another method, which sometimes provides a little excitement, is hunting with the aid of a Verey pistol on moonless nights when the hippo raid the food crops. The Verey light lasts long enough to give you two aimed shots even with a magazine rifle. I have never used a repeater with a Verey light, but Blunt* mentions doing so for marauding elephant on several occasions and sometimes getting two shots off before the light came down (for the benefit of those who may not know what a Verey light is: it consists of a ball of flame fired from a special large-bore pistol. Such lights, incidentally, and shooting lamps too, are illegal throughout Africa except for use against marauding elephant and buffalo, or man-eaters, cattle-killers, etc.).

There isn't a great deal one can say about hippo hunting. I rarely shoot them except when they are raiding the natives' food crops or upsetting their canoes. To make sure you get the actual rogue you are after, the best method is to paddle around his known haunts until you provoke him into attacking you. It may not be generally known that a hippo wounded in the body will leave the water so as to get the wound out of it. I expect this is to prevent his drawing water into the wound when he breathes, and I know it is also because little fish are attracted by the blood in the water and worry him by nibbling at the edges of the wound. White hunters often don't know of this habit because they usually take head shots; but the native hunters know it well. They spear or shoot a hippo with an arrow, not caring much where it hits so long as it's not the head, anticipating that the animal will come ashore where they will be able to surround him and finish him off with their spears.

By far the most sporting method of hunting hippo is that practiced by

* Commander David Blunt, who wrote that excellent book *Elephant,* was one of the early officers of the Elephant Control in Tanganyika when that scheme was first started there, around 1925.

the natives of the lower Zambezi. And I've never come across or heard of any other tribes' using this method in any other part of Africa. I refer to harpooning hippo. This is a real man-sized game and genuine sport. I have accompanied the hunters on two or three such occasions, purely as a spectator, and will take you along in my canoe so that you can see for yourself. The hunters use their oldest canoes because they can be pretty well certain that at least one will be smashed before the hunt is over. They lash two or sometimes three of these little old canoes together for greater stability, and they are accompanied by several fast light canoes which act as outriders, sometimes serving to keep large crocs away and at all times acting as rescue craft. The men that man them will, of course, lend a hand during the final stages of the hunt, when it's merely a matter of finishing off the hippo and butchering him. We will have ringside seats in one of the outrider canoes; but first a word about the equipment used.

The harpoon iron is of conventional shape with just the one large barb. It is loosely fitted to the stout bamboo shaft that carries it, because it's not thrown but driven into the hippo with both hands. The shaft is then pulled free and dropped into the canoe. A line is, of course, attached to the iron. And this line is deserving of special mention—it's really a work of art. Although as thick as a man's wrist, it's as flexible as a snake's body and as free running. It's hand-made from tough palm leaves twisted and plaited together, and then single strips of the same leaves, not twisted, are bound tightly around the rope for its entire length. The finished result is a really strong line that you can do almost anything with. It's so smooth that if it is suddenly pulled when you are gripping it tightly, it won't burn your hands. At the same time it is, as I say, beautifully free running. I've never seen one become snarled.

The procedure is to go out to where some hippo has been marked down by scouts, in the hope of finding him enjoying his midday siesta. He'll probably be entirely submerged, just his nostrils showing, or not even that if he has them under the sudd or other floating vegetation. But that doesn't worry the harpooner. Usually there is only the one harpooner with two steersmen, one in the stern of each of his tied-together canoes. Just occasionally there may be two harpooners. If so, they will both harpoon the same hippo at a given signal. But first they have to decide exactly how the animal is lying so that they can drive the harpoon(s) into the best place. This is done by prodding down fairly gently with a reed or cane until they have placed the hippo's outline. The hippo takes no notice of this prodding. He must have plenty of things prodding and sticking into his tough hide from time to time, to say nothing of the fact that hippo consider it quite the correct thing to use one another as pillows and cushions. Besides, the hippo knows that he is quite safe from the ordinary rifle-armed hunter when under water and therefore relaxes completely: his only danger is one of these harpooners, and there aren't many of them left. Having satisfied himself of the hippo's exact position, the harpooner raises his harpoon and, after a glance around to see that all are ready for action, drives it with all his strength into the hippo's back immediately abaft the withers. And then the fun commences. The harpooner wrenches off the shaft of the harpoon and drops it into the canoe behind him. The steersmen backpedal like fury so as to get the lashed-together canoes around and facing in the best direction for the hippo's rush. On feeling the iron, the hippo gives a convulsive plunge and looses a startled, explosive snort. He ducks down, wheels around, and dashes away. The harpooners let him run for a spell, and then gradually snub the harpoon line; and the chase is on. That first snort of astonishment has pretty well emptied the hippo's lungs, so he'll soon break surface. In the meantime the hunters are crouching in the bows of their canoes with keen and watchful eyes on the line where it enters the water ahead of them. The canoes are well under tow, the bow waves creaming out on either side. Suddenly the line slackens and everyone holds his breath as the hippo comes up for a quick gasp of air: will he charge or won't he? The canoes' momentum is carrying them rapidly forward to overrun the line. Apparently the hippo does not yet realize just what's happening. He ducks under again and the tow line tightens with a jerk. We, along with the other outriders, are paddling furiously so we will not get left behind. Spectators we may be, but we've got to be ready and in position to lend a hand if necessary when the first charge comes. A charge is a practical certainty sooner or later, though, curiously enough, more than one is considered unusual. Occasionally, of course, the natives get hitched to a tartar which will attack again and again.

After another spell of high-speed work the hippo has seemingly cooled down a mite, enough to enable him to reason some, and he decides to see if he can't rid himself of this infernal thing which is following him so closely. The line again goes slack and all hands cease paddling as the hippo's head again breaks surface to breathe. The harpooners and their steersmen adopt crouching positions—at least, the steersmen do, for the harpooners have been crouching all along. Sure enough, having filled his lungs, the hippo turns around to look behind him. He gives just the one look and then dunks under. There is no indication at first that he's coming, but those heroes know. For a little while they watch, then with one accord they slip overboard and swim rapidly and silently away from the immediate vicinity of the canoes. In an astonishingly short space of time the hippo has covered the twenty-five or thirty yards separating him from the canoes and one can now see a slight wave approaching. It's not much of a wave, but the hippo must be causing it because there's nothing else to do so. Suddenly he rears up just in front of the canoes and, with a grunt of rage, brings his forefeet down with a smashing blow on the bows of the craft. Only one forefoot gets home, the other misses; but that one foot breaks a large piece out of the bow. Still he isn't satisfied. His vast, cavernous mouth opens and engulfs the remainder of the bow of that same canoe. There's a rending and splintering of wood, and the enraged animal shakes his head as pieces of wreckage fall from his mouth. He gazes at his handiwork for a moment and then, doubtless figuring he's settled his enemy's hash nicely, he turns around, dunks under, and moves off. The harpooners and their mates race for the canoes and scramble aboard. Those in the damaged craft give it a quick once-over to see whether it's still seaworthy or must be cut adrift. They decide it will hold together if they both keep aft, so they bail for dear life, since the vessel is pretty well awash. They naturally don't want to cut adrift if they can possibly avoid it, because by being there they give greater stability to the other craft for the scramble aboard after an attack.

The hippo has apparently reckoned he has freed himself from his tormentors, because he starts off again quite slowly. But as soon as he feels the pull of the harpoon and line he again makes a rush, and again we paddlers take up the chase. Up, down, and across the river he leads us. The water is all of three miles across right here, but he takes it in his stride. Since he did not make another attack shortly after the first the hunters know it is extremely unlikely he will do so later. He has been tiring all the time, but it is all of three hours before we succeed in killing him. He makes for the bank eventually and scrambles ashore. He drags the harpooners' canoes right to the bank, while we outriders paddle alongside and exchange paddles for spears. I did not bring a rifle with me that first time, for I wanted to see the whole performance as the natives themselves did it. However, on subsequent hunts I did bring a rifle along in order to hasten the end.

It has been a never-ending source of regret to me that I did not have a small movie camera in those days. I'm certain that this sport has never been photographed. I suppose it's in every way comparable to old-time whaling. And if any folk on earth deserve their meat, those hippo harpooners do.

Hippo have a peculiar trait which I've never seen described in print. Other hunters must have observed it but possibly they reckon it's not enough of a drawing-room topic to mention in their books. I'm doing so here because I think it may be of interest.

When a hippo is in the water and wishes to empty his bowels he either gets into water sufficiently shallow or, if that's not convenient, cocks his backside up until his anus is just level with the surface. As he relieves himself he flaps his little stumpy tail rapidly from side to side so that it slaps the water loudly, sounding not unlike a goose having a bath. The reason usually attributed to this is a desire to break up the droppings so they will rapidly disperse, preventing the possibility of his getting a mouthful of them. The fact that on coming ashore he backs into an evergreen bush and there goes through the same performance is considered merely force of habit. But I don't believe this is a particularly rational explanation. I suggest that a desire to discourage the unauthorized entry of inquisitive leeches is far more reasonable, because it also accounts for the habit's persisting when the hippo comes ashore, when there may be leeches clinging to his backside. It is noteworthy, moreover, that when the hippo reaches his feeding grounds, which may be quite close to the water or anywhere up to three miles away from it, he abandons this habit and his droppings may be found in heaps like those of young elephant. It would seem that, leeches or no leeches, he has no desire needlessly to foul the grass on which he will presently be feeding.

Incidentally, rhino also dislike leaving their dung where it falls. As I have said, they are inclined to return to the same spot to relieve themselves when they come in for water. Having done so, they kick their droppings around and scrape with their forefeet like a dog. (I cannot find any good reason for this.) I've had hunters tell me that they use their horns, too, to toss the dung around, but I don't think that is so. From my own observations I would say they use all four feet, but mostly their forefeet. It seems to me that a rhino would need to have deformed horns to be able to use them for that purpose.

There's no creature on earth, not even burros or servants in an Irish kitchen, that yawns so persistently, so widely, so hugely—or so infectiously!—as hippo. Their yawns are positively heart-rending. They swing their heads right back until their enormous mouths are gaping straight up to heaven, remain like that for a long time, and then allow themselves to fall over backward into the water with a mighty splash. They seem to derive more satisfaction from their yawns than any other animal. They yawn again and again until you find yourself and all your canoemen yawning in sympathy!

Hippo do an immense amount of fighting among themselves. Nearly every one is covered with scars, both old and new, and not infrequently has a dreadful bite or two on neck or shoulders or both, showing where those long curved tusks sank in deep. Even the cows don't come off unscathed: only the other day I shot a big cow with a terrible bite through chest and shoulder. But I wouldn't like to swear that that bite hadn't been inflicted after death, because there was no indication that it had begun to heal.

A number of years ago, around Lifumba, a most unusual battle took place one night. It was between a hippo and a wounded buffalo bull. There was a Dutchman camped there that year and, like many of his species, he had a habit of blazing off at anything that moved. The result was plenty of wounded buffalo that year. He admitted having wounded and lost this particular buff when it made its way into a very dense thicket back of camp. There was a deep pool close by, and hippo sometimes took up residence in it. The Dutchman told me he had heard a battle in progress for a considerable time during the night. I went out with him to see what the spoor had to tell us, and there was no earthly doubt that a wounded buffalo had come out of the thicket for a drink at the pool and had run afoul of the hippo, which was grazing around the edge of the water. It was impossible to say definitely which had attacked which. Chances were that the buffalo, having been wounded so recently, was the aggressor. But he had bitten off more than he could chew in tackling a hippo! Judging by the amount of blood scattered around, and the puddles of it here and there on the battlefield, the old hippo had got in at least one bite—and a hippo's bite is an awe-inspiring thing. It's difficult to see how the buffalo could have injured the hippo; and it's unlikely that the hippo, unprovoked, would have tried to prevent the buff from having a drink. Anyway, the buffalo finally cleared off without his drink.

I've had occasion before now to remark on the strange coincidences that take place in the bush; but I think even stranger are the whims and vagaries of stray bullets.

When an unaimed shot is fired, or a bullet passes clean through its target, nobody under the sun can tell where it's going to come to rest. When one thinks of all the stray bullets about Africa, it's a never-ending source of wonder to me that there are so few persons accidentally killed. My friends the Portuguese used to be very bad offenders in this respect, and to some extent still are. Sitting on the riverbank across from the township of Tete it can be considered an unusual day, especially if Saturday or Sunday, if numerous shots are not heard being fired from full-powered rifles. I have on many occasions had bullets whizzing and whistling over my head, and thudding and smacking into the tree under which I was sitting with my old friend McKenna. We would just move around and sit on the other side of it. On one afternoon as I was walking back to my camp higher up the river a burst of shots from what must have been a pair of automatic pistols whistled and screamed past me, followed by five shots from a rifle. The bullets weren't, of course, intended for me;

it was just that someone was blazing away at bottles or something without looking to see what was beyond. But the point is that, while the chances were all against my stopping one of that shower of bullets, they were whizzing across a river which is only about a mile and a quarter wide right there, and the opposite bank is invariably lined with innumerable dhobi washing clothes and other laundry. Why it is that those men and women *never* are hit by the showers of stray bullets is something I cannot attempt to explain.

Yet Wilfred Robertson once told how some sportsman missed a kudu bull on the brow of a hill way out in the wilds and had his bullet sail across a wide valley, pass through the tops of the trees on the other side, and take a lone native fairly between the eyes as he was looking up into the treetops for wild honey or something! There was only that one native on the opposite hillside, and he would have been quite invisible even had the hunter been high enough to see over the brow of the hill, because the treetops on the other side of the valley would have concealed him; yet the bullet traveled with deadly accuracy straight for him.

I've never been so unfortunate as to kill anybody unintentionally; but I've had three or four astonishing, incredible, unbelievable flukes take place when I was out shooting. I call them "unbelievable," and they will doubtless be so to those unaccustomed to rifles. Yet I would wager that all who hunt game with the rifle have been equally astonished—and pleased—at sometime or another by bringing off a kill they didn't really deserve. And, after receiving the plaudits of all witnesses, how many had the honesty to admit that the shot was sheer chance.

I remember one of those incredible flukes I had long years ago. I was going out after elephant in Portuguese Angoniland but didn't expect to meet them anywhere near where I was camped. We needed camp meat so, when within a quarter-mile of camp I 'saw a reedbuck's head showing through the grass, I was tempted. But almost instantly I realized it was an impossible shot: only the head and about three inches of the neck were visible; the animal was fully a hundred and seventy-five yards away; there was no tree against which I could steady myself, and the grass prevented my firing from any but the standing off-hand position. There *may* be men who can bring off such a shot successfully, but I know my own limitations. Nevertheless, I brought up the rifle with the intention of aiming just to see how steady I could hold it. From force of habit I rolled over the safety. Now this weapon was fitted with double set triggers (hairtrigger mechanism) and was the first rifle so fitted I'd ever used. I was a long way from being accustomed to it. Without thinking I clicked back the rear trigger and thereby set the firing trigger on a hair. As I brought up the rifle my finger accidentally touched the firing trigger and the rifle went off while the butt was still two or three inches from my shoulder. Boy, did it kick! But the little buck disappeared and my men yelled that it had been shot. They went haring across. I, however, remained where I was. I hadn't aimed, the butt hadn't yet reached my shoulder, I hadn't intended to fire—I *couldn't* have killed. But had I been firing from a gunmaker's bench rest I could not have placed that bullet more accurately. It had taken the little buck fairly in the neck, just where I'd been looking, and killed him instantly. It was no good trying to tell my men it was a fluke: they wouldn't believe me. Had I not prepared the rifle for firing? Had I not brought it up to aim? Had I not fired it? Anyway, there's no word in their language for "fluke."

I had another such experience only last month. I was trying to get a shot at a very shy hippo. Mostly he would raise just his nostrils above the surface at intervals for a breath, but from time to time he would also raise the top of his head for a quick reconnaissance. Had the rifle I was using been fitted with a hair trigger, and had he always raised his head in the same place, it would have been comparatively easy to hit him because I was using a scope sight. But the rifle had a very heavy trigger, and the perishing brute kept moving around in a small circle. Time and again I only just missed getting him; it took too long to squeeze off that heavy trigger. Since he was gradually getting farther and farther out, and I getting more and more cramped in the wretched little dugout canoe, which was too narrow to permit me to get my hips into it, I was about to give him best. But I could not resist just one more attempt. As I concentrated on my aim and tightened my trigger as much as I dared, waiting for him to give me another chance, a goddamn fly of some sort made a crash dive at the speed of a jet-propelled plane right into my shooting eye. I gave a gasp and a jump and shut both eyes tight. The jump was sufficient to jerk off the final fraction of an inch that was needed to fire the rifle. And Aly loosed a yell of delight: "Got him! Got him nicely!" And so I had. It was a hair-raising fluke, because both my eyes were tight shut when the rifle went off, and even when I opened them on hearing Aly's yell the tears streaming down my cheeks prevented my seeing anything. Had that accident not happened, I very much doubt that I would have succeeded in bagging that hippo.

9: BUFFALO

The African buffalo is the biggest, heaviest, and most massively boned of all buffalo. He's a magnificent fellow. Next to elephant hunting I prefer the hunting of buffalo to that of any other species of big game. I know that except for elephant I've shot many more buffalo than any other animal. But although I deprecate those men who allow the thought of buffalo to scare them, I do not suggest you should become contemptuous of them. Far from it! The African buffalo can hit back and hit hard. What I do say is, don't let all the tales you hear about the African buffalo start your imagination working overtime, so that you get all steamed up and are scared stiff before you ever see your first buffalo. I've met a number of men who have done just that. They were so frightened that they completely lost their heads when they got their chance for a shot. They seemed to have the notion that a buffalo will attack the instant he sees you, even though you haven't fired or in any way interfered with him. There are others who believe that a buffalo will invariably whip around and charge the moment he feels the lead if you don't kill him stone-dead with your first shot. I'm not making any dogmatic statements, but I have never experienced such a charge in all the years I've been hunting buffalo—and I've killed close to twelve hundred of them. It's possible that you *might* experience such a charge; I can only say that I never have, and give it as my belief, based on personal experience, that such an instantaneous charge would be definitely exceptional—unique. I am, of course, referring to an unwounded buffalo. The situation is entirely different if you are following up or have encountered a buff that has been recently wounded either by yourself or by someone else. But then, we all know that a wounded buff can be horribly dangerous. He's quite a different proposition.

The fatalities and maulings which have occurred among African buffalo hunters have almost all been caused by wounded buffalo. The few others were caused by the nervous and inexperienced sportsman's losing his head and imagining that a general stampede in his direction was a mass attack, and endeavoring to run for it. The herd would then run him down, in all probability without knowing they had trampled a man underfoot. In exactly the same way a large herd will sometimes come toward you when you encounter them out in the open with all grass burned off, so that there is no cover. They will start at a walk, but those in the rear are so anxious to see what it's all about that they will jostle and push until the whole mob breaks into a lumbering gallop. The dust and black pall of burned ashes of the grass thrown up and the clashing and rattling of mighty horns are certainly awe-inspiring if you aren't accustomed to them, and the beginner might well be excused for believing that it's a mass attack. But it's nothing of the sort; it's merely curiosity. And the bigger the herd the more curious they are. If there are several hundred of them, as there well may be, don't let them scare you. Just wait until they are within perhaps forty yards or so, and then loose a yell: "Hi-ya, there!" Anything will do. They'll stop. A couple of mighty bulls, the leaders of the herd, will come perhaps their own length out from the dense black mass of the remainder of the herd, and paw the ground and snort and toss their great heads. But that's sheer bluff. Don't take any notice of it. Throw up your rifle and drop the better of the two, and then slam your left barrel into the other as he wheels around to go. It's quite in the cards that if you should lose your head and run, the herd would come on and run you down without having any evil intent. They can be dangerous in that way, just as a bunch of heifers in a paddock can be if a dismounted man ventures across it. But it's almost unknown for *any* species of big game to attack en masse. I'll go further and give it as my considered opinion, based on my own observations and experience with some of the very elephant and buffalo herds which had the reputation of being mass killers, that no such mass attack has ever taken place. In every case I investigated I learned from survivors that the hunter had lost his nerve and tried to run for it or make for the nearest tree. When I went out to tackle that same herd a day or two later, or a week or two, or a month or two, as the case might be, I found that only one or at the most two bad beasts were responsible. When I shot them the remainder halted. Let me remind you of that party of elephant cows and immature bulls which looked as though they were making a concerted attack on me in the elephant playground, and which I've described in an earlier chapter. When I shot the two bad ones the others proved entirely innocuous. And I've found this to be so everywhere else. I admit I also used to think that entire herds, after most of them had been wounded by excitable and inexperienced sportsmen, were apt to turn man-killer; but subsequent experience has convinced me of the falsity of this notion—irrespective of whether it's elephant, buffalo, or lion. Shoot the bad ones—they will be in the lead—and the danger evaporates.

Perhaps, since I've permitted myself to make a categorical denial that such mass attacks have ever taken place, it might be well to go a mite more fully into the question. I have personally tackled herds of elephant and buffalo which had for years the most evil reputations as mass man-killers: there was an elephant herd in Uganda; a buffalo herd in the Congo—not the big Cape buffalo but the smaller forest variety; there was another elephant herd, all cows, in the coastal belt in Kenya; there was a buffalo herd in the Luangwa valley in Northern Rhodesia; yet another buffalo herd in Portuguese East, in the Zambezi valley; and a big elephant herd in the Makossa area of the famous Barui district, also in Portuguese territory. I had heard the most gory yarns about all these herds, and there was no doubt that they had all killed a number of hunters and natives; but they most certainly didn't deserve their reputation as mass man-killers. When I came to tackle them I found this so, almost without exception. The exception was that herd of cow elephant in Kenya; but even they didn't live up to their reputation. In no single instance did I get evidence that more than one animal had taken part in a killing. In the case of those Kenya elephant it would seem that any member of the herd which found man close by would turn and kill him if she could catch him; but there was no evidence that more than one elephant was ever concerned at the same time; no evidence that even two, much less the whole herd, co-operated in the killing. When I opened fire on the beasts I was charged several times, but never by more than one elephant at a time. And it was the same elsewhere. The Luangwa buffalo had fright-ened white hunters out of the valley for years far more effectively than the tsetse fly had; yet when I came to tackle them I found that there were only two bad bull among them. When I shot those the remainder showed their usual healthy respect for man. The Makossa elephant had killed several native hunters, one or two half-breed hunters, and had either killed or badly scared one or two whites, but I found that the damage had been done by one old bull and one big old cow. When the bull charged me he came alone, but when the cow came she was accompanied by the remainder of the herd, who obviously looked upon her as a leader. Nevertheless, when I dropped her the others halted and made no attempt to press home the attack.

I admit that a mass stampede directly toward you can have just the same results as an attack if you fail to split the herd so that they pass on both sides of you; but if you do fail it's probably your own fault. Stam-peding animals aren't usually difficult to split or turn, whether they are elephant or buffalo. Generally speaking, the danger is more apparent than real—it depends greatly upon the conditions under which the stampede takes place.

I remember tackling an immense herd of buffalo one day, a herd I had seen and shot up several times previously. I wouldn't like to be asked to estimate how many head it contained, but I've seen them walking head to tail, six or eight abreast, and extending over upward of a mile of bare burned-off plain. On this occasion I caught up with them on the near side of a low undulation covered with palmetto scrub and four-foot grass. I couldn't tell how many had passed over the rise, but guessed the greater number of them must have done so because I seemed to be near the tail end of the herd. They were passing me from left to right. I slipped up behind a small clump of palmetto and opened fire, dropping a bull and a cow, and grabbed my second rifle as the herd swung around and commenced stampeding back the way they had come—which might almost be described as a definite buffalo characteristic. I was just about to fire again when something made me glance up to my right. I saw a black wave of buffalo pouring over the rise to come sweeping down directly toward me like a great flood. I turned to face them. As I raised my rifle I saw a second wave pouring over the rise beyond them, and so let the close ones come on until they were within about twenty-five yards. I then opened fire, killing one that was directly facing me with a bullet between the eyes, and then swinging on another one beside him. I drove the bullet into his chest, which brought him down on his nose. This made a gap in the line, and the buffalo on both sides made frantic efforts to swing outward. Since they were coming shoulder to shoulder at full gallop, it wasn't too easy. However, panic could clearly be seen in all eyes, and they succeeded in swinging out sufficiently to clear us where we stood behind our little clump of palmetto. I just had time to exchange rifles again when the second wave of buffalo reached the carcasses of the two I'd shot. They also made frantic efforts to swing outward, the bodies of the fallen acting like a breakwater for us now. I killed one of the new wave with a frontal head shot and then brought another down with a bullet through the shoulder as he swung out to clear one of the dead, and again exchanged rifles. As I fired I'd seen yet a third wave of terror-stricken beasts come pouring over the brow of the rise. I waited for them, knowing that they wouldn't cross the bodies of the four dead buffalo in front of us. Accordingly, I had two easy shots as they broke their line and thundered past on both sides and was in time to exchange rifles once more and bag another brace from among the inevitable stragglers.

These buffalo are classed as varmints because of the devastation they cause when they raid the natives' food crops and cotton gardens. Everything is swept bare. Moreover, buffalo are the worst carriers and spreaders of the dreaded tsetse fly. Toward the end of the dry season, when the water in the hills dries up, the buffalo come down into the low districts, combining into immense herds, and cannot get away again before the rains because there is no other district able to support their vast numbers. I used to concentrate on them for about four months a year, for some four or five years, by way of a vacation from elephant hunting. The Nyasaland natives used to come down with the money they had received for their tobacco and cotton crops and buy the carcasses of the buffalo then and there where I shot them. They would have their own porters butcher and dry the meat and then carry it back into Nyasaland to retail there. I had no expenses worth mentioning: a gunbearer, a cook, and a youngster to help him clean pots and pans and fetch firewood and water. Just sitting around doing nothing isn't my notion of a vacation. This game proved interesting and profitable and gave me great experience in buffalo hunting and a real insight into their habits and characteristics. I'd shoot from five to fifteen or even twenty a day, depending on the number of buyers and how many beasts each wanted. So long as there was a buyer I would shoot, but I'd leave the herds alone as soon as all buyers were satisfied. I fixed the prices to ensure that every buyer would double his money—make a clear 100 per cent profit—on each beast he bought from me. That helped them, pleased them enormously, and secured me their good will. Word whizzed around Nyasaland, and soon after the herds came down from the hills you would see long strings of porters with great loads of dry meat trekking north, and other long strings, without loads, hastening south lest they miss the harvest.

I remember two youths in particular, brothers they were or very close pals, who arrived with shining eyes full of hope. Shyly they told me that they had only enough money between them to pay for half a buffalo, and half a small buffalo at that. Would I please shoot a beast for them: perhaps I could sell the other half to someone else? Well, I have always had a very soft spot in my heart for youngsters, and since these two had such frank, open, ingenuous expressions and so obviously had scraped up every available penny they could, and moreover had built such glowing hopes on the success of this venture, I couldn't possibly refuse. Besides, I like to think I'm helping these people. So I shot the biggest bull I could see in the herd and told them their money would pay for half of him, and they could take the other half on credit. Furthermore, I would get them as many local lads as they needed to help them cut him up and dry him and then carry the meat back over the border to their homes. They could pay the labor out of their profits when they sold the meat. They were delighted: this surpassed their fondest expectations. They came to bid me farewell when they were ready for the road, and to assure me that just as soon as they'd sold the meat they would be back for more. And back they came, their eyes sparkling, again and again, each time buying twice as much as on the previous occasion, until by the end of the season they were buying up to thirteen, fourteen, and fifteen buffalo on each visit. They were really a remarkable pair of lads and should go far—if given a square deal.

There were a number of big herds, though the one described a few paragraphs ago was the biggest. There were also a number of smaller groups and many old bulls that lived either alone or with a solitary companion. In addition, there were several parties of old bulls consisting of four, five, or seven. These old fellows had all been wounded in previous years by pseudo-hunters—mostly armed with totally unsuitable rifles—and so had lost their places in the herds. They lived all the year around in certain big clumps of very dense bush and heavy forest and didn't evacuate the district as did the herds after the first rains. It was, and is, one of the very finest districts for buffalo I have ever come across in all my wanderings. There are some magnificent heads there. I remember shooting one which must have run pretty close to the world's record. I had no tape, but it was truly enormous. Since as a tent dweller I have no use for such trophies, I gave it to another fellow who told me later that he sold it for a big price to a wealthy American tourist who happened to be passing through Beira. So it probably was a really good one.

Old buffalo bulls that have left the herd and live in these small bachelor groups do a good deal of fighting at night. There was one party of seven that used to visit one of my camps almost nightly and graze close around. Scarcely a night would pass without at least one fight between two of them: we could hear the pounding of hooves, the clash of horns, and angry bellowing as they wrestled and twisted after charging one another head-on. But they never seemed to do much damage—at least, I never found any blood after these fights and they were always together next morning.

When wandering along and feeding at night, the herds make a considerable noise. In addition to contented grunts they give vent to growls and snorts, and rattle their horns together. If it's a large herd, the clash of the horns is tremendous. I rather think all this must be with the hope of discouraging the ordinary hunting lion from venturing an attack (though it would take a good deal more than that to scare the big buffalo-killers) because you don't hear them making such noises during daylight hours, and it's very, very rarely that lion will tackle buffalo by day.

There is nothing to compare with actual personal experience, provided you have enough of it. In my very early days I used to be terrified of buffalo, for I had heard so many tales of their ferocity. I hated the very thought of walking after dark through bush frequented by them, even though I was armed with a good rifle. Then one night during my first season in this very fine buffalo district I've been describing a local headman who gloried in the name Frying Pan visited me. He sat drinking the palm wine I had in camp until a very late hour. Eventually, when the wine was finished, he got up, thanked me, and said he must be going. Since I knew his kraal lay between two and three miles away, and that the path he would use crossed a dry river bed with long matetti growing along both banks, a favorite haunt of several big old bulls who crossed and recrossed the path nightly, I protested. His only weapon was a light spear which was more of an ornament than anything else. I reminded him of those old bulls and asked him if he weren't scared.

"Scared! Me scared!" He laughed. "Why, if I do meet the buff it's they that'll be scared, not I!" And off he went with his characteristic swagger.

I can assure you that gave me much food for thought. If that was the attitude of a man who had lived his entire life surrounded by buffalo—then why should I be afraid of them? I deliberately began to go for walks at night, first carrying a rifle, afterward without it, to prove to myself that my fears were groundless. On some of these walks I met buffalo, and occasionally lion; neither molested me and I have never since felt frightened.

Normally, buffalo are not credited with outstanding intelligence, but when I was hunting in this same district I noticed a custom of theirs which would seem to show they are not out-and-out stupid. The big old bulls which live all the year around in the dense heavy forest growing in the triangle formed by the L of the lake or lagoon of Lifumba find all their feeding at the margin of the water. Here and there around the lake the leeches are very numerous, and it would appear that the buffalo swallow a great many, which attach themselves either to the insides of their gullets or, for all I know, to the linings of their stomachs. Anyway, these old bulls from time to time make their way around the long arm of the lake until they reach the hot springs which are in the range of low hills running around that side of the lake. These springs are medicinal, strongly impregnated with chemicals—sulphur probably predominating—and the buffalo drink the water to the point of vomiting. Then they turn away from the water and let rip, and out come balls of leeches.

I remember a fellow, a white man, who had allowed himself to get badly run-down by living on a very poor diet. He was covered with veld sores—tropical ulcers—and had all the usual symptoms of serious food deficiency. Naturally, this condition must be tackled from inside if there is to be any real benefit; but, that seen to, the healing of the ulcers—extremely stubborn things—can be greatly hastened with the aid of these springs. I took this fellow along to them, made him strip, and then told him to get into the hot mud and bury himself. He did so and I kept him there with only his face showing until he was well cooked. When he was much the color of a boiled lobster I said he could get out and wash off the mud in the water from the springs. We repeated this treatment for several days, and I've never before nor since seen veld sores heal up so quickly.

By the way, onion seed would not germinate on the island in the lake on which I had my base camp in the angle formed by the L. A creek ran down into the lake not far away and must have brought some of the chemicals with it. At least, that was my explanation, because the seed germinated perfectly on an island in the river a couple of miles away. Other seeds, however, were not affected—unless the chemicals actually hastened matters. For I have never seen seeds germinate so quickly as here. According to my diary, turnips were half an inch above the ground thirty hours after planting. (The only water the vegetables got was lake water, as I had started the garden in the dry season.)

The buffalo gained his reputation for savage vitality and fiendish vindictiveness in the days of black powder and lead bullets. It is practically impossible to stop a charging buffalo with certainty with anything much smaller than an 8-bore or a very heavily loaded 10-bore. The animals can, of course, be killed with much less powerful weapons—the trouble arises when the hunter only wounds and has to follow up. Time and again a man would fire, drop the charging beast, and, thinking he was dead, lean his rifle up against a convenient tree or even against the "dead" buff while he sits himself down for a rest and a smoke. And the next thing the hunter knows the buff has come to life and is savaging him to death. It has happened on innumerable occasions, the lead bullet coming up against the mighty boss of the horns, where they meet in the center of the forehead, and failing to penetrate. If one hunter has been killed that way, scores have; but although the African buffalo is a magnificent antagonist he would never have won his deadly reputation had those old-timers been armed with modern rifles and bullets. All the same, you must not despise him. Men who permit familiarity with any species of dangerous game to make them contemptuous are themselves deserving of a real hunter's contempt.

I knew a Dutchman* who professed scorn of buffalo. "Why they're only cows," he would say. "They're easy." Yet a buffalo killed him. There was another, also a Dutchman, who sneered at lion (though he admitted he was afraid of elephant). He caught a lion in the ribs with his Mauser one day and then strolled carelessly into the long grass to finish him off. But he didn't get a chance to fire again: the lion ripped him open. He had in the same way stated that lion were only cats and were easy. There

---

* Throughout the continent "Dutchman" refers to a South African of Dutch descent. A visitor or settler from Holland is called a Hollander.

was another, an Englishman, who reckoned it was bunk to class rhino as dangerous game; but a rhino finally impaled him on a twenty-two-inch horn, which gave him several very unpleasant hours before he died. Then there was another Englishman, one of those know-it-alls, who had shot two or three elephant—lone bulls—and gave it out that there was nothing to elephant hunting, that those professionals who spoke and wrote of the dangers of their profession were merely putting it on so that the uninitiated might be persuaded they were braver fellows than they really were. He was killed by an elephant next time he went out. One could go on like this almost indefinitely. As I have said, the hunter who allows himself to become contemptuous or think slightingly of any particular species will inevitably become careless when hunting, and that is likely to have but one result. Don't let the thought of an animal frighten you before you leave camp; but being cautious is different from being either frightened or contemptuous.

An unwounded buffalo is unlikely to attack, but once wounded he can be infernally dangerous in thick cover—and, like any wounded beast, he will make for cover if there's any around. It's a never-ending source of amazement to me how little cover is necessary to conceal entirely some big beast like an elephant or buffalo which has decided to ambush you. The inexperienced man naturally pictures the animal standing behind the thickest clump of bush in sight and so passes over with the most cursory glance, if that, some lighter, smaller bit of cover on the opposite side of the trail. Yet often as not it's there that the animal is waiting. His very bulk is his best camouflage—that, and the fact that he will be standing absolutely motionless. I once looked clean through a tuskless elephant bull when he was ambushing me behind a sapling no thicker than my wrist, scarcely forty paces away and no other cover about. Had he not commenced to swing out his ears, in all probability I should have walked right into him. You can do exactly the same thing with buffalo. And since a wounded buff will usually be found standing within twenty to thirty yards of his spoor, on one or the other side of it, and if he sees you coming and decides to attack will have sufficient cunning to wait until you have actually passed before charging, you will find it disconcerting to have to swing around for a quick shot in an unexpected direction. (Buffalo are well known for this tactic.) Moreover, you are usually accompanied by native followers, and since the charge may be directed toward them there is all the greater possibility of confusion. The men's agility will usually enable them to get clear without much difficulty, but fear of accidentally shooting someone may make it necessary for the hunter to hold his fire until the charging buff is very close. It has even been known for one of the men inadvertently to bump the hunter and knock him off balance just as he was about to fire. It might be asked, "Then why in hell go wandering around with a gang of spare men?" The answer is that when you are hunting dangerous game, and especially when following up a wounded animal, trackers are not only desirable but, in my considered opinion, essential. It's their job to keep their eyes on the spoor and follow it while the hunter's eyes are constantly roving ahead and around for the first glimpse of the quarry. Remember, far more often than not, it will be but a glimpse you'll get before the charge—if that. Eyes that have been glued to the spoor will inevitably become tired far sooner than if they have just been roving ahead at their own level. Moreover, the quick and hasty glance thrown ahead won't always be sufficient, and you may easily overlook the animal that is standing there waiting for you to come a mite closer. Another thing: if you have more than one rifle with you, you will naturally want someone to carry it for you; and since it's the height of folly to load yourself down with water bottles, spare ammunition, and various other odds and ends in addition to handgun and knife, you will also be wanting someone to carry those things. In addition, if you are hunting for camp meat you should have at least one other fellow to act as guide to the butchers later —if you haven't brought the butchers themselves, that is. Naturally, when following a wounded beast you will tell your followers to keep well to the rear, all except your gunbearer and trackers; but if the chase has been a long one, or the bush very thick, the lads will naturally close up both for moral support, if you're following a dangerous beast and so as not to lose you. They may be very much closer than you suppose.

There have been men who boast they go out entirely alone to hunt dangerous game. In my opinion that's nothing to boast about—quite the contrary. I consider it the act of a fool. Curiously enough, buffalo seem to affect men this way more than any other game; or, possibly, it's because so many hunters get themselves killed when they are out alone after buff that one hears of it mostly in such connection. (Let it be clearly understood that I'm referring to the average white man in Africa. What Jim Corbett did in India is not in question. The conditions are utterly different, and Corbett was a man of very different caliber from the usual run of hunter in Africa—just as he was from the usual run of hunter in India.) But what's the object of going out alone? If you kill your buff you certainly won't be able to carry him back to camp yourself. That means you'll have to guide your men out. What do you gain by that? Any keen hunter will get all the walking he wants without needlessly doubling it.

I'm thinking right now of a fellow I knew, a South African Dutchman, who went out alone after buffalo one day although his men begged him not to. He wounded a bull with his Mauser and followed him into very dense bush. The buffalo was waiting not ten yards within the fringe of the bush. The hunter, with his eye glued to the animal's tracks, actually passed the buff, as his spoor clearly showed, and failed to see it. The bull then charged from a range of less than ten paces. It would seem that the charge came from the hunter's right rear, so that he would have had to turn around to face it. He wasn't quick enough, didn't get a chance to fire his rifle at all, and was trampled and savaged to death.

Back in camp his men had heard the shot and then, as hour followed hour with no sign of their boss, began to get worried. Finally they decided they had better go out themselves to see if they could pick up any sign. They went in the direction from which the sound of the shot had come, finally reaching a spot where a herd of buffalo had been. They then scouted around until they found the place where the herd had stampeded, and then where one big bull had left the herd and gone off on his own— showing that he had probably been wounded. Proof positive came when they found blood and saw that he had made for the thick bush. They very cautiously entered the bush and there for the first time struck the spoor of shod feet on the sandy soil: obviously those of their boss. They found him in a pool of his own blood, with his unfired rifle beside him. The tracks told the whole story. There was no sign of the wounded bull; he must have wandered away into the depths of the forest.

Don't have the idea that your men will think you are a hell of a fine fellow if you go out like that after dangerous game. Nothing of the sort! The native is no fool and fully realizes that the average white man is a babe in arms in the bush as compared with himself. And far from admiring the hunter who takes needless risks, he gives him the opprobrium he deserves. If a white man dies or gets himself killed while out hunting, it spells endless trouble for his men. They dare not just bury him decently and let it go at that for fear they will be accused of murdering him. They have to put his remains into a *machila* and carry him whatever the distance may be to the nearest government station or *boma*. He'll be whistling to high heaven by the time they get there, as it may be several days' journey. And even then they will be held and there will be endless questioning. Furthermore, they can be certain they'll be blamed for allowing him to go out on his own. It will be of no earthly use to say he insisted on going out alone and that they had not dared disobey him, that they naturally hadn't thought he intended to go hunting but assumed he had a date with some local woman and didn't want them to know it. That is what your men will almost inevitably think in similar circumstances. Why not? *Why* otherwise should the boss go out alone when he has perhaps a score or more followers in camp? There just *cannot* be any other rational explanation. The native, naturally, looks at

life and the behavior of others (including the exalted white man) from
the point of view of his own philosophy, assessing it with that yardstick.
And the African outlook on life is different from that of the white man.
I don't suppose that there's one white man in many thousands who has
lived on sufficiently intimate terms with the African to look out on the
passing world through his eyes. (For one thing, few white men in Africa
nowadays speak any African language even reasonably fluently, much
less idiomatically and colloquially, and you can never really get to know a
people until you do.) I flatter myself that I'm the exception, because I'm
certain there isn't another white in Africa at the present time who has
lived on such intimate terms with Africans as I have and do. Once upon a
time in days gone by, yes, but not now.

The African is a real hunter, and although he may take what you
would consider grave risks you must not forget his altogether remarkable
agility, his fleetness of foot, his ability to run up trees in his bare feet—
trees you would describe as unclimbable without a telegraph lineman's
irons—and the remarkable way in which he can render himself invisible
by just standing motionless beside a tree or crouching in bush or a little
clump of grass. His dark skin makes him seem merely a shadow. On
top of all that, his eyesight and hearing, especially his hearing, are far
superior to those of any white man I've ever met. His ability to see at
night is unbelievable. He is fully aware of all this and is equally aware
of how infinitely far below him the ordinary white man is in all such
physical matters. Without doubt some tough backwoodsman from the far
north of America—say from Alaska—or from the back blocks of
Australia could open the African's eyes to what the white man *can* do;
but even he couldn't carry a dead buff back to camp unaided. And under
the African sun meat won't keep so long as it will in the Arctic—to say
nothing of its vulnerability to vultures and other scavengers.

I must admit that I often go out unaccompanied to shoot a buck for
camp meat. But the shot is fired well within earshot of the camp and my
men know that there will be meat and start out right away toward where
they heard my rifle. They know me well enough by now to realize that I
don't waste ammo taking chancy shots. Having killed, I just sit down for
a smoke until I figure my men are within earshot of my whistle. Then I
blow a blast or two on it to give them the exact position. When they arrive
I leave them to bring in the meat, and return to camp alone. I thoroughly
enjoy these lone hunts because when natives are along inevitably much
of the actual hunting is left to them. When you are out alone you have
only yourself and your own bushcraft to rely upon.

Here are some general rules. When following up wounded and potentially dangerous animals you must on no account hurry. Move slowly and carefully, rifle ready for instant use, eyes searching out every bit and scrap of likely *and unlikely* cover. Don't bother about the spoor—that's your tracker's job, and he'll make a very much better job of it if he knows that he can rely upon you to spot any movement ahead. It doesn't have to be a movement of your quarry: the movements of monkeys and birds can sometimes tell you where he is if you are walking with your eyes and ears open; you may spot some other animal, such as a small buck, looking fixedly at one spot. It's more than probable, then, that he's watching the beast you're following.

I remember a kudu cow's showing me where a bull elephant was one morning. He had been raiding overnight and I had picked up his spoor at daybreak. I'd been following him for about three hours through fairly easy open forest, and he'd led me through the worst of it trying to make me lose his tracks. This is a well-known trick of marauding elephant who suspect they may be followed next morning. However, I had very good trackers and he hadn't been able to shake them off until a heavy downpour of rain came and washed out all spoor. There was a fairly clear open piece of country in front of us where the grass hadn't yet grown to more than some four feet. There were scattered trees about and little clumps of bush. We stopped under a tree while waiting for the rain to ease up and wondered if it would be worth while trying to pick up further traces of our elephant. It didn't look too hopeful. It was then I noticed a kudu cow about sixty yards away on my half-left front. She was standing in a clump of fairly long grass with her head well up and staring fixedly at something away on her left. I at once whispered to my trackers that that kudu was watching our elephant—he must be over there somewhere and she could see him. From where we stood we couldn't. The breeze was blowing across, so I whispered to my trackers to move over to our right so as to get well downwind of the kudu. That would prevent our scaring her and, through her, the elephant; it would also ensure that we would be well downwind of the elephant too. We did this, and presently I spotted his back about ninety yards away. He'd been plastering himself with red clay so that he looked something like a red anthill; and he was almost invisible, for the rain had caused some of the clay to be washed off in streaks, leaving him irregularly striped red and gray. When we were roughly halfway around the semicircle the kudu spotted our movement, but we were too far, besides being downwind of her, to alarm her unduly. She watched us for a spell, then turned around and cantered easily away for a short distance where she again pulled up and looked around. There was nothing to scare the elephant, even supposing he'd been able to see.

I had an easy approach and was able to kill him without difficulty. But it was entirely thanks to that kudu cow. The elephant had been so superbly camouflaged that we might easily have missed him.

If you're careful you will usually spot your wounded buffalo in time to get a shot before he comes—that is, unless the grass is very long or the bush very dense. In the more open types of scrub he may spot you coming and clear off himself without giving you a shot. He has halted to ease his wound, just as any other wounded beast will do—stopping doesn't always mean a charge or ambush. In the thicker bush and long grass he may not have deliberately waited for you, it may have just happened that he was unable to see you coming until you were right on him. In such circumstances a charge is almost a certainty.

The answer to all this, of course, is: *Don't wound.* Take care to kill or cripple with your first shot and you have nothing to worry about. Despite all the buffalo I've hunted and shot, I can honestly state that I've very, very seldom been charged. And of those charges practically all were made by buffalo which had been wounded by someone else. Since there is no telling when you also may meet a buff which somebody else has wounded a day or two previously, it obviously behooves you to be carrying your rifle, and a rifle with a decent punch. You may spend the rest of your life wandering around the bushveld without ever bumping into a buff wounded by someone else—but you may also do so the first day you go out. I know many men who have spent a lifetime in the bush without stumbling across a buff wounded like that, yet I have encountered three or four myself. I would certainly have been killed on at least two of the occasions, and at the best badly mauled on the others, if I hadn't been carrying a powerful double rifle at the ready. The attacks were so unexpected and came from such close quarters that I would never have succeeded in getting a magazine rifle into action in time. I'll tell you of just one to make my point clear.

I've mentioned that there had been a Dutchman wounding a lot of buffalo in this district. The authorities had sent for me to try and kill them off because they had been responsible for a number of deaths, women and children and elderly men who accidentally encountered them when out collecting wild fruit and firewood. Having undertaken the job, I advised the powers to chase that fellow out of the district because he was a menace. They had done this—he had left the previous year. During the ensuing months I hunted down and slew all wounded buffalo in the district that hadn't been pulled down by the big buffalo-killing lion that follow the herds. I'd done a good job and knew it. There was no other hunter in the area, and I myself hadn't wounded and lost a buffalo for many years. Accordingly, I had no reason under the sun to suspect that there was a wounded buffalo anywhere in the whole district on this day in question. Still, I'm a hunter and bushman of considerable experience and it is my pride to live as I consider such should live—that is, I never become careless, never omit reasonable precautions, never act contrary to established practices which my long experience has proved wise and sound. And so, when making my way through a wide patch of long grass to where I knew I'd find a herd of buffalo, I was carrying a powerful double rifle. My gunbearer, who was breaking trail through the grass, carried my second rifle in front of me.

For no discernible reason I suddenly began to feel uneasy. I tapped my gunbearer on the shoulder and signed to him that I would take the lead. I didn't even speak—I knew this feeling so well that I felt in a moment or so, if I advanced, I would run into very real danger. As I have said before, you must never attempt to weigh inner urges like this against your very limited powers of objective reasoning: you must, without hesitation, accept and *act* upon them. That is what I did. As I always do when I do not expect to be wanting it immediately, I had been carrying my rifle muzzle foremost on my shoulder. I now reversed it so that I could get it into action with the minimum delay if and when it was needed. I advanced through the grass, slowly enough to be always collected and balanced. And I had gone scarcely ten paces more when there came a rush through the grass close beside me. As the barrels of the rifle came down into my left hand my right thumb shoved forward the safety. It was then time to fire, there was no time to get the butt to my shoulder: I just pointed the muzzle and fired with the butt inside my forearm, pressed against my side. Had I been carrying the rifle wrong way round I would almost certainly have been unable to get it into action sufficiently quickly. I had no reason to suppose there was a wounded buff anywhere around, but as it transpired this one had been wounded the previous day, or rather night, by a native armed with an old muzzle-loader. As well as I can recall, I fired that shot from a range of less than three feet.

IN CAMP
ANGONILAND, PORTUGUESE EAST AFRICA

Oh, you fool! You triple-distilled bladder-headed fool! Don't you know by this time that a buff does not lift his head to look at you, but only his nose? And you call yourself a hunter!

That outburst was occasioned by a piece of momentary forgetfulness on my part before I had acquired the experience I now have. I was hunting for meat for my men and encountered a troop of twenty-five or thirty buffalo. I let drive at the big leading bull, placing a hard-nose bullet immediately under the great boss of his horns where they meet in the center of his head—always a most tempting shot. He dropped instantly, and I presumed I had blown his brains out of the back of his head. I turned my back on him to see if I couldn't get a shot as the animals stampeded in a semicircle past me, and was about to fire when there was a yell from one of my followers. I swung around, saw my bull on his feet, shaking his head to clear it, and dropped him again with a bullet in the neck just as he started a rush.

This brings up a point you would do well to remember if you ever try your hand at African buffalo—or, for that matter, any buffalo. All buffalo carry their heads low, and when they want to look at you they don't lift their heads like other animals (except hogs): they only lift their noses. This means that the face is practically horizontal, and if you try to slip your bullet in under the boss of the horns, which is so tempting, your bullet may pass *over* the brain and out the back of the head. It will knock the bull out but won't necessarily kill him. You should take an imaginary line between his eyes and place your bullet just *below* it. Then when you examine your kill you will find that your bullet has actually entered the upper part of the nose and not the forehead. I've read that the buffalo of Ceylon when contemplating a charge advance quite slowly toward the hunter with their heads held high. But the writer of that article omitted to mention that they still hold to the buffalo characteristic of carrying their noses stuck well out in front of them. This doesn't apply to the American buffalo (which isn't a buffalo but a bison). At least, every picture I've ever seen of them shows them charging heads down and noses tucked in like domestic bulls. I have also read how the hunter places his bullet on the front of the withers, which would certainly seem to indicate that the head is carried in that manner. The African buffalo hasn't the high shoulders of the American and lowers his head only at the last moment, to use his horns. He charges with his eyes open; it's no blind rush.

Blunt, in his excellent book *Elephant,* speaks of the only time he was charged by a buffalo. He and his men were returning from a hunt along a small path when suddenly and without warning a buffalo—a lone cow— came full tilt down the path toward them. They scattered, but one elderly fellow failed to get out of the way in time and was knocked down. Blunt stepped behind a small bush at the side of the path and waited. As the cow rushed past he shot her in the neck from a range of about six feet. He says he cannot explain her charge as she had not been wounded, wasn't in calf, and had no calf. Personally, from my own experience with buffalo, I have no hesitation in saying that that wasn't a charge at all, that the cow rushed through the men without knowing she was doing so. Take the old fellow who was knocked down: he declared that the cow "pushed him with her nose." Had she been charging she would have seen him and lowered her head when on him—it wouldn't have been her nose he felt. My own explanation is that in all probability a lion strolled close past the cow and upwind of her. In her panic, and with all her senses concentrated on her rear, where she thought the danger lay, she stampeded blindly through Blunt's men without realizing they were there, as they had been approaching either up or across wind.

Which reminds me of another incident involving a cow. I had been chasing a very big herd all morning, but they wouldn't leave the forest and make for the open. They knew they had a better chance among the trees. I could catch only glimpses of them, but there was a bit of a clearing and as the stragglers came past some of them passed through it. I was waiting, in the hope that a nice fat young heifer would offer me a shot, for we wanted some camp meat and also cooking fat. Sure enough, very near the end of the procession came exactly the girl I wanted, obviously in calf. I got ready to shoot. I stepped out from behind the bush which had concealed me and swung up my rifle. The little cow had stopped and was standing not more than a dozen paces away; and the imploring look of despair that appeared on her face when she saw me—for all the world as though she were saying, "Oh, Lordy, look what I've done! Here it comes!"—was so comically human that I burst out laughing and was unable to shoot.

Let me tell you now about the hunting down of the Maiembi mankiller. He was the last of the wounded buffalo left around by that Dutchman. I have always thought that the hunting down of this beast was one of the most difficult and dangerous jobs I have ever undertaken. The brute had taken up his residence in an impossible patch of impenetrable bush that extended over many acres. He only came out at night to water and feed close around the outskirts of the bush. There were four other big old bulls that lived in there and they had without doubt been wounded in previous years by other near-hunters; but they had long recovered from their wounds, their tempers had cooled off, and they were now quite innocuous. They lived together in a bachelor party—the brute I wanted was still solitary. It is true that if he were now left alone he *might* become as harmless as the other four, because nobody ever attempted to enter this patch of bush (he'd done all his killing before taking up residence in here); but since the bush abutted on lands near the kraal I didn't consider it fair to the villagers to take a chance on his good behavior. If any of them were late down at the river, which ran along the far side of their fields, they might easily bump into the killer on their way back up. The bull's spoor showed that he came out nightly, crossed the field, and made his way down to the water. He then fed along the river's edge where there was young grass, returning later to the bush for the day.

I mooched around the edge of the bush looking for an opening, but there was none. The greater part of the growth which comprised the patch was fairly free of leaf for about two or two and a half feet from the ground, but from there up it closed like a curtain behind anything entering. The big buffalo could brush through this, but no man could. And although the greater part of the growth was free of leaf for some distance from the ground, there was other vegetation growing among it which carried leaf and small twigs right down to the ground. Crawling in there to try to hunt any unwounded buffalo would have been difficult but not particularly dangerous provided you took the greatest care to kill outright. To go in after a wounded man-killer could only be considered as a last alternative if all else failed.

It seemed that my best bet was to try for him by night when he came out. Had there been a moon all might have been well; but just then there was no moon. I clamped a flashlight on the barrels of my rifle. Unfortunately, the cells were nearly worn out, so I sent runners off to try to get me some fresh ones. In the meantime I determined to see what I could do with what I had—and bitterly regretted it afterward.

I went out about an hour after dark, knowing that buffalo must have their water and in a hot district like this would come out of the bush as soon as they felt it safe to do so. I strolled slowly along toward the river, swinging the beam of my flashlight around in all directions. For a considerable time I saw nothing and was drifting slowly back toward camp with the intention of waiting awhile and then trying again (so as to save my batteries as much as possible) when I picked up a very large eye in the ray of light thrown by my torch. I halted and stared at it. It was unlike anything I'd ever seen. As an eye it looked like a buffalo's, but it was only about five inches off the ground. Moreover, when it moved it did so with a curious undulating gait: like a rabbit feeding, and hopping along a bit farther to halt and nibble again. I decided it must be a rabbit, though it had the biggest eye I'd ever seen in a rabbit. Still, what else could it be?

I watched it seadily. The light wasn't strong enough to show up the animal's body even though that was only about twenty yards away; it showed just the eye. And then another eye appeared, rather more than a foot from the first one but on the same level. That must be another rabbit. If the two eyes had been a decent height above the ground I would now have said that it was a buffalo looking straight toward me, but who ever heard of a buffalo with his head so low that his eyes were only five inches off the ground. One eye disappeared and the other continued to move along now, parallel with my own route, but with that strange undulating movement. I strolled along more or less level with it but it gradually got ahead of me. That didn't matter. It was a buffalo I wanted, not a rabbit.

And then suddenly and most unexpectedly the eye soared up until it was about four feet from the ground and immediately in front of me. It was now about twenty-five yards away and just on the edge of the bush. For the first time I realized it was my buffalo. The brute had been coming back from the river along an old hippo path which had been worn some three and a half feet deep there. It was this that had caused the eye to seem only a few inches above the ground, and the roughness of the track accounted for the undulating movement that had deceived me into thinking it a rabbit. It was only now, when the bull scrambled out of the hippo track, that my weak batteries dimly showed up horns and body. I took a despairing shot as the buffalo disappeared into the bush. I heard the thump of the bullet but knew I'd hit him too far back because his head and shoulders were already concealed in the bush. I don't normally shoot unless I'm sure of killing or crippling. But this wasn't a harmless unwounded beast; it was a man-killer which had already been wounded by someone else. As I looked at it, wounding him again could not make him any more vindictive than he had already shown himself to be, while my heavy soft-nose bullet, even though badly placed, would certainly not improve his health or strength. This is perfectly legitimate practice in the case of a man-killer, though naturally I wouldn't resort to it if I could avoid it. However, what I failed to realize was that my firing like that would inevitably put him on the alert in the future. He had never previously been shot at by night, and up to now hadn't associated the bright light of the flashlight with danger. I could have walked right up to him had I only realized in time that it was my quarry I was watching. In the future things would be different. It wouldn't be possible to stroll around and expect to get an easy shot. The instant the bull saw the beam of the flashlight he would make a beeline for safety—or would charge. Moreover, an additional reason, if it were needed, for him to associate danger with light was the fact that he must have got a whiff of my wind just before he received my bullet: that was probably why he had climbed out of the hippo track and made for the bush.

A careful examination of his spoor next morning showed that he habitually left his sanctuary at the same place, crossed the field, made his way down to the water, which was low at this season, and then after feeding for a while made use of the deep hippo track to get back to the bush. Standing in the field about fifteen yards from the buffalo's tracks and about the same distance from the fringe of the bush there was a good-sized tree which the owner of the field hadn't bothered to fell. I decided to squat at the foot of this, on the river side, and hope for a shot when the bull came out that night. Accordingly, just before dark I took up my position. I had been sitting there only a short half hour when my quarry appeared. But it was a pitch-dark night and against the black background of the dense bush I was unable to see him until he was broadside-on to me and silhouetted faintly against the horizon.

Unfortunately my flashlight had not been designed for sitting up like this or it would have had a switch which could have been turned on with the rifle and held ready for instant use. My light had only the ordinary side, which meant that after switching it on I had to return my left hand to the forearm of the heavy rifle in order to raise it to my shoulder. And that took too long in the circumstances. I had hoped the bull would stand for just a moment gazing at the light—that short moment would have been sufficient—but he now knew well just what the light portended. He didn't give me a chance. The instant the light sprang out he whipped around and was all out for his sanctuary. My dim light was not enough to show me his outline for a shot before he was gone.

I got up in disgust and returned to camp.

The following night I tried sitting in the same place without a light— my batteries were practically finished anyway—but except for a visit from a lion, which, I think, got an even greater shock than I did when he came around my tree from the opposite side and found me within a few feet of him, nothing happened.

My runners returned a day or so later to tell me there were no flashlight batteries to be had. So that was that.

Well then, there seemed no alternative but to try to make my way into that impossible patch of bush by day. Having wounded the bull myself now, I felt it incumbent upon me to kill him. I didn't fancy the notion of that bush, but there was nothing else to be done. I wasn't a wealthy sportsman who could stick around indefinitely: I wasn't being paid for this work (if I had been I would probably have waited until there was a moon and tried ambushing the bull). As it was, I had to kill the brute as soon as possible so as to be free to push along to where I could make my modest living.

Accordingly, the morning after my runners had returned I went out to reconnoiter again. I decided to wait until close to midday as I guess the bull would be lying down then—and he *must* be lying down or it would be impossible for me to kill him. I decided it would be best to enter the bush where he was in the habit of coming out. There was probably some tiny clearing around the foot of a tree or under some bush which would give him shade during the hot hours. It would be my job to snake up along his spoor and hope to spot him before he spotted me. The one and only advantage I would have would be that he wouldn't expect to be hunted in there and so might not be on the alert. But it would call for very careful stalking, because if he became the least bit suspicious he would instantly scramble to his feet and then I would be helpless. The bush would completely cover all his vitals and I would see nothing but his feet and lower legs. If he sighted or winded me coming and decided to charge he could trample me underfoot without the slightest difficulty and I wouldn't be able to do anything. My only hope was to take him unaware when he was lying down so that I could see him under the bush. It wasn't a pleasant prospect to dwell on. It was best to think of something else until the time came to get on with it. So I returned to camp and picked up a miniature rifle with which to stalk spur-winged geese down by the lake shore.

By eleven o'clock I was back again with as many geese as my men and I could eat. I drank the pot of tea my cook had waiting for me. Then, taking my heavy rifle, I commenced what I still consider—as I say —probably the most dangerous stalk of my career. I would much rather have stalked a wounded lion under such conditions than a buffalo, because a lion's vitals would have been vulnerable whether he was standing or not. However, it was no use wishing; thinking about it would only make me more scared than I already was. Oh, I was frightened all right— make no mistake about that! I'd had enough experience to know just how dangerous a proposition it was, and how quixotically foolish I was to attempt it.

I reached the place where the bull habitually emerged from the bush. My men tried to dissuade me from entering, as they already had before. They also realized that their arguments weren't worth the candle. My courageous gunbearer looked hurt when I insisted he remain outside with the others. But, as I explained to him, he would be unable to help me if things went wrong, and if the buffalo chose to come for him when we were both down on our bellies, I wouldn't be able to help him. I told the men they were on no account to enter the bush. If they heard a shot, or heard the bull bellowing, they were to wait at least an hour before doing anything. If I hadn't returned by then, they could come and look for me—and scrape me off the ground if they could be bothered to (but I said that last sentence to myself).

As I got down to start the crawl I grinned at my men, thinking to cheer them, but nary a grin responded. Instead they gave me that blank dead-pan look that only the African can produce. They knew I wasn't acting with my usual modicum of common sense, and they didn't like it.

As I have said before, the African does not applaud those who take needless risks, stupid unnecessary risks; he looks upon it as plain damned foolishness. In which, of course, he's perfectly right. Far from sneering at me for being scared, if I had turned back now at the last moment they would have been greatly relieved. But I was determined to go ahead.

It wasn't possible to proceed even on hands and knees: I had to lie right down and literally snake along by means of elbows and toes. My greatest difficulty, and a serious and most important one, was to make sure that the muzzles of my rifle didn't pick up sand or other dirt. It was easy enough to keep on the spoor because the bull had used the same track a number of times. I would edge forward perhaps two or three times my own length and then pause for a careful reconnaissance in all directions; then on again for another short distance. The ground was a light sandy loam covered with thick compost—the annual grass fires never entered here. There were no stones or pebbles and remarkably few dry twigs or dead sticks to bother about. The result was that I was able to move in absolute silence just so long as I was careful—and I was very careful!

I cannot give you any estimate of the distance I crawled or the time it took me. At first it was ghastly: sheer hard labor mixed with fright. But as I kept going and became more accustomed to the mode of progress and realized how quietly I was getting along, my spirits rose and I found myself tingling with excitement. My fear gradually departed and I became more optimistic of success. I came to realize more fully what I had learned long before: that anticipation of possible dangers is always worse than the actual danger itself. I had scared myself beforehand by thinking of all the unpleasant things that *might* happen; but now that I was actually on the job I found it was becoming the most thrilling I had ever experienced. It was difficult and dangerous, yes—it would be foolish to forget the danger—but I knew now that when I eventually placed my bullet where it would do the most good I would derive greater satisfaction from that one shot than from any I had ever fired before.

My greatest danger lay in the possibility that the bull was lying downwind of me. However, there was nothing I could do about that, so it was best not to worry about it. At long last I came to a tall tree with a tiny clearing around its base. It was plain to see that it was used by buffalo from time to time, possibly by that party of four to which I've referred. There was nothing there now but droppings. Still, I welcomed the site because it gave me a chance to stand up and have a bit of a rest. Moreover, it suggested that there must be other similar places where these bulls lay. I gave myself a full ten minutes' rest here and a smoke. I could see no harm in the latter, because if my quarry were lying downwind of me and could smell the tobacco, well, he could smell me also and that would have more effect on him than all the smoke in Africa.

Then on again. The god of hunters must have been on my side that day. When I think back over all the impossible places in which I might have encountered the wounded bull, and then remember just where I did find him, I have much cause to be grateful.

I was continuing to advance in exactly the same manner as that in which I'd started. It was, I suppose, some fifteen or twenty minutes after leaving that little clearing under the tree that I found I was approaching another similar little clear patch with a tall tree in the center of it. And there was something else there also, something blacker and more solid than bush. Some of it was concealed by the tree trunk and some of it extended out to the right of the tree. It might have been an anthill, of course, or the trunk of a long-dead tree—but I had a feeling that it was my quarry. I could see it only indistinctly as yet and would have to go several lengths farther forward to be certain; but I had no real doubt as to what it was. And it certainly wasn't the quartet: the clearing was so small that they would have been lying all around the tree, easily discernible.

I snaked forward twice my own length; and again. Then I slowly took hold of my rifle with both hands and slid forward the safety catch.

The bull was lying down asleep with his nose on the ground like an old cow taking her ease in a meadow. His hindquarters were concealed by the tree, but the rest of his body was broadside-on to me with the head turned away. I could have shot him then and there from where I lay, and I sometimes wonder why I didn't. But apart from the fact that I don't like shooting from the prone position if I can possibly avoid it, there was also the fact that if anything went wrong I'd be at a grave disadvantage. I had, of course, expected to be compelled to fire while prone, but it seemed to me now that it was worth making a major effort to get a bit farther forward so I could at least kneel, and possibly stand upright. So I very carefully inched forward until I was clear of the bush and in the tiny clearing along with the bull. I was now within three and a half steps of him (measured later). And still he slept.

I slowly got myself into a kneeling position, one knee down and the other up, raised my rifle and drove a heavy bullet into the bull's shoulder. He rolled over on his side without a murmur or a kick, dead as a kippered herring.

Thus, in spite of the difficulties of the approach, my bridge was easily crossed when I came to it. And so I have generally found it throughout life: one worries oneself ill beforehand, only to find later that there was no need.

It would have been nice now to find a clear track along which I could stroll. But there was no such track, so I had to get down again and snake my way back through that infernal bush. But the return was a great deal easier. I could unload my rifle and not worry if it did pick up a bit of sand, and it no longer mattered if I made a little noise. So I covered the distance back to where I'd left my men in about a third of the time it had taken me to get in. I heard their voices long before I saw them. They were arguing that something must have gone wrong: it was a long time now since they'd heard my rifle, they ought to be doing something. It would certainly have seemed a whole lot longer to them than it did to me, because they had had nothing to do except sit around and wait and worry. But my gunbearer, the most reliable of them and the one who knew me best, was insistent that all was well and that they must follow my instructions exactly. I'd told them they must on no account attempt to look for me until a full hour had passed from the time of my shot. That hour had not yet passed.

Then I stuck my head out of the bush. My gunbearer was the first to spot me. He jumped to his feet with a yell and came dashing across to help me to my feet and take the rifle from me. He didn't need to ask questions. My grin and the freshly severed tail I held out to him were answer enough to everything. The men yelled and danced around me. The villagers heard the noise and came running. I was escorted in triumph to my camp. My gunbearer was one huge grin from ear to ear for the rest of the day as he basked in reflected glory.

Far from allowing familiarity with dangerous game to breed contempt, I find that the greater my experience the greater my respect. I don't mean by this that I'm growing more frightened: quite the contrary. I used to be scared stiff in my early days, whereas nowadays I'm not— provided I have a decent rifle in my hands and equally reliable ammunition for it. What I mean is that the more I see of wild animals and the punishment they can take, the more I realize their potentialities for mischief when wounded and vengeful. My nervousness in days gone by was due to an overactive imagination's playing upon inexperience. There are many others who suffer from the same defect. Provided they realize it in time and have the courage to admit it there will probably be no harm done. The trouble is that so few of them *will* admit they're scared. They don't or won't realize that there is nothing to be ashamed of in being frightened—it's perfectly natural, and there must be something wrong with the man who can honestly say he has never been afraid when first facing death, whether from bullets, bombs, or a wounded elephant, buffalo, or lion. More especially, perhaps, in the case of game, for in that case he has himself and himself only to rely upon to get him out with a whole skin. The real danger arises when the beginner has a couple of easy kills, say at lone elephant, and jumps to the conclusion that there is nothing to this sort of hunting. If he can kill the biggest of all big game so easily, why, there is little to worry about with lesser animals. That is a very foolish attitude and will inevitably lead to trouble.

I have already shown how on certain occasions a powerful double rifle is preferable to a magazine when tackling buffalo. And those are the occasions that will matter. But when you are using a powerful rifle of any sort against a herd, *don't use hard-nose bullets*. There is grave risk of the bullet's driving through the beast at which you're shooting and possibly wounding another or even several others standing beyond. And if they are standing in long grass you may be completely ignorant of the fact that there is another wounded buffalo in the vicinity. Having admired your fine trophy you may be returning to camp well pleased with life, feeling right on top of the world—only to find yourself unexpectedly attacked by one of those wounded beasts about which you knew nothing. It's happened time and again.

Where to hit a buffalo? Where I recommend that you hit every animal if you possibly can: slap through the shoulder. Bring him down with such a shot and if your bullet was any good he's yours. He'll be knocked out with spinal concussion and will be dead of rapid internal hemorrhage before he can get to his feet again.

I've already referred to a buffalo's characteristic method of raising his nose rather than his head when he wants to look at you. So—to repeat—be careful to aim *below* an imaginary line drawn between the eyes, and not above it.

Practically every writer on the subject states that when taking the heart shot at buffalo you must aim much lower than on any other animal. Why? It beats me. I advise you not to take any notice of such statements. Remember what I had occasion to say when discussing heart shots at rhino: a shot through the bottom of the heart is not nearly so deadly as through the upper regions. If you bear that in mind you'll do. Slam your bullet centrally through the shoulder blade and don't worry your head about the alleged position of the heart. In the same way, if you are taking the frontal chest shot, just place your bullet nicely at the base of the throat—assuming you're more or less on the same level as the game. You'll bring him down with either shot: he won't be wanting any more.

These two shots will kill anything; but the snag is that when you are hunting in very close cover you can't always pick and choose your shot. If you could you would do just as well with a small-bore gun as with a large one. But when it's a case of knocking down some savage beast at very close quarters by merely slamming a bullet into him almost anywhere at all, a heavy slug is essential.

Some men are always talking about the neck shot, and sometimes it's the only shot you can make, but personally I don't like it. Bell even goes so far as to say that you don't have to hit the bone to kill. That certainly hasn't been my experience: I've had a few disappointments when attempting the neck shot at various beasts, including buffalo, and although some of them came off successfully, others didn't. I see that Elmer Keith (and nobody living has had more experience with American game, including the Alaskan species), who is an incomparably better marksman than I am, says much the same and has admitted in print that he eschews the neck with all game if he can possibly get anything better.

Not long ago I was reading a book in which the author claimed great experience with African buffalo, and among other things he spoke of the "dying grunts" of a buffalo—of a buffalo's "grunting" as he died. I cannot permit that to pass because it could be dangerously misleading for the beginner. A buffalo grunts contentedly when feeding at night (and possibly to scare off lions), but he doesn't grunt when dying. Shot through the lungs a buffalo runs, staggers, falls, and then, but not until after he's fallen, he gives vent to a mournful bellow usually repeated three or four times. There is absolutely *no* comparison between a grunt and a bellow, and no possibility of confusion. If you have shot a buffalo and he has run and disappeared in some grass, and on following him you hear a grunt, you must on no account become careless, because he certainly isn't dead or dying or anywhere near it; but if you hear a series of *mournful bellows,* or even only one, you needn't worry. I've never heard a buffalo loose that sound unless he's handing in his chips. It's one of the very few aspects of hunting to which I've never known an exception.

A buffalo bull with a broken shoulder or foreleg looses a series of bellowing roars deep and throaty and pregnant with meaning when he charges after being hit. I've seen him, after a badly placed shot had broken the shoulder at the joint—much too low—charge his companions again and again, scattering them and bowling some of them over. For more than an hour he had kept up that continuous series of deep throaty bellowing roars, until I finally succeeded in killing him.

But there can be no confusion between that sort of furious sound and the mournful bellow of a dying buffalo shot through the lungs.

After a heart shot there will seldom be a sound—death is too rapid.

10: LION

Curiously enough, I have difficulty remembering my first few lion. This is not because I have shot such a colossal number but because my first ones were so easy. There just wasn't anything to make an impression on my memory. Naturally, since they were my very first, for some time afterward I had no difficulty picturing them; but subsequent not-so-easy kills have tended to obscure those early ones. It is perhaps fortunate that I have a well-developed bump of self-preservation, or the ease with which I killed those first few—say about a dozen—might have made me careless and inclined to think there was nothing to this lion hunting. As I have said, it has happened to other men, not only with lion but also with elephant and buffalo. Some of them lived to regret that attitude—others didn't! It's the height of folly to underestimate the potentialities for mischief of *any* of these animals. You may kill a score of lion without any trouble—and then have the twenty-first turn the tables on you. You must treat *every* lion as that potential twenty-first. They are unaccountable creatures; you can lay down no hard and fast law concerning them. The experiences of one hunter may be directly contrary to those of another. Nevertheless, lion have certain traits that may loosely be described as characteristic.

For instance, it may fairly safely be said that lion don't look for trouble—leave them alone and, generally speaking, they will leave you alone. You may meet lion, possibly several of them, face to face when you are armed with nothing more formidable than a walking stick; and, provided you don't do something foolish, it is improbable that they will interfere with you. They will just stand there gazing at you until their curiosity is satisfied, or until they realize that it is indeed man they are looking at. Then one of them will give a low purring growl and the lot of them will clear off into the grass. But if you were to lose your head and run, or attempt that fatuous business of climbing a tree, one or more of them might come after you—their instinct seemingly being to chase after anything that runs. As for the tree climbing: unless you have a very conveniently forked tree right beside you it's but a pious hope to imagine you can climb out of reach before the lion has you—if he is close and means business. Don't forget that lion have been known to pull men off platforms fifteen feet or more above the ground by merely springing up and grabbing, just as an ordinary cat will spring up and grab a mouse off a rafter in a barn. Selous mentions having one of his men pulled off a platform close to seventeen feet high, I think it was, one night.

What is likely to cause the inexperienced man to lose his head in such circumstances is if one of the troop—probably a female suffering from the usual curiosity of her sex—comes forward for a closer look. She probably has no animosity whatever: it's apt to look far worse than it really is. And if you just stand your ground and look steadily back at her, she will stop and gaze at you once more. To turn and run is simply asking for trouble.

As with bear, the female of the species is far more dangerous than the male, and far more likely to attack, wounded or unwounded. Nevertheless, she will rarely attack without some provocation. Of course, the provocation may not be intentional on your part, but she cannot know that. If she is close by with young cubs, your sudden unexpected appearance in the grass or upon turning a bush may well precipitate an attack; yet cases have been known of the lioness' just clearing off and leaving her cubs to their fate. (I must admit, however, that such examples of faintheartedness are very rare.)

Then, if there are a male and female before you, and you shoot the male, you can certainly expect to be charged by his mate. Exceptions occur even here, but it's advisable for beginners to shoot the lioness first: the lion will seldom charge unless wounded. There are experienced hunters who say that you should shoot the lion first if you want a pair, since you are practically certain to get a shot at the lioness then, taking it as she charges.

You will sometimes hear the argument that since a wounded tiger in India won't hesitate to charge a trained shikar elephant when bayed, and lion do not attack full-grown elephant in Africa, then the tiger must be a braver and fiercer beast than the lion. But such an argument is quite meaningless because we don't use trained elephant for hunting in Africa. Therefore nobody is able to say whether or not a wounded and bayed lion would attack as readily as a tiger would in such circumstances.

Whenever sportsmen from India and Africa forgather an argument invariably arises as to the comparative ferocity, strength, and killing power of lion and tiger and the comparative dangers of hunting them. But all such debates must of necessity be academic, conditions being so dissimilar. There are a few lion left, carefully preserved, in the forests of Kathiawar in India; and in the early part of the present century the late Maharaja of Gwalior imported several pair of half-grown lion directly from Africa and turned them loose in the state jungles in the Sheopur district in the hope of re-establishing them there. The experiment was a failure. Not only did the lion dislike their new environment, but they all turned into cattle-killers and man-eaters. In the circumstances this was almost inevitable: Blaney Percival, at that time game warden of Kenya, had been given the job of collecting the young lion, and after they were brought to him by the Masai he hand-reared them and made great pets of them. When they were eventually shipped across to India and turned loose to fend for themselves they had no fear of man. Percival had played and wrestled with them and even allowed them to sleep on the foot of his bed until they got too heavy for it. Game being not nearly so plentiful in India as in Africa, it was only to be expected that these lion would take to cattle-killing and later would be forced by hunger to start killing the cattle's owners. They were all eventually shot.

Such experiments are foredoomed to failure. The game warden of Tanganyika at one time spoke of wishing to introduce tigers into his territory; but the outbreak of World War II put a stop to this notion. I'm not apologizing to anybody when I state that in my opinion it's the essence of outrage for princes, governments, or their officers to be empowered to indulge in such experiments at the expense of the unfortunate natives of their countries. How would the stock owners of Britain and the United States like it if some wealthy sportsmen turned lion and tiger loose so that they, the wealthy sportsmen, and they only, might have the "sport" of hunting them under conditions of perfect safety: would there be an outcry or would there not?

There are men who describe the lion as an arrant fraud, in no way deserving his title the King of Beasts. They will say there is little or no difficulty in stopping a charge. Ask those men where they have done their lion hunting. You will probably find that their entire experience has been in the great East African plains or other open stretches of country. If a charge comes on a more or less flat plain with the grass burned off, perhaps, and in any case too short to conceal a lion, it's true he's not too difficult to kill provided you are suitably armed and don't lose your head. But it's a different pair of boots if you are compelled to follow your lion into thick cover after wounding him. A charge across the open and a charge through thick reeds or long grass are by no means the same. I've known men with quite a considerable bag of lion, all killed in open country, who wouldn't attempt to follow a wounded lion into close cover. There are men in India who, claiming the tiger as a more formidable antagonist, say it would be madness to follow one on foot into thick jungle, as so many hunters follow wounded lion into thick cover in Africa. A wounded lion in thick cover is just as likely to charge as any wounded tiger. But because trained shikar elephant can usually be found to assist in following up wounded tiger, men not unnaturally use them. We have no such safe and useful assistants in Africa, and wounded lion in inhabited areas *must* be followed up and finished off to prevent the possibility of their turning into man-eaters. No man *likes* following a wounded lion into thick cover; we don't do it from choice, we do it simply because it has to be done.

Most tiger in India are shot for sport, but an immense number of lion are killed every year throughout Africa by ranchers, farmers, and others possessing livestock, considering it all in the day's work. In all probability the farmer's only weapons are a medium-bore Mauser and a cheap shotgun. True, where you have any quantity of livestock it's mostly reasonably open country; but there is generally no scarcity of long grass and clumps of bush just waiting to hide wounded lion. They can sometimes be beaten out of such places, but generally speaking little beating for lion is practiced in Africa—at any rate, not compared with the amount of beating for tiger there is in India. Sometimes, and in some districts, the lion are too numerous for the ranchers and farmers to cope with—the necessary time cannot be spared away from work. This is when a professional hunter is called in to take on the job. You will notice I have used the word "killed." I have done so deliberately, because any means, including traps and poison, are legitimate for cattle-killers and man-eaters. Naturally, the hunter, if he's a real hunter, will prefer to shoot the animals if he can, but sometimes it is necessary to employ other means. Professional lion hunting isn't a job that appeals to many men. However I must say I found it interesting. What I also discovered was that if the hunter goes all out to clear a district he can find he's shot himself out of a job. But that didn't worry me because I had no intention of remaining permanently anywhere.

I met a fellow who was running a few head of stock, hoping someday to be justified in calling himself a rancher. He was looking mighty blue when I met him and had only one topic of conversation: Lion with a capital L. I gathered from him that most if not all the lion in Southern Rhodesia had formed a conspiracy to prevent his getting ahead. He had shot some—eight or ten or a dozen, he hadn't counted them—and had tried to trap others. But he wasn't a hunter and it didn't seem to do any good. There were always plenty more just waiting their turn to get at his stock. Anyway, he hadn't the time to do things properly. (Apparently there is more to cattle ranching than just sitting around with your feet on a box waiting for the beasts to grow up.) He asked if I would like to come along and give him a hand. He was baching it and I could live with him. He couldn't afford to pay me much, but he'd give me my keep and a bonus for each lion. It sounded all right to me so along I went. It was then I fell for that grand little gold-inlaid Martini-Henry and invested in it.

Ted's property (I forget his surname) adjoined one of the big ranches down West Nicholson way. His house was a wattle-and-daub affair with a thatched roof like the kind everybody else started off with in the Rhodesia of those days. He had a few good black polled Angus stock from which he hoped to grade up the half-bred scrub stock which comprised most of his herd. It was nice parklike veld with clumps of trees here and there, though it looked as though the grass would be pretty long during the rains. There were a couple of large *kopjes* not far away, and he told me the lion seemed to live somewhere up there between them. He had only one horse left and two mules; the lion had killed the others.

I had bought an acetylene night-shooting lamp along with the new rifle. I knew nothing about such things, but Ted had insisted it was essential. The lamp was strapped around the head and the generator slung on the belt, a rubber tube carrying the gas up to the burner. (The modern electric edition had not yet been introduced.) I'd never used such a thing but it seemed to have possibilities. Of course, it wasn't very powerful and merely showed you the animals' eyes. You had to rely upon your experience to tell you what manner of creature you were looking at. I had merely thought of sitting up for the lion, much as they sit up for tiger in India, but I could see immediately that with a lamp I'd have much greater scope.

And while I'm on this subject of shooting lamps let me slip in a word of caution: If you have never used one before, be sure to try it at a target or some nondangerous animal first. Some men shoot extraordinarily well with these lamps with any pattern of sight; but I found, and have always found, that I am very likely to shoot high by taking too much foresight in my endeavor to see the foresight at all. I would strongly advise you to have one of those "Folding Moon" night sights fitted to your rifle if you expect to be doing much night work. It is merely an extra-large enamel-faced bead sight on a somewhat longer stem than the regular foresight. It folds down out of the way when not in use. But it's the longer stem that balances your tendency to shoot high. I find such sights excellent if I haven't a scope sight for the rifle I'm using. Fortunately for me, my little Martini—as I said, it had been built to special order for one of the Indian princes—was fitted as a matter of course with one of these night sights. I used it because it was there and consequently shot well; it was only later when trying to shoot with another rifle which didn't have one of the sights that I discovered my tendency to aim high.

There is another point that might be mentioned in connection with shooting by head lamps. Edison Marshall in his book *Shikar and Safari* tells how he tried to use one in Indo-China, and he says that the animal's eyes invariably blinked out just before he was ready to shoot so that he actually fired blind. This shows that his guide hadn't instructed him properly in the correct use of the lamps. When you are wandering along you should keep the lamp centrally in your forehead so that the beam of light is thrown wherever you look; but when you pick up—that is, shine— some animal's eyes, you must pull the lamp over your *left* eye if you shoot from the right shoulder. Then, when you aim you must hold the rifle with one hand at the same time your other hand adjusts the lamp so that it will show up both your sights and the animal at which you're trying to aim. For this reason, these head lamps are something of a nuisance. With experience you get to know pretty accurately just how much to pull the lamp around—though you will be very lucky if it doesn't need a final adjustment. However, if your quarry hasn't been shot at before at night you will find that all game with the exception of leopard are very accommodating, since they can't see you behind the light and so usually give you ample time to make these essential adjustments. Once you've made them properly you get, with the modern electric shooting lamp, a perfectly clear view of your target right through the firing of the shot. However, I must say I very much prefer the kind of light that clamps on the barrel of the rifle, provided it's been definitely designed for this work: the Parker-Hale system is by far the best—if you can get it.

I was some days on Ted's place before anything happened. Then one morning about ten o'clock a breathless and perspiring herdsman came running up to the house, where I happened to be having a cup of coffee, to tell me that three lion had just killed a cow not far away. I finished the coffee, wiped the oil out of the Martini, and out I went with him, Joro naturally accompanying me. (This was in the early days when Joro was still with me.) About a third of a mile away we came on a herd of cattle all gazing toward a clump of bush with some trees in it. The herdsman told us that the lion had killed on the far side of the clump and had probably dragged the carcass into it. I strolled around the bush to see if the lion were visible, but as there was no sign of them I decided to sneak through the bush, which was not particularly dense: perhaps I could take them unaware. I told the herdsman to take up a position at the foot of a tree which he could climb easily if necessary, some twenty-five yards from the clump and so situated that he could see the spot where the kill had taken place and the probable direction the lion would take if they happened to slip away. If they did he was to shout to me. Then Joro and I entered the bush and stalked very carefully toward the most likely place, close to where the lion had killed and where they most probably had dragged the dead cow. Joro took the lead, since we both knew he would spot the lion more quickly than I would. I followed close on his heels, rifle ready for instant use and the customary two shells between the fingers of my left hand, where they would be immediately available when needed.

It didn't take us long to work through the strip of bush to the place where we expected to find our quarry. As we closed in, Joro stopped frequently to listen. At last he heard something, waited for an instant to be sure, then turned toward me and pointed ahead as he whispered, "Lion, *Bwana.*" And then I also heard it: a grating and a deep purring. It was very close. There was a bush immediately in front of me as I exchanged places with my companion, and as I very cautiously moved around that I saw, first, an indubitable lion's tail and then the hindquarters of its owner. I edged farther around the bush until I could see all three of them feeding on the carcass of the kill. Although I was barely ten paces away they hadn't a notion I was watching them, so thoroughly were they enjoying their stolen feed. The party consisted of a lioness and two almost full-grown cubs. (Lion, like all other carnivorous animals, keep their young around until they are almost mature—doubtless for instruction purposes.)

The lioness was closest to me, and I determined to kill her first, not only because she was such a good shot, but because I knew enough to realize that she would be by far the most dangerous of the three, particularly if one of her cubs were shot in front of her. Since the ground was clear between us, I knelt down, drew a bead on the back of her head, and squeezed. She was killed instantly, and I immediately reloaded. On the shot, the two youngsters—nearly as big as their mother—sprang back from the kill, one of them spinning around to stand broadside-on to me and the other just to face me. Since I didn't expect the one facing me to attack without the moral support of either his mother or his brother, I shot the other one through the heart and again reloaded. While I was doing so, I saw the second cub look down at his mother, then around to where his brother had been a moment before—that one had cleared off on feeling the lead—and then, just before I was ready to fire again, he wheeled around and followed his brother.

I grinned at Joro, who was standing just behind my shoulder watching it all with my loaded Webley in his hand, and told him I was certain we'd find one cub dead but to watch out for the other—he would probably be sticking around close. So, after making sure the lioness was really dead, we took up the spoor of the cubs and followed it very cautiously. Although I guessed I'd find the second cub close to where I'd find the first one dead (I felt certain), I didn't anticipate an attack. I had a hunch he'd clear when he saw me coming. After all, he was only a youngster, even although almost full grown; but I naturally hoped to get a shot at him also. We had only covered about fifty yards when, on turning a bush, I saw the first cub flat out. There was a little clear space where he was, and even as I entered it I saw a movement on the far side. But it was gone almost instantly, long before I was certain what it was, much less get an aim. It was, of course, the second cub; but I had to make sure the other was dead before I could safely turn my back on him. He was dead right enough, so we started after the other one. But while still some distance from the open ground we heard the herdsman shout that a lion had broken cover and was streaking away. We hurried through the remainder of the bush but were far too late to get a shot at the vanishing youngster. I might have taken a very doubtful aim at his rump at longish range, but even in those early days I was opposed to such chancy and uncertain shots.

However, we weren't despondent. Even if one of the youngsters had got away, I'd killed his mother and the other young one; and it was in the last degree improbable that this one would continue cattle-killing on his own after the morning's lesson. Besides, I at once realized that he was almost certain to come back again later, probably that night, to look for his folks. I might get a smack at him then. The type of ground made the spooring of an unwounded lion almost an impossible task; and anyway I felt so sure he'd return that night that I wouldn't even attempt it. As there was no need to waste the good beef of the cow by leaving it out I had it butchered and taken away and then had the two dead lion skinned and their carcasses dragged just clear of the bush. They would be a greater attraction for the second youngster than all the cows on the ranch. I then borrowed some of Ted's men and had them disembowel the two carcasses and drag the guts around in a big circle half a mile or so in diameter, now and again dragging the stuff back to the carcasses. In this way I hoped to attract any other lion that might come around. It was my intention to stalk the bait that night immediately after dark in the hope of bagging the second youngster and again at the first crack of dawn in case any other lion had arrived.

That day seemed one of the longest I'd ever known, but the sun did finally drop. Ted had offered to accompany me, but as he obviously wasn't the least bit eager to and anyway was paying me to do the job and was therefore not under any obligation to help in it, I told him not to bother. But I borrowed his shotgun. It was a cheap-grade weapon in very poor condition, but with a single-shot rifle it's desirable to have something as a stand-by and when loaded with SSG it would be a better weapon for Joro to carry than my revolver. Besides, no matter what weapon I'm using I like to have a good handgun on my belt when I'm after lion.

As soon as the sun was down we started out. We walked slowly, keeping the clump of bush between us and the bait. We had to wait for a short time when we reached it since it still wasn't sufficiently dark for the lamps to do their work properly. (I had borrowed Ted's lamp for Joro to wear.) Then around the clump of bush we went, all set for instant action. And sure enough, the lamps picked up a pair of large glowing eyes immediately beyond the carcasses of the two dead lion. They blazed red-gold in the rays of the acetylene gas. This could only be the fellow we were after. I closed to within about fifteen paces. The eyes never left me, never moved. To make sure the angle was right, I dropped to one knee and aimed for the left eye. When I had it nicely balanced, as it were, on top of the large enamel night sight I squeezed. An orange-red flame leaped from the muzzle, and a cloud of smoke from the black powder blotted everything out for a few moments. When it cleared sufficiently for me to be able to peer through it, there were no eyes to be seen. I had, of course, reloaded automatically after firing and while waiting for the smoke to clear, and I now advanced toward the dead lion. Out of the corner of my eye I could see that Joro was at my shoulder, with the muzzles of the shotgun pointing at a misty something we could just distinguish beyond the bait. It was our young lion; and no lion could have been deader. My big lead bullet had taken him fairly in the eye and shattered the back of his head.

Do I need to tell you that you must never attempt to shoot a lion between the eyes unless you're right on top of him and very definitely shooting down? A lion looking at you appears to have a good forehead, as though specially designed as a bullet trap—especially if he has a good mane—but it's a snare and a delusion, as many a man found out in days gone by. If you examine a lion's skull you will find that it's quite flat on top—*he has no forehead at all.* Accordingly, if you are aiming at one of his eyes you should choose his left eye if you shoot from your right shoulder. Then if you yank at your trigger it will merely spell a clean miss; whereas if you aim at his right eye and do the same thing you will send your bullet between his eyes. This will merely crease his scalp and send him raging mad. A savage charge is a practical certainty after such a shot.

On the return to the ranch house I seemed to be walking on air. After making sure that the young lion was dead I had of course swung the light around on the off-chance that there might be other lion in the immediate vicinity; but no glowing eyes had rewarded me, apart from the deep ruby eyes of a nightjar and the scintillating diamond-bright eyes of a spider.

When the first cocks were crowing next morning Joro and I were up drinking a pot of scalding-hot coffee. I wanted to time things so that we would arrive at the bait when there was just enough light to see the sights. Since this wasn't a game district, any lion that came around would know very well that they were poaching and would beat it before full daybreak. In good game districts where they haven't been shot to any noticeable extent lion will frequently lie around until the sun gets too warm for comfort, but not on a cattle ranch.

We had timed things nicely, but there was no lion at the bait when we came within sight of it. However, there were very clear indications that a lion *had* been there. The freshly killed lion had been untouched but the other two had both been half-eaten. Hyenas had been there and had certainly enjoyed themselves; but so also had a big lion. His spoor was plainly discernible, and there was every evidence that he had filled himself with the hindquarters of the young lion. What was the betting he'd come back again tonight for another feed? There wasn't much game about—there seldom is on a ranch—and there was still plenty of feeding left on the two carcasses, to say nothing of the third. As this was a big lion we could take it for granted that he was experienced. There was no telling at what hour he'd arrive, though it was doubtful if he would risk it until fairly late; while this morning had shown that he knew better than to wait until daybreak. Consequently, I decided it would be best to sit up for him. There was a young moon which wouldn't set until close on to midnight. If he were coming he would probably come before then as he'd know all about hyenas and similar scavengers.

But I decided not to sit up on the ground level. I doubted very much if, even with careful nursing, our gas lamps would last through the night. The moon while it was out might or might not give enough light to shoot by, though I very much doubted that it would—I had no scope with hard-coated lenses like the one I have today. There was a big tree with a convenient fork about a dozen feet from the ground growing close to the edge of the bush, and I had a notion to have a stout platform built in that fork. Joro and I could both sit up then, taking it in turns if necessary to get forty winks of sleep. As our gas lamps were only suitable for close-range work, we would have a rough native-made ladder down which we could come more easily and more silently than by climbing, if and when the lion arrived. Moreover, it occurred to me that, twelve feet or so above the ground, and fairly well back from the edge, we could keep one lamp in reserve in case the lion was very late, and possibly be able to light it under cover of a blanket without scaring him. In this way the two lamps might possibly see us through the night. I certainly didn't want to be left without a lamp, for if the lion turned up I could do nothing about it.

This attended to we arrived back at sundown with a couple of blankets and a pillow and made ourselves comfortable. I ought perhaps to mention that our lamps had black-out shutters which could be closed or held open by means of a spring clip. These enabled me to have one of the lights all ready to use, and yet there was no fear of the lion's spotting it too soon.

Our first two visitors were a couple of jackals who seemed to have springs in their legs, so keyed-up were they and ready to bolt at the first sound or movement. They were really scared stiff. Of course, they knew very well they were stealing someone else's meat; but it was curious they should be so terrified since it must be a nightly performance for them. We did *not* have a bag of stones to throw at them as so many men say they do. I've frequently heard and read of men sitting up for lion, tiger, or leopard filling their pockets with stones or bringing a bag of them along to throw at the hyenas and jackals to scare them away from the bait. But surely that's all wrong. The big cats must be well accustomed to finding these scavengers on their kills whenever they return to them. If you throw stones at them they will usually just clear off a short distance and sit there waiting for a better opportunity. If a lion arrives and sees the hyenas sitting around like that, he will immediately guess there is something at the kill which scares them. If it's not another lion— then what the heck is it? He'll circle around at a respectful distance and perhaps pick up your wind. If he knows anything about this sitting-up business, that's all you'll see of him. It's obviously better to ignore the jackals and hyenas—they won't finish the bait before the lion arrives unless it's very small. If he finds them on the kill he won't be suspicious and you'll have your shot.

It may be worth mentioning that on dark and stormy nights lion are incredibly bold. Their determination to have a feed seems to override completely all their customary caution. I know a case of a man's firing no less than four shots at a lion on a kill before he took any notice, and then all he did was to drag the kill out of night range. (The man wasn't using a lamp.) On another occasion four or five lion arrived on the bait. One of them, a lioness, was killed with the hunter's first shot. The others cleared off a short distance but almost immediately one of them, a big lion, came back to the kill, completely ignoring the dead lioness. But on bright nights lion seem to be much more cautious.

As we waited a hyena howled dolefully some distance away, and then was answered by another. Their howls came closer and closer, and finally ceased. Our two little jackals were even more on the *qui vive* now, and suddenly disappeared. In the next instant a hyena appeared, to be followed shortly by another. Their howls were hideous as they told the world and any distant pals of the free feed they had found. As they settled down to it the two jackals would dart in now and again to snatch a mouthful. The hyenas took no notice of them. How long we watched them I don't know, but suddenly they were gone. This could only mean one thing—lion, or just possibly leopard. But it was a lion. He walked up to the kill as though it were his own, completely ignoring the scavengers. For a few moments he stood looking at it, seemingly estimating its possibilities, his tail waving from side to side. Then without more ado he crouched down beside the fresh carcass and started feeding off the rump.

I tried to get an aim, but it was too chancy. The branches of the trees overhead kept the moon off my sights, and I didn't want merely to wound. I whispered to my companion that I was going down. Very carefully, so as not to make a noise, I descended our ladder. Almost as soon as I was off our perch the intervening bush concealed me from the lion. Joro followed me, shotgun in hand. Then, as I turned the bush, I opened the black-out shutter on the front of my lamp.

The light seemed to leap out, but for quite a little time the lion took no notice. He was feeding heartily and doubtless figured the ray of the lamp was merely the moon shining a mite brighter after coming from behind a cloud. I walked up to within about thirteen paces of him before he looked up. It was necessary to get really close with these low-powered lamps if there was even a little moonlight—and with a full moon they were useless. It was as I halted that the lion looked up at me. It took but a split second to aim, and then I let him have it slap between the eyes. This was possible because he was lying down and I standing close. His head dropped and never moved again. It was as easy as that.

Having assured ourselves that he was a "good" lion, and having admired him by the combined light of the young moon and my lamp, Joro and I climbed back to our platform. We might have returned to the ranch house, as most men would have done, but both of us were keen as mustard and intended to bag any other lion that took it into their heads to come around. We chatted quietly for a while and then took turns sleeping, while the other kept watch. But nothing further occurred.

In fact, for some weeks nothing further occurred, and I began to get a bit bored. Then one night there was great yelling and shouting. We gathered that a lion or lions had either broken into the kraal or had caused the cattle to break out. Greatly excited herdsmen took us to the place, and there was no doubt the lion had played the game of getting the cattle to break open their kraal. There were scared and dazed oxen standing around not knowing what to do: wherever I looked I picked up their big eyes in the ray of the lamp. It was a fine dark night, for the moon was waning by this time and hadn't yet risen. But I had to be careful, because I didn't want to shoot any of the cattle, mistaking them for lion—as I once heard of someone's doing elsewhere. There was little or no breeze, but what little there was gave me the most probable direction in which to look for the lion: they would almost certainly have killed on the downwind side of the kraal. I moved around there and, sure enough, scarcely fifty yards away I found two of them on the carcass of a big bullock. I walked slowly up to within fifteen or twenty yards, dropped to one knee, and shot the nearer one fairly in the eye. The smoke prevented my seeing for the moment it took me to reload, but as it thinned I could see the second pair of eyes some little distance away. Apparently the second lion had bounded off when the rifle roared, and then stopped to see what was detaining his pal. He was a mite farther away than I would have chosen, but I was keen to bag him also. In addition, I was steady and had great confidence in my little carbine, and I was afraid if I tried to close in on him he would clear and I might not get a shot at him at all. So, still kneeling there where I had fired the first shot, I drew a steady bead on this second one's eye and squeezed.

When the smoke cleared there were no eyes, and I didn't know whether I'd killed or missed clean. As soon as I had reloaded I advanced to where he'd been standing, Joro with his lamp and shotgun alongside me. He had murmured, "You have killed him," when I fired, and was quite sure I had. He being slightly on one side had not been blinded by the smoke to the same extent that I had. And he was right. The lion was as dead as the first one.

These first easy kills might well have had the effect of dangerously lowering my respect for the King of Beasts. But from what little I'd read and from all I'd heard about all potentially dangerous animals, elephant, buffalo, lion, and tiger in particular, it's not the actual hunting and shooting of them that's so dangerous. Provided you are suitably armed and don't lose your head, none of them are difficult to kill so long as you get a clear shot at them. What struck me was that the real danger came when they were wounded and being followed up. From all I had gathered, the fatalities and maulings and similar unpleasant happenings occurred only after the animal in question had been shot and wounded. So right from the beginning I endeavored to make sure of my shots. I didn't want to have to follow up any wounded beast, which of course I would have to do if I muffed my shot. The obvious answer is not to muff it, and that is the principle I've worked on right up to the present day. True, I'm only human, and I've yet to meet the man who *never* misplaces his bullet—I guess he has yet to be born. Not even the late Annie Oakley, one of the greatest shots of all time, was entirely infallible, and neither was the great Karamojo Bell.

I didn't have to follow up a wounded lion at all on this ranch. (By night, of course, if using a lamp as I was, there is no excuse for missing or wounding; and I shot most of my lion here by night.) I remained for about three months, killing some fifteen or sixteen lion. Then, as I was made a very much better offer for a similar job by a big ranching company in Northern Rhodesia, and as there had been peace on Ted's place for quite a long while, I decided to quit.

The new ranch was located in the Lusaka district, and it was bleak and bitterly cold when I arrived. I had a hunch I wouldn't remain long—I don't like cold. Nevertheless, I put in some seven or eight months on the place. It was up there I had to face a charge. A big lion had killed and I determined to sit up for him. As there was a full moon I knew my lamp would be of no use to me. And since there was no suitable tree close by I was forced to wait on the ground. Most men in a situation like this have a small enclosure made of bushes and sit in that, which is all right if there are other bushes around; but if it is bare open veld the sudden appearance of bush where no bush had been before would be likely to arouse the lion's suspicions. At least, that's how I look at it. Let me add that these enclosures are not primarily for safety—no such hastily erected fence would stop a determined lion from getting at you. They are merely to conceal you, and, to a lesser extent, to break the force of a charge should one eventuate and give you a chance to do something.

A much better method on bare open veld is to have your men dig a pit about three feet deep with a stout cage of sticks erected over it about a foot higher. You leave an opening at the back into which you crawl, and then when you are inside your men tie a tarpaulin or ground sheet over the entire show leaving just a loophole in front through which you can see and shoot. A few branches or bundles of grass can be scattered over the top. Since light is only contrast, and it's pitch-dark inside your enclosure, you get an excellent view of your target. Moreover, since the muzzle of your rifle is shoved through the hole and therefore outside, you should have no difficulty in seeing your foresight. Another very real advantage of this method is that you can kill with much greater certainty than you can when shooting down from a tree—at least you can in most instances. I think it was Selous who inaugurated this method. Anyway, I have found it very satisfactory.

I had one of these pits dug, big enough to contain Joro and me, and we settled ourselves in it shortly before dark. About an hour later we heard a deep sigh from somewhere close behind us. Then for what seemed a long time there was absolute silence. As the pit was entirely closed except for the loophole in front we could see nothing and do nothing but wait. Had the lion winded us and gone? Was he lying waiting and watching to see if we were really there and potentially dangerous? It was impossible to tell. We sat as still as two mice and hoped. And presently our hopes were rewarded by another deep sigh over on our right side. It seemed to be right beside us. (And next morning we found the lion's spoor a bare four feet from the pit. As the breeze had been blowing from that side, it's quite possible that he didn't actually know we were there—he was just being unusually cautious before approaching for a feed. But he had finally decided there was no danger.)

The lion now came into view very close, and I was greatly tempted to shoot. But it would have been a rear-view raking shot at an awkward angle, and I had doubts of a clean kill, so I waited. As events developed I might just as well have fired then and there. When the lion reached the kill he lay down and immediately commenced feeding, and except that he was lying instead of walking he was in exactly the same position and at exactly the same angle. For a long while I waited for him to turn. I should have continued waiting, but I foolishly became impatient. My excuse was that clouds were appearing and had begun to darken the moon at intervals. I wanted to get my shot off under the best possible light conditions. I realized later, of course, that my excuse was not really a valid one in the circumstances; but at the time it appeared legitimate.

At all events I drew a bead on the lion's short ribs and squeezed, hoping that my bullet would drive forward diagonally toward the point of the off shoulder and so traverse lungs and heart. Had I placed it properly, without doubt it would have done so; but something must have gone wrong. Instead of the bullet's taking him through the flank it broke his doubled-up knee joint on the left side, as I later discovered. If you picture a lion lying down and facing not quite directly away from you, you will see that I must have hit him some three inches to the right of where I intended. He loosed a surprised roar, leaped clean over the kill, and was gone before I had time to reload.

Mentally I kicked myself for not awaiting a better chance. I knew instinctively that I had missed the shot I intended, and only wounded. There was a possibility, of course, that I had killed, but somehow I didn't get much consolation from the thought. I don't know why I should have been so certain I had muffed the shot—I can't remember any feeling that I'd pulled instead of squeezed my trigger. It must have been just a hunch. Anyhow, it was correct.

As the pit wasn't big enough to lie down in, and as there wasn't much likelihood of anything else turning up, we struggled out and made our way back to the cottage the company had given me.

Next morning after a pot of coffee we went out to pick up the spoor. I carried the Martini I'd used the previous night; Joro the Greener (a second rifle I'd bought when I took on this job—a single-loader chambered for Rigby's excellent .400/.350 cartridge). The kill was undisturbed, showing that we had been wise in not sitting up for the remainder of the night, and the lion's spoor indicated he was lame on the near hind. There was no cover near by, and spooring was fairly easy. The trail led us toward a fair-sized clump of longish grass about half a mile away. It looked a likely spot for him to be lying up in; consequently I decided that if nothing happened when we approached it, I would circle around and see whether he had come out on the far side. It wasn't necessary to do so. When we were within some thirty paces of the fringe the lion could contain himself no longer—he must have been lying just within the edge of the grass all night and had watched us approaching. There was a grating roar, and next instant I saw what appeared to be a ball of concentrated fury, all mouth and teeth, come flying toward me across the short grass. I dropped to one knee in order to give myself a better chance of stopping the charge. As the sights lined up fairly in the center of that open mouth, from which came the rapid succession of furious throaty roars, I found they were rock-steady—I had had no time to get scared—and I had but a split second to wait until I reckoned the lion was close enough. Then I let him have it—slap in the open mouth. A roar, choked off short, became a cough. I dropped the Martini, grabbed the Greener which my companion was holding out to me, and stood up as I brought it to my shoulder. The lion had staggered and lurched on receiving the bullet, but he hadn't fallen. Now, after coming on for another couple of lengths, he'd halted and was swaying and retching, head down, about twelve feet from me. He looked drunk and very, very sick. But he was still dangerous, damned dangerous. I took steady aim with the .350 and drove its soft-nose bullet into the top of his head.

It was all over.

I reached for my companion's shoulder and squeezed it. I was proud and pleased at the way he had stood by me during the charge, and the way he had held the second rifle out in the best possible position for me to grab. After all, this was his first charge. On a previous occasion when I was charged—*my* first charge—I had had to stalk a lion and lioness across the open and so had left Joro at the fringe of the last cover (much against his will) because two of us stalking them would have meant a greater possibility of the lions' spotting us. That time I had carried both rifles during my stalk, and when opening fire had laid one of them on the ground with its muzzle on a leaf so it would not pick up sand if I had to grab it in a hurry.

Having got away with two charges without any trouble I was naturally feeling good. But then, just to square things, as it were, came a series of inexplicable misses. At least they seemed inexplicable at the time, though I got the answers to them eventually. But what mattered was that they badly upset my confidence, besides being a sore slap in the face to my self-esteem. This latter may or may not have been a good thing, but the blow to my confidence was serious. I'm sure now that all this came about by my deciding to use the Greener at night to avoid the smoke nuisance, which was, of course, more noticeable by night than by day. But the Greener wasn't fitted with one of those folding night sights as the Martini was.

Well, it was the better part of a week after the adventure I have described before anything further happened. Then one day a herdsman came running to tell me that two lion had killed an ox about two miles away. He and his fellow herdsmen had driven them off before they had had time to feed. I went out at once to see what could be done. By the time I arrived there was only about an hour or an hour and a half to go before sundown. There was a useful-looking tree close by, so I told the men to build a platform in it right away, with a ladder leading up to it. Joro and I would sit up there with our lamps. We then returned to the cottage to eat. That done, we got the lamps fixed up and rode back, reckoning the herdsmen could bring back our horses. They did that, and we settled ourselves to wait for the lion, which would almost certainly return to their interrupted feed.

They returned, two of them, about an hour after dark. I waited until they started eating before attempting to climb down from our perch. I figured they would be so engrossed then that they'd be less likely to notice any small noise I might make. All went well until I knelt for my shot. Both lion were looking toward me now, but without seeming alarmed. I drew what I thought was a certain bead on the left eye of the near one, and squeezed. The rifle spoke, there was a flash but no smoke, and the eyes disappeared. Reloading instantly, I waited for the second one to look around for his mate. Sure enough, just as I completed re-loading, a pair of glowing eyes sprang out of the darkness. But even as I raised my rifle I was astonished to see a second pair of eyes close to them. "Ye gods!" I thought. "Were there actually three lions there all the time? I could've sworn there had only been two. Well, anyway, here goes for another." I fired. And again the eyes disappeared. Certain I had killed two lion, I reloaded and waited to see if the third would give me a chance. For a few moments there was nothing to be seen, then a pair of big eyes glowed from some distance away—too far for a shot with a gas lamp. And when I rose to my feet with the intention of closing in on them if they'd let me, damned if a second pair didn't appear just beyond them! To say I was amazed in no way describes my feelings. What on earth. . . . This must be a troop, or "pride," as they like to call it nowadays, of lion, and the first two were an advance guard. All right, let's see how many I can bag. But as I advanced toward the eyes, Joro at my shoulder, I naturally took a good look to see that the first two were dead. I swung my lamp. Nary a dead lion. I could see two pair of eyes ahead of me—and even as I looked they vanished. I whispered to my companion to swing his lamp on the "dead" ones while I tried again to pick up the eyes. But he couldn't find them either. As there was no further glimpse of the eyes, we both then set to work to try to find our two kills. But neither sight nor light of them could we find. So, very disconsolate, we had to climb back to our platform. I *couldn't* have missed *both* those shots. It didn't make sense. Then what had happened? Surely the .350 couldn't have blown both lion to atoms—but if it hadn't, then where were they? Could the others have carried them away to eat at their leisure? Can you imagine the fantastic possibilities that passed through my bewildered mind?

Since I knew I'd get no sleep for many a long hour I suggested that my companion try to take a nap while I took first watch. There was a good chance of the lion returning later though possibly not much before dawn. Anyway, I'd keep watch until I felt good and sleepy, then wake Joro for his turn. So I quenched his lamp and shut the black-out shutter on mine. As the long hours passed I went over and over those two abortive shots. I was positive I hadn't flinched or jerked my trigger—then why hadn't I killed? True, it hadn't been too easy to see the sights, as compared with the big night sight on the Martini, but I had seemed to be getting a good enough aim—then why hadn't I killed? My ammunition was fresh; the rifle was in good condition; I'd killed other lion with it by day, as well as buck for the pot—then why the hell hadn't I killed these two lion? If I had been scared or nervous or overanxious I could have understood it. But I hadn't been; on the contrary, I'd felt perfectly confident. Around and around in my head the questions buzzed and shouted—but for the life of me I couldn't find the answers. And I didn't get them either when, long after midnight, I wakened my companion and took his place. However, I got no sleep. Shortly after I lay down I felt his hand squeeze my thigh. I sat up quietly and picked up the rifle. With his lips against my ear, Joro whispered that there was a lion creeping back to the kill. He wasn't sure, but he thought there was another waiting a little way off to see if the coast were clear. These would almost certainly be our two back again. Anyway, they were lion, and that was what mattered. Again I waited until they were satisfied there was no danger around. But they were very, very cautious. The first of them circled around several times before he ventured to approach. We were sufficiently high to prevent his getting our wind. However, for a long while it looked as though he would never make up his mind that all was well. Finally he did. In absolute silence he walked up to the carcass of the ox, and then stood there with his tail waving from side to side. At last he lay down and took a bite into the rump. When the other saw that he also came up, just a shadow moving through the darkness.

When the sound of their feeding reached me, I very slowly and quietly went down the ladder, Joro naturally following me. I was again carrying the Greener. I wanted the smokeless ammunition in the hope of being able to bag both lion—I would have done better to use the Martini for one certain kill, and just hope for a chance at the other.

One lion had his back to me; the other was concealed by the carcass. I walked up quietly until I was within thirteen or fourteen paces of the nearer one before opening the black-out shutter on my lamp—I had a hunch they'd go before I could get a shot if I opened it too soon. It was quite an experience to walk up like that to two lion feeding at night, so close without a light. I don't recommend it. Anything may go wrong, and then you'll be very much at their mercy. With an electric lamp you would be all right—you could switch it on instantaneously; but the shutter on the old gas lamps was apt to stick. However, on this occasion all went well. As the light sprang out the near lion spun around with a low deep purring growl. I swung up the rifle and fired the instant the butt came home on my shoulder. The lion dropped. I reloaded and swung on the second one. He had bounded away a short distance as the shot was fired. He was possibly twenty to twenty-five paces away when he halted, and looked around toward me. As the carcass of the dead ox might have prevented my getting a shot had I knelt down, I took a standing off-hand shot at him, aiming for his left eye. At the shot the eyes disappeared. I reloaded, glanced down to make sure the lion in front of me was dead, and then made for the second one. Again disappointment: there was no second lion there. This didn't upset me quite as much as the previous misses had, because I realized I had tended to hurry and it had, after all, been an offhand shot at a small target. So we again climbed our ladder to spend the remainder of the night wondering if the second lion would return to look for his mate. There was a good chance that he would, in spite of the fact that he'd been fired at twice. After all, the firing might have alarmed him, but it certainly hadn't hurt him.

However, we saw nothing further of him, though we both sat there with eyes skinned until my lamp went out. Under a blanket I then lit Joro's, which I'd extinguished earlier in the hope of saving some gas. But we had no need for it. Nothing came near the kill. As soon as it was light enough to see we took up the spoor of that elusive second lion, in the faint hope that he might have been wounded—though when I failed to kill him I knew very well that I must have missed clean. We lost the spoor eventually and couldn't find it again. So we returned to the kill and had the men, who had arrived by this time, go through the usual procedure of dragging guts and bloody meat around in a large circle and then back toward the place where the kill had been. The best of the meat was butchered and carried away, but enough was left to make an attractive pile and, with the carcass of the dead lion would act as bait for either that second brute or for any others that might come prowling around.

That night we again took up our position in the tree. But nothing happened. The east was graying before anything approached. I then saw a shadow creeping up carefully toward the bait. I extinguished my lamp by pinching the rubber tube (I guessed I'd do better without it) and squeezed my companion's thigh. I was glad to remove the lamp from my head: it had grown heavy with the hours. Joro and I then sat motionless and waited for what the gods were going to give us. Gradually the day dawned. The lion—for a lion it was—took a long time to come close. There could be little doubt that it was that elusive second one come to look for his mate. He prowled around and around, and I followed him with my sights whenever he was in front of me. At last, when it began to look as though he were not going to venture right up to the bait, I was tempted to let drive. But I was overanxious. Those misses had upset me; my confidence had been badly shaken. Instead of sitting easily for the shot, I foolishly tensed myself and thought too much about it. One shouldn't do that: one should shoot naturally and instinctively. I was using the Greener. I squeezed, but raised my face too soon from the butt in order to see the result of the shot better. I must actually have raised my cheek before the bullet was out of the barrel. And since my muscles were tensed this was equivalent to flinching. Instead of my bullet's taking the lion through the heart and lungs it hit him too far back and too high. He spun around with a coughing roar, biting viciously at his flank. Hurriedly reloading, I fired again and—clean missed. Again I reloaded. The lion, after spinning around several times, started to leave. He was traveling directly away from me at a slow canter. I drew a bead on the back of his head and this time fired a good and steady shot without thinking about it at all. The lion crumpled and fell and never budged again. My bullet had taken him where the neck joins the base of the skull. Then and there I learned one of the most important lessons a marksman must learn: *Don't think of the actual mechanics of firing.* Up to this time I'd never consciously given a thought to such matters, but I now found I had developed a tendency to do so except in the case of a quick shot with no time to think about it. I quit using the Greener for night work, too, though it wasn't until later that I discovered just why it had been responsible for those first misses.

Loss of confidence has affected me several times during the course of my career, though fortunately only at remote intervals. I now know that it has always followed the use of some rifle not built to my measurements and exacting specifications so that it did not really suit me and the work for which I intended it.

My next two or three kills were easy ones, yet in spite of that I very nearly muffed both of them because of this lack of confidence—I was scared, not of the lions, but of missing. The first occurred a few days after the events just described. I had stalked a kill made the previous evening and was given a fair chance at a big lion at about sixty yards' range. Everything was in my favor: there wasn't a breath of air stirring; the sun was on the horizon behind me; the lion, full-fed, was dawdling over the remains of the kill as though reluctant to leave it. I had sneaked up behind a tree and had him in clear view. Nothing could have been easier. And I felt no trace of nervousness until I came to raise the rifle for the shot. Then a fit of what amounted to buck fever suddenly came over me. I started panting and trembling and had the greatest difficulty in steadying my rifle, although I was leaning against that very convenient tree. As I came to squeeze the trigger I found I flinched so badly that I actually raised my cheek from the butt before I made the squeeze! Had I actually fired I believe I would have completely missed the lion. But fortunately I realized in time what was happening and stopped myself before the rifle went off. Again I tried to steady myself. I took a long, long time over that shot; but the lion was apparently in no hurry to go. At last I steadied sufficiently and let him have it. There was no doubt about it this time. But it had been a doubtful thing.

The next occasion wasn't quite so bad but bad enough to act as warning *not* to think of the mechanics of firing but just to throw the rifle up, line the sights, and let drive automatically and naturally. There were two lion this time—a male and a female. Again it was a daylight encounter. They had killed in the evening and the herdsmen hadn't driven them away because they figured they'd be able to call me in time. I galloped out to where the kill had taken place—accompanied by Joro, who was becoming quite a horseman—dismounted when I came in sight of the lion, and proceeded to stalk. The stalk was quite an easy one, and I closed to within some seventy to seventy-five yards. The fact that I'd killed three roan antelope since I'd last shot a lion, and killed them all without any trouble, had gone a long way toward restoring that lost confidence of mine, but it wasn't entirely back again even yet. When I came to shoot I once more found myself trembling slightly, though not nearly so badly as last time. Yet it was enough to make me flinch a bit, with the result that the first lion, a female, wasn't killed outright. I'd hit her a mite too far back. She loosed an angry growl, spun around, and bounded away. The lion jumped to his feet, looked after her, then toward me, undecided what to do. Reloading instantly, I threw up the rifle for a quick shot at him. And just because it was a quick shot it went true— I hadn't time to think about it or flinch or anything else. He bounded away for a short distance, staggered, and fell. After making sure he was dead I took up the spoor of the wounded lioness. It was obvious she was hit hard. There was plenty of blood along the spoor, and great puddles of it where she had halted momentarily here and there. I expected to find her dead, nor was I disappointed. Within a quarter of a mile we found her stretched out, quite dead. But it was the quick shot at her mate that did more to restore my confidence than anything else. I was enough of a rifleman to get the answer: *Don't think about the shot.*

There was one confirmed old cattle-killer I was very anxious to bag at this time. He'd been shot at several times by others but had always managed to get clear. I'd tried for him myself a couple of times but had failed to get a shot. Then one day he killed a Wemba herdsman who had tried to drive him away from an ox he'd just killed close to a drinking place. I was called, rode out, and found him feeding. He hadn't interfered with the body of the herdsman after killing him, but had immediately returned to the carcass of the slain bullock. When I was about one hundred yards away I dismounted, walked up behind a small bush, and knelt down for the shot. But he must have been watching me all the time out of the corner of his eye. Even as I knelt, he suddenly and without the slightest warning whipped around and came for me openmouthed. It was most unexpected. His killing of the herdsman—the first man he'd been known to kill—must have given him a swollen head. I was using the Martini. Since he was now within about forty yards of me, I didn't have much time to think. As my sights lined up in the center of his open mouth, I squeezed. He coughed, staggered—and came on. I dropped the Martini and grabbed the Greener, which, as usual, Joro was holding out ready for me. But as I took it the lion suddenly pitched onto his nose, rolled heels over head, and lay facing back the way he'd come. He was stone-dead.

This is the *only* time I've ever had an unwounded male lion attack unprovoked.

My experiences with lion have been almost exclusively with man-eaters and cattle-killers. I don't interfere with the ordinary "hunting" lion and, above all, not with the magnificent big buffalo-killers. These last deserve special mention. They're much larger than the ordinary lion and generally wander around alone or with one other mighty companion. I've never seen more than two of them together and have never seen a female with them. They follow the buffalo herds and will not lower themselves to kill lesser game—always excepting porcupines, the lion's favorite tidbit. He seems to look upon porcupines as I look upon oysters, and his method of killing them is interesting. If he thinks he can get away with it he will just pounce and rip open the throat; but if porcy has rolled himself into a ball the lion lies down close by and just taps the ground quite gently close in front of the porcupine. Porcy gets curious after a bit and sticks out his nose to investigate. That is what the lion is waiting for. He gives his victim a tap on the end of the nose, which knocks him out, and then rolls him over and kills him. But the technique doesn't always work so easily. I remember I shot a magnificent big dark-maned buffalo-killer one morning around ten o'clock when I was returning from a buffalo hunt. There was a lot of scrub and grass about, and the lion was only eleven paces away when I spotted him as he made to cut across my bows. He was just walking along with his mouth open as though he found the heat somewhat trying. He was making for a water hole I knew of and didn't see me. It must have been some kind of reflex action that caused me to throw up the rifle and kill him. Had I waited an instant longer I would have realized it was one of these fine buffalo-killers and let him pass. When I came to examine him I found that he must have pounced all too impatiently upon a porcupine some two or three days previously. He had twenty-six quills stuck deep in his chest. Some of them had been crumpled against his breastbone; others had been driven up to four inches deep. Whether that had been done when he pounced on the porcupine, or later when he tried to kill some bigger beast, I cannot say; but it seems improbable that he would have pounced so heavily on so small an animal as a porcupine that those tough quills would crumple against his breastbone. It was clear, however, that he would have been unable to kill a beast of any size until sufficient pus had formed around the quills to let them drop out. What struck me as extraordinary was that he had apparently made no attempt to draw any of them out with his teeth: he might not have been able to get hold of all of them with his teeth, but there aren't so very many places on his body that a member of the cat family can't reach. It was quite obvious that he was unable to kill, because he had absolutely nothing in him— nothing at all. Never have I seen an animal so empty—even his intestines. Yet he was fat enough.

I was greatly interested to learn from Corbett of the numbers of tiger that get themselves stuck like pincushions with porcupine quills.

Apparently this is in large measure the cause of their becoming man-eaters (though I cannot remember ever killing a man-eating lion and finding him stuck with quills). Corbett says that the Indian leopard does not get himself stuck, though he is just as partial to porcupines as the tiger: he grabs the porcupine by the head. And Corbett wonders that animals with the agility and intelligence of tiger should be so clumsy. He also states that the quills in tiger are invariably broken off flush with the hide, and that sores form where the tiger has tried to get hold of them with his teeth. This makes me wonder even more why my lion that day, and other quill-stuck lion I have encountered, did not attempt to pull out the quills.

Ever since I killed that big buffalo-killer I've regretted it, because such lion do real good. They kill off a large number of buffalo that have been wounded and lost by inexperienced, excitable sportsmen, buffalo that would otherwise injure and kill women and children going out to collect firewood and wild fruit. And the lion do no harm at all. On many occasions I've had two of them come quietly past where I was sleeping, stop not more than eight feet or so from the foot of my camp bed, as their spoor has clearly shown next morning, stand there gazing at me fast asleep, and then drift along down to the water for their drink. On their way back they would go through the same performance and then wander on. They never attempted to interfere with me, and I didn't consider it necessary in any way to take precautions. This has happened not once, but many times. My men got to know these two lion too and also took no precautions—they were all sleeping about ten yards behind me. Time after time we would meet the two great tawny-maned beasts when we were following up the spoor of a herd of buffalo in the morning. I'm perfectly sure the lion knew they were safe from us and got to recognize us too. They would merely draw aside some fifteen to twenty-five paces from the spoor of the buffalo, and then sit down under a tree and gaze at us as we passed. There was no evidence of fear in their behavior. After we had passed they would drop into place astern of us, perhaps fifty to a hundred yards or so, and follow along. Nothing would induce me to fire a shot at them. Year after year when I visited that district I met them. There were others we occasionally encountered, but we never became so friendly with them as with those two.

Cattle-killers are far easier to deal with than man-eaters, if only because of the very much easier conditions under which they're found. Moreover, they don't usually develop the cunning that's so characteristic of the confirmed man-eater. When you get a man-eater in easy open veld, you can pretty well bet on it that he is some wretched creature which has been wounded and become lost. By far the worst man-eaters are those that have been bred to man-eating by their parents. These brutes are mostly found in thick bush and scrub country, where it is practically impossible to get a shot at them by day unless you're very, very lucky. You can hunt them for months without getting a shot by day; and then one red-letter day you may be allowed to bag two or three at a sitting around ten o'clock in the morning. But you can't bank on that. And anyway, they kill several times a week. In this sort of bush the man-eaters romp the countryside in bands of three and five; occasionally you'll get a solitary one, and sometimes a pair, but the usual number seems to be three. And where the ordinary "hunting" lion will generally be satisfied to kill perhaps a couple of times a week, these man-eaters are seldom satisfied with less than three kills, and sometimes four or even five a week. I've known them to kill nine natives in one week. There are some districts in Africa that are notorious for their man-eaters, districts that have been notorious as far back as man can remember. Livingstone spoke of more than one and referred to them as notorious even then. I've been in some of those districts and can say that they are still notorious, and for the same reason. It doesn't seem to matter what you do, you can't rid them entirely of their scourge. You may wipe out the three brutes that have been creating a reign of terror, but scarcely has the sign of relief had time to fade away than another three take up the good work. I'm not exaggerating. There are times when the wretched inhabitants may have a spell of peace lasting for a few months, or even for a couple of years, but sooner or later the drums will roll their warning through the night again.

It's true that in many of these bad districts game is scarce; but why don't the lion clear out to other districts? It isn't only scarcity of game, anyway; I know other bad districts where game, if not actually plentiful, is certainly not scarce—yet man-eaters are nearly always to be found there. There is no doubt that a lioness will bring up her cubs with man-eating tendencies if she is herself a man-eater. She will teach them to kill man just as an ordinary "hunting" lioness would teach her youngsters to kill game. I can give you an instance: The headman of a certain kraal went out of his hut just as day was breaking and squatted down a short distance away. (The African's notions of sanitation are primitive.) Presently he gave a series of yells which by his own account must have gone on for quite some time before anyone in the kraal woke up sufficiently to realize that something was wrong. The men then came yelling and shouting and brandishing spears and tomahawks, and drove a half-grown lion off the headman's back. It seemed—I saw the spoor myself about an hour later—that a lioness with two half-grown cubs had come wandering past just as the headman squatted down. The mother must have directed one of the youngsters to try his hand at killing, because the spoor clearly showed where she and the other youngster had stood about a dozen paces away and watched while the first had sneaked up and sprung on the man's back, knocking him forward onto his face. However, the young lion must have been nonplused by the unfortunate man's yells and lost his head. He used his weight to keep the fellow down but apparently didn't know how to kill him. With the arrival of the other natives he decamped. It seemed quite obvious that those lion had just had a feed; otherwise the lioness would have seen to the killing herself. But the old girl figured this time she could let the youngster practice. Ordinary "hunting" lion would almost certainly not have interfered with the man at all; he would never have known that there had been lion watching him.

There is a widely held belief that all man-eaters are old and mangy, incapable of killing alert game. Experience doesn't bear this out. That some man-eaters are old and mangy is indisputable, but I've shot many which were in their prime, not infrequently mothers of cubs. If all old lion took to man-eating, Africa would be infested with the brutes since —just as there are lion born every year—lion age every year. But, generally speaking, the man-eater is the exception.

Why some lion should take to man-eating and others not is a question frequently asked. I have never yet heard a satisfactory answer. Man is not the natural prey of any animal—if we except lice, bedbugs, and possibly carnivorous croc, to whom anything in the meat line is acceptable. Then what starts some lion off on a man-eating career? In the case of the solitary man-eater, my experience tends to show that wounds or hunger or both are usually responsible. When a lion has been wounded in a densely populated area and his wound is sufficiently serious to incapacitate him for some days, there is a grave risk of his becoming a man-eater. Men, women, and children will be wandering around possibly quite close to where he's lying licking his wounds and starving. Finally one of them will approach too close and one clout of the lion's paw will slay him. But it's in the last degree improbable that the lion will start right in to feed. If he doesn't wander away he will just lie there until the smell of the freshly spilled blood gives him the notion that here's something with which to satisfy his hunger. Thereafter, as his wounds slowly heal, he will start killing deliberately and become a dreaded man-eater.

That explanation may be acceptable in the case of the lone man-eater, and understandable, but it doesn't go far enough. It covers him and, when he recovers from his wounds and takes a mate, it would account for her being taught to kill man. When the cubs arrive she will almost certainly feed them on human flesh, since cubs will naturally eat anything their mother provides. But do those same cubs continue as man-eaters after leaving their parents? I think that, at any rate in some districts, they do, but I wouldn't like to generalize. Corbett says that he has never known a tiger cub automatically to continue killing man when it has started out to provide for itself, even though it was brought up on human flesh and trained to assist its mother in procuring it. My own belief is that in the great majority of cases lion cubs are the same; otherwise some of the bad districts I know of would be very much worse than they are.

Of course, one cannot really compare lion and tiger—conditions are dissimilar and so therefore are the habits of the two species. The tiger is a much more solitary beast than the lion and lives alone except when actually mating. If one of the mating pair is a man-eater the second will almost certainly share the kills; but I don't think there is any reason to suppose that when they separate again the second one will now continue preying on man—though under force of necessity it will doubtless take to man-killing more readily than it otherwise would because its natural fear of man will have diminished.

The hunting of man-eaters, if it is to be done successfully, is a rather specialized undertaking and doesn't appeal to many men. Yet it's fascinating sport. If I could afford to quit the elephant trail I would concentrate on man-eaters exclusively. It's because so very few men ever go after them that the lion have it all their own way in those bad areas. The bush is of such a nature that it is practically impossible for the native inhabitants to round up the lion and kill them with spears, as the Masai and Nandi can and do when lion attempt to interfere with their herds on the great open plains where they live and wander. (I've heard it said that if the Masai lived in a bad district they would wipe out the man-eaters. I yield to nobody in my admiration of the Masai and Nandi, but I honestly don't believe that even they could do anything in dense continuous scrub jungle.)

The contention so frequently put forward, that it's because of the extermination of the game by the natives themselves that their districts are overrun with man-eaters, won't bear close examination. No native methods of hunting would ever exterminate the game. They have used those methods since the world began, and yet Africa from the Sudan to the Cape was literally teeming with game when the first white man set foot on the continent. Every one of them remarked on it. It was the magazine rifle that was the cause of the extermination of game and its threatened extinction in those parts where there is some left.

However, the natives themselves are greatly to blame in another way.

Until a number of their companions have been killed they will not believe that it is anything but witchcraft. They are firm believers in were-lion, were-hyenas, and were-crocs. Nothing can alter their belief in a witch's or wizard's ability to transform himself into a lion, say, for the purpose of getting his own back on someone who has done him a bad turn. Those who know they haven't done any particularly bad deeds therefore take no precautions whatsoever. I knew one man who went to sleep on the ground in his garden without a fire or anything, in an area where there were man-eaters: this in order to scare the wild hogs that came to raid his crop by night. All they found of him next morning was his hair.

There was another who was visiting with a friend, got a skinful of home-brew, and, much against his friend's wishes, insisted on leaving. After going a scant fifty yards he decided to have a sleep on the path. All that was left of him by morning they could have tied up in a handkerchief, had they possessed such a thing. As is well known, once a lion takes to man-eating it is often the case that nothing else will satisfy him. This is usually attributed to the quantity of salt in human flesh and blood—lion are very fond of salt. Even more probable, however, is the fact that there is no tough hide here to be torn off, and that man is very much easier to hunt and kill than alert game. It is when he learns how defenseless man is, and how easily killed, that the man-eater loses his natural, instinctive fear of man. Then his boldness becomes incredible— incredible to those who haven't had personal experience with man-eaters.

I suppose that Paterson's *Man-Eaters of Tsavo* has been read by many of my readers. That is the classic dealing with this subject, and there isn't a word of exaggeration in it. As a matter of fact, Paterson could have made a great deal more of it if only he'd had a bit more writing experience. I don't mean that he needed to add fiction—it surpasses all fiction dealing with the subject as it stands. But there are parts of Africa I know where the exploits of the Tsavo man-eaters pale into insignificance beside what takes place regularly year after year. The outside world doesn't hear of them because their depredations are exclusively among the natives—and nobody here considers them worth newspaper space.

The determined man-eater has lost all fear of man and man's contraptions: even fire won't keep him at bay. The only thing I know that will is one of those pressure-fed storm lanterns. The usual size is three hundred candle power, but I had a peach of a little one giving just one hundred candle power. I was mighty glad to have it when in a man-eater's area. We used to light it and put it on a box, and then my men and I would all sleep around it as though it were a fire. It was advisable to wake up just once during the night and pump it up a bit as the level of the juice dropped. (You can train yourself to wake up like that, do what's necessary, and then drop back to sleep without its interfering with your rest.) I certainly wouldn't care to be in a bad man-eater's area without one of those lanterns. I can assure you it's a nerve-racking business.

Naturally, any means are legitimate for the extermination of man-eaters, including (as I've said before) traps and poison. I won't discuss those here as they don't belong in a book about hunting. Besides, they are apt to be disappointing, since the confirmed man-eater rarely returns to his kill in Africa—assuming he has left any of it. The only sure and satisfactory way to catch these brutes is to outguess them and tackle them at night with the aid of a good flashlight or night sight clamped on the barrels of your rifle. It's of little use to sit and wait for them; you must be free to wander around. A car—and nearly everyone has a car or station wagon or light truck nowadays—will be of real help, for lion are fond of strolling along any roads or paths there may be in preference to walking through the bush. They will wander for miles along a road at night—either a motor road or railroad. They know very well that such tracks lead to human habitations and that they have a much better chance of encountering man on a road than in the bush. Moreover, there are fewer thorns to be picked up on paths.

The inexperienced sportsman, burning to get a smack at the man-eaters, goes haring around the country whenever news comes in of a kill. But it's of little use making for the scene of the last kill because the man-eaters travel anywhere from twelve to twenty miles after they've had their feed. They usually cover a roughly circular route and, having taken up residence in a more or less densely populated district, with native kraals scattered about all over the place, they will inevitably miss several kraals or groups of kraals before another killing. The same thing will happen again, and another group of kraals will be passed by before the following kill takes place. You must collect all the information you can, sort things out with the aid of a map if you can find one, and then endeavor to outguess the lion so that you can get ahead of them and be at the most likely kraal or group of kraals for the next attack.

You'll appreciate that there will be many disappointments before you succeed in guessing right. Some men are luckier than others; but you will never succeed in this game if you are easily discouraged. All hunting requires patience, and I think the hunting of man-eaters requires more than any other kind.

The procedure is as follows:

Having decided that a certain kraal or group of kraals is your best bet for the next attack, you drive there in your station wagon, if you can, or as close as possible if you can't. Then, having seen to it that your men are safely housed for the night, as soon as it's dark have your driver drive you slowly along the road for a few miles in both directions with your head lamps dimmed. This will enable you to get close to lion if you are lucky enough to meet them. If you do, have your man let the car roll along slowly and quietly until you're within say forty or fifty yards of the animals. He is then to stop the car and switch on the full lights. You should be able to kill at least two of the brutes now, if not all three (supposing it is a group of three). Lion are very accommodating at night. Naturally, they can't see you behind the glare and just stand there staring at the lights and wondering what they are. At your first shot, which should kill one, the others will usually spin around in a complete circle and then, in the most obliging way, stand broadside-on to you looking over their shoulders at the lights and their fallen companion. You should have no difficulty in dropping another now. The third will often take a bound off the road at your second shot, and then stop and look back to see why her companions aren't following her. (These brutes are mostly found as male and two females.)

There is no question that a magazine rifle has advantages over a double if you are tackling more than two man-eaters from a car at night. It's the only kind of shooting for which I prefer this pattern of rifle. That third quick shot can make all the difference. For one thing, if you're sitting in the front seat of a car it's awkward to reload a double rifle.

However, you can't bank on always getting your man-eater like that. Suppose you have driven your several miles along the road in both directions and have seen nary a lion. You get back to camp, attach your flashlight to the left barrel of your rifle (which is, of course, loaded), and then turn in if you like or sit up with a book—I prefer the latter. The lion, if they come at all, may come early or late. You can please yourself: just read on through the night until there's an alarm, or take a stroll around the immediate vicinity of the kraal from time to time with your rifle, muzzles-foremost, on your shoulder and your flashlight switched on. That was what I did originally. Lately I don't bother. I just sit and read until the hue and cry is raised and then go out. Provided no one has been foolish enough to leave his hut there is no harm done. Probably the lion made an attempt to get into one of the huts, which started the hullaballoo. Man-eaters often lie down on the doorstep of a hut and from time to time stick a paw around the edge of the reed door, for all the world as though they were trying to wake up the occupants in the hope that one of them might come out. Sometimes they will take up a position immediately alongside the door and spend the entire night there, knowing that by daybreak someone will certainly come out.

When the yells start you put down your book, knock out your pipe, pick up your rifle, remove the muzzle cover, switch on the flashlight, and out you go. Carrying your rifle in both hands more or less at the ready, the light will be directed in front of you. You turn around the nearest hut and there are your man-eaters, maybe a bare ten paces away. They will all stop whatever they are doing and stand staring at your light. You should be able to kill two of them with two quick shots, because they will act exactly the same as those you met on the road earlier. Here again you would probably prefer a magazine rifle if there are more than two lion, but we'll use the double since we started out with it. You will naturally have slipped two spare shells between the fingers of your left hand to save having to fumble for them. You have these as you break the breech. But first a word of warning: One naturally presses down the muzzles of the barrels of a double gun or rifle when opening it to reload, but you will have to remember *not* to press them down quite so far at night—try to keep your light on that third lion. If you press the muzzles down in the usual way the light will be directed to the ground close in front of you. And that means that that third lion *will no longer be dazzled by it.* A lion is unlikely to attack something he can't see, and if you keep your light directly on him he will generally just stand wherever he stops. But if you drop the ray of your flashlight to the ground, that third lion will start moving toward you. He can now begin to distinguish you back of the light. It was an episode like this that taught me the absolute necessity for keeping that ray directed as nearly as possible on the brute's eyes. I'd killed the first two man-eaters, a lion and a lioness, with a quick right-and-left from my double .400—a fine little gun for the job—and then broken the breech. I didn't bother about the light because I knew it would take me only a moment to reload since my rifle was fitted with ejectors. But when I closed the breech again, thereby raising the light, I saw the third man-eater, a lioness, scarcely eight feet in front of me! She had apparently crept up quite silently with the intention of springing when she could see better. She stopped as the ray of light came up again and dazzled her. As I raised the gun butt to my shoulder she moved her head up, to one side, and then lowered it right down close to the ground, in an effort to see over, around, or under the light. I killed her with my next shot before she'd made up her mind what to do.

And here's a useful tip which you'd be well advised to keep in mind when using a double rifle and wanting more than two beasts, whether they're elephant or man-eaters: If the survivors don't show signs of bolting immediately on the heels of the first shot, don't try for a quick right-and-left just then: reload your right barrel and *then* take your quick right-and-left. Tackling man-eaters at night usually gives plenty of time for this maneuver, and you will more often than not be able then to bag all three; whereas, had you taken two quick shots to start with, the third beast might not have waited for you to reload and get your sights on her. What it all boils down to is not getting steamed up and flurried.

The actual killing of man-eaters isn't hard; the difficulty is in getting in touch with them. There are no hard and fast rules about it and it's almost impossible to give helpful advice. But I assure you you will find it one of the most fascinating games in the world, once you get well into it —that is, of course, if you are a genuine hunter who honestly wants to hunt his game and not have it handed to him on a silver salver. It is satisfying, besides, to men who don't need to hunt for their livelihood and therefore feel unjustified in doing much killing, though they'd like to do a whole lot more if only they could find an excuse that would pass muster with their somewhat sensitive consciences. Well, these sportsmen can get all the hunting they want by concentrating on varmints like man-eating lion. No license or permit is required, apart from an ordinary gun permit. You'll be encouraged by the authorities to kill all you like and can, and nary a soul, official or otherwise, will ever object to your dropping an occasional buck, large or small, for camp meat. You will have the added satisfaction of knowing that you are doing real good every time you kill. There's a bounty on man-eaters, too, but it's only Esc. 200$00 (about ten dollars), so you can't expect to grow fat on it.

It's surprising how few men ever go out after man-eaters. The modern generations in Africa seem to prefer to do their big-game hunting from a comfortable seat in some movie theater.

Corbett says he overheard a high government official trying to persuade a group of so-called sportsmen to go after the notorious Rudraprayag leopard, and their response to his appeal was: "What! Go after a man-eating leopard that has killed more than a hundred people? Not on your life!"

I've heard those very words on similar occasions. Many men who consider themselves sportsmen and most certainly like to think others believe them so are not averse to having a crack at some inoffensive hunting lion, particularly when shooting from the safety of a tree or a closed car; but the hunting of man-eaters entails constant danger, whether or not the brutes have been wounded and that doesn't seem to appeal. I know a number of these pseudo-sportsmen who have wounded lion and made not the slightest attempt to follow them and finish them off. Some of those lion quite possibly became man-eaters.

In some of those notorious man-eater districts known to me I have not heard of anybody's making any attempt to shoot the animals for many years. The Portuguese don't lay claim to being the sportsmen the British insist *they* are; but I'm not concerned solely with Portuguese territory. I know of three very bad districts in British Nyasaland that are scarcely ever free from man-eaters, and right now I can recollect hearing of only *one* party within the last twenty-five years which tried to do something about it. On that occasion three bank clerks went down to Chikwawa and the District Commissioner took them out to a kraal a certain man-eater was known to pass nightly. On arrival there, because they didn't think it was yet time for his passing, they sat around having some refreshment and chatting. It was a dark night and the lion grabbed one of the clerks and started to clear off with him. It would seem that his two companions hadn't even loaded their rifles—at any rate they didn't get them into action; but one of the District Commissioner's rifle-armed police loosed off a shot which, whether or not it hit the lion, caused him to drop his prey. That was the end of man-eater hunting in that locality. (The man wasn't badly injured, and since he was rushed to the nearest doctor there were no complications.)

Nowadays, all that happens when man-eaters appear in a district is for the District Commissioner to give one of his police, or some local native who can use it, a rifle and a few shells and, possibly, a shooting lamp, and let him do what he can. For more years than I can remember I haven't heard of one of these commissioners' going out after the lion himself. Some of the natives are good. There was one who shot two man-eaters just over the border from where I am camped right now, and when another two came along later he killed them also.

But it certainly seems that British sportsmen of the present day, in Africa at all events, are only interested in sports which entail no risk. Jim Corbett was one of the outstanding exceptions. I admit that man-eater hunting isn't everybody's game: as witness the fact that in spite of Corbett's unrivaled experience, knowledge, and stamina, he found himself unable to spend more than four, five, or at most six consecutive weeks in a man-eater's area. If he hadn't succeeded in killing within that time, he was compelled to quit because he found the constant strain on his nerves unbearable. He would usually take a break of two or three months and then return refreshed for another go.

I rank the hunting of man-eaters next only to elephant hunting as the grandest and most absorbing sport in the world; and I well know how grim it is to live under the reign of terror they create. I remember one very bad one, a magnificent big black-maned fellow. He terrorized a large area for a period of three years and was known to have killed more than two hundred natives—some accounts said three hundred. He had also mauled at least two white men who had tried for him and killed another, a decent cheery lad named Jimmy James, who was well known to me—poor Jimmy! It was after Jimmy's death that I took the warpath after his slayer. This lion lived in good game country—which convinces me that he wasn't naturally a man-eater but had been wounded and become lost—nice open parklike veld with grass that grew longer than two and a half feet only in some of the depressions and with scattered clumps of trees having not-too-thick undergrowth among them. This lion differed from the majority of man-eaters in that he didn't usually wander far after killing. Having decided to feed up a bit in a certain locality, he'd usually remain there for several days or weeks, killing just when it suited him. Many men had tried for him (this happened a number of years ago) and several had had a shot at him, but he had always managed to outwit them and get clear. He was known to have been wounded several times, but obviously the wounds weren't serious—except the first, the one which had presumably started him on his man-eating career. The result of all this was that he knew as much as, if not more than, those who hunted him about all the usual methods of hunting. I heard it declared that no one intended to try for him again after Jimmy's death. For Jimmy had had not a little experience.

In this particular case the obvious policy was to make for the area in which the lion had last killed. I did that, arriving in my station wagon with just a gunbearer and cookboy. I'd heard so many reports of this fellow's cunning, and of the number of times he'd escaped unscathed when doubling back and breaking through the beaters who were trying to drive him toward where the guns were waiting—and where he knew darned well they were waiting—that I decided to try a trick I'd worked out long years before when shooting confirmed cattle-killers (lone ones) which had also been tried for on several occasions by other hunters. The trouble with most men is that they don't credit these animals with any horse sense at all. They forget that a lion's ability to keep out of your sight is only equaled by the care he takes to keep you in sight if he figures you're after him. These sportsmen come out to where the lion has been marked down accompanied by several gunbearers and all the natives in the locality all talking at the top of their voices. They then halt and have a discussion as to where they'll take up their positions. That done, they tell the beaters to go around to the far side of the cover in which the lion is supposed to be and drive him toward them. The lion, who has been watching all this taking place, has probably slipped away long before the beaters are in position to start the drive. If not, then he'll do so the instant they commence yelling and beating their drums and tin cans. These cunning old fellows take good care to have a reasonably safe line of retreat from anyplace they choose for lying up in. If they can't slip away in that direction, they'll break back through the beaters—quite possibly without being seen. That done, they just stroll away in the most unconcerned manner, knowing perfectly well that, being now behind the hunt, they are safe.

As I say, I had several times in days gone by been beaten by a cunning old cattle-killer in just such a manner and had at last bested him by going through the above performance with the beaters in full view of where he was known to be, then clearing off to take up my position a full quarter of a mile *behind* where the beaters were to start the drive. There was no gun waiting along the route the lion would normally have been expected to take, but the beaters had instructions to go through with the drive just as though there were a gun there and continue until they heard me shoot. This stratagem proved beautifully successful. The cattle-killing lion broke back just as I had expected he would and came strolling along past me not twenty paces away. I won't go so far as to say he was chuckling to himself at having outwitted those fools of human beings once again, but he did halt when he was directly opposite me and glanced back over his shoulder to satisfy himself that the racket raised by the beaters was still continuing. As his head came around again I drove my bullet through his shoulder. I don't think he knew a rifle had been fired.

So this was what I intended to try with the old man-eater. I was fully optimistic of success. I'd played the same trick on lion on several other occasions and had never known it to fail.

Word came the morning after my arrival that the lion had killed a native belonging to one of the neighboring kraals and was almost certainly in a particular clump of bush in which he'd been known to lie up each time he visited the area. This clump of bush was about half a mile from the kraal, which in turn was about two and a half miles from where I had camped. The lion had caught his victims early in the morning and had calmly had a feed in the open after carrying the body a scant hundred yards from where he'd killed him close to the huts—this in spite of the yelling villagers who came to see. They told me that if any of them attempted to approach too close he'd take a short rush toward them, growling horribly, and then return to his interrupted meal when they skedaddled. He just didn't give a damn for them.

My gunbearer and I climbed into the station wagon with the fellow who had come to call us and drove off to the scene of the killing. There was just a faint hope that I might get there before the lion had finished feeding. But we were too late. The gruesome remains of the kill were still there; that was all. I told the relatives they could bury them and then went out to examine the place where the lion was said to be. From a slight eminence I got a good view of the terrain. The clump of bush in which the lion was presumably concealed covered about half an acre and had some tall trees in it. About fifty yards away to the northeast there was another smaller clump of bush, with some short grass covering the ground between. There was a slight depression running along the center of the grass, in which somewhat longer grass grew. Beyond the second clump of bush another fairly open patch led into an extent of light bush which wouldn't provide much in the way of cover for an elephant, but would be ample for a lion. Since it's mere waste of time trying to drive a lion into the open if there's no good cover in front, this was the obvious way to drive our fellow. He'd willingly face the open with that other clump of bush only fifty yards away and with the long continuous stretch of cover beyond. I say that was the obvious way to plan an ordinary drive, and it was the way this same lion had been driven on two previous occasions. The gun or guns had taken up their position between the two clumps of bush, and on at least one occasion had wounded the lion, though apparently not seriously. The next time someone had tried to drive him, he'd broken back through the beaters and got away, they didn't know how. However, from where I stood I could bet on it that he'd broken away to the south. In that direction there was a stretch of flat ground covered with short grass, scarcely a foot high. But I could see a depression running along through that too, and, as usual, somewhat longer grass grew in it. This open flat extended for perhaps ninety yards and then merged into very lightly bushed veld, the little bushes being rarely more than three feet high and widely scattered. It wasn't the sort of stuff into which you would normally try to drive a lion, particularly in view of the much better cover to the northeast. Nevertheless, it was into that lightly bushed veld I intended to drive this lion—only I'd do it without his knowing I was doing so. Satisfied with my reconnaissance, I turned to the locals and told them they were to behave exactly as they had with each of the other hunters who had tried for this brute, but that instead of accompanying them to where the other men had taken up their positions, I was going to dip down right now and make my way along to the south, making sure to keep well out of sight of the bush that was harboring the lion.

They, however, having given me plenty of time to get where I wanted to be, were to go along in a body, talking and discussing things, to where they had placed the other hunters. Having done this they were to return, encircle the bush, and commence the drive just as though there were a gun waiting for the lion to break forward. I didn't want to go with them because I had a hunch the lion would break to the south as soon as he saw the beaters returning from where they had supposedly placed the hunter. I guessed he'd be watching them and would know what all this portended, and I figured he wouldn't wait for the actual beat to start but would make his break right away. Accordingly, if I delayed getting into position he might well beat me to it and get clear.

The men were delighted with my scheme. The notion of outguessing a lion and having what seemed like a game with him tickled their fancy enormously. They were all agog to get started and see how it worked out. I slipped away and in due course took up my position about a hundred and fifty or two hundred yards from the bush, sitting myself down beside a little solitary bush that grew some twenty paces away from the slight depression along which I felt the lion would come. When I got to the place I signaled the beaters with a wave of my hand and saw them start off, talking and laughing as they went. They passed beyond the bush in which the lion was lying, and presently I saw them again. When they were about halfway between the two clumps of bush they halted and stood talking for a few moments, then started back the way they had come. They were surely doing their stuff. (The African is a splendid actor, throwing himself so completely and unselfconsciously into his part that he actually lives it.) They encircled the bush and then at a given signal all started whooping and yelling and beating drums and tin cans as they commenced to enter the undergrowth. Nobody saw the lion slip away. I'll bet he did so when he observed the beaters returning to take up their positions around the bush.

Guessing this, I had been watching the beaters with only half an eye. When they were still whooping and yelling somewhere in the bush I spotted a movement in the grass to my left. Through the top of my little bush I watched the spot intently. Sure enough, it was my lion. He was coming along at a crouch, making himself small, as only a lion can when he doesn't want to be seen. He was neither hurried nor scared; it was just that he wasn't going to expose himself like a fool any more than necessary. As I watched, he halted and slowly raised himself to his full height, looking back over his shoulder as he did so, to see through the tops of the grass and make sure the racket wasn't following him. Satisfied that it wasn't, he turned again and came on toward me at a slow slouching walk. He hadn't a notion there was danger in front of him. The breeze was blowing across, and I was downwind of where he would pass.

I was using a double .400, and slipped forward the safety catch. As he came opposite, a bare twenty paces away, I slowly raised the butt to my shoulder. He must have seen that slight movement. Suddenly he halted, looked straight into my eyes, his face breaking into a savage snarl as he crouched, and he seemed to swell to double his former size when he realized how he'd been tricked. But my soft-nose .400-grain bullet took him through the shoulder before he could do anything about it. He dropped instantly, his back toward me, and I drove a bullet from my left barrel straight in through the top of his head. But the second shot wasn't necessary.

As soon as they heard my rifle the beaters quit their noise and came haring along to see what luck I'd had. Rarely have I seen Africans so excited as that lot were: they whooped and yelled and laughed and sang, dancing and leaping into the air, twirling and whirling until it almost made me giddy to watch them. I tell you I had my work cut out to prevent their tearing the lion to pieces then and there. I wanted his hide. It would have been a fine enough trophy in the best of times, but since the lion had been such a notorious man-eater I knew I'd get a big price for it. I had to stand over it until my men had skinned the beast. The instant I gave the word, then, those locals made a rush, spears aloft. Every man among them wanted to blood his weapon in this lion. They danced around and around, every now and then one of them leaping forward to drive his spear through the carcass again. By the time they'd finished it was little better than mincemeat.

Word of the kill whizzed around the district, and men and boys came from all over to see it for themselves. Needless to say my reputation received a tremendous boost as a result of that morning's work. I had never previously been in this district, though I was known to the tribe from various elephant-poaching expeditions. But after I had killed the brute that had so many of the tribe chalked against him, those Awemba couldn't do enough for me. Thereafter their country was mine. When I returned later there was never any shortage of porters for my ivory or of food and beer for the porters, while the offers to assist as guides and trackers were almost embarrassing, as I hate turning away keen and willing volunteers. These Awemba are a really fine tribe. They remind me in many ways of the Masai, although the latter are Nilotic whereas the Awemba are essentially Bantu. They are intensely black and both men and women have most pleasing features: clean-cut, with small, straight, delicately chiseled noses and by no means unduly thick lips.

They are generally tall and slim and of fine physique. I reckon they come next to the Azandi as elephant hunters, being utterly fearless. But, in common with the Masai, probably their most outstanding and notably praiseworthy characteristic is their splendid sense of loyalty. And by that I'm not thinking of loyalty to absent kings and such, but to *you* the individual, if they have reason to like you and feel grateful.

And since I've mentioned the word grateful I'd like to say a word about it, because you'll hear on all sides, "Hell! These black African bastards have no sense of gratitude." To that I reply, "In the name of Allah, what have they to be grateful for?" In days gone by, before the advent of the white man, none of them wore clothes or wanted to; but with the exception of the Masai and Nandi in Kenya, and the Shilluk, Nuer and Dinka in the Sudan, nowadays they have all been compelled to—so as to boost the ruling race's trade in cotton piece goods. They've got to work for the white man for a pitifully meager wage to get the money with which to buy that clothing and pay their hut tax. In most parts of British Africa they have been booted off all the best land so that it may be reserved for nonexistent white settlers. In view of the very small amount of the monthly wage, the deductions that are made out of it by the boss for small breakages, which are *never* deliberate, are entirely disproportionate and grossly unfair—anything from half a month's to a full month's pay being deducted for some little damage that was entirely accidental. They are knocked around and beaten up because they fail to understand what is wanted of them, the vast majority of white men nowadays not bothering to learn the native languages. "Who wants to talk to the bastard anyway? Let him learn my language. If he does it wrong, kick him; and if he does it wrong again, kick him again! He'll soon learn the right way to do things." If I've heard that said once, I've heard it scores of times. And then that same white man expects the native to show gratitude. For what?

There is no word for "thanks" in any Bantu language or dialect with which I am acquainted. (The Kiswahili word *"asanti"* comes from the Arabic.) The African doesn't therefore say "thanks" or "thank you" like the white man and straightway forget all about it; he waits his time and then shows his gratitude by actions, it may be years afterward. I have personally experienced this on countless occasions.

I'll give you an instance. Sometime around 1935 to 1936 I was shooting in a district the natives of which were described as outlaws and runaway criminals. Except that they were desperately poor, I found them much the same as any other natives who hadn't been spoiled by the white man and labor recruiter. But traditionally they never paid the annual hut tax. When the police came around to collect they got warning of course and cleared out of the kraals, taking everything with them, including their fowls. Incidentally, it was rather amusing to see how they managed: they had to gag the roosters by tying their beaks so that they couldn't crow and disclose their hiding places! The gags would be removed from time to time to allow the birds to feed and then replaced. The people didn't walk in the usual single file—that would leave an easily followed trail; instead they all took their own way out to where they had decided to hole up. They would build themselves little shelters of branches and grass and just lie doggo until their scouts gave them the all-clear.

But in the deserted kraal beside which I was camped there was an aged crone—she looked about a hundred and fifty at least, and was probably a good centenarian—practically blind and quite incapable of doing much for herself. For instance, she could never have made the mile trek to the water hole and back. I naturally figured that when the villagers scooted from the kraal they left one or two little girls—too small for the police to interfere with—to look after the old woman. But apparently they hadn't done so. It's just possible they hoped the old lady would peg out if neglected—in this respect the women are infinitely more callous than the men. Be that as it may, I awoke one dirty cold wet night and heard a curious moaning and crying somewhere out in the forest. I wakened my gunbearer, who shared the hut with me, and asked him what on earth it could be. It sounded human, but who could be doing it? He replied that in all probability that old crone had gone out for some reason, got herself lost owing to the wind and rain, and was unable to find her way back to her hut.

Cussing a good deal, I lit the lantern and we started out to see what was the matter. We had no raincoats or umbrellas, and it was cold and miserable; but naturally we couldn't leave the poor old thing to die of exposure, perhaps, before morning. We found her and took her back to her hut. There, since she was shivering uncontrollably with both cold and fright, I had my cookboy warm up some soup for her and fed her myself with a spoon, for she was quite incapable of doing so herself. I then had plenty of dry firewood brought and a decent fire built that would last the rest of the night, and put more wood within reach of her hand. I also wrapped her in a little old blanket I didn't use much—I don't expect she'd had a blanket around her before in all her life—and then left an empty can close by and told her to beat it with a stick if she wanted anything, as we would close the door from outside. With that we left her. I'm quite sure she hadn't had such a fuss made about her since she had been an infant. We looked after her daily after that: my lads took food across to her, got water for her when she needed it, and saw that she had a good fire every night. There was nothing to it; anyone would have done the same. I left the district shortly after the villagers returned, berated them soundly for leaving the old lady unattended, and promptly forgot the incident.

But about three years later, when I was shooting buffalo around Lifumba, more than a hundred miles away, I was sitting in my *macheza*** one scorching hot midday when I noticed a somewhat elderly man accompanied by a youngster arrive and sit themselves down under a tree not far away. Presently the man sent the youngster around to ask my fellows for a drink of water. As we'd plenty of food in camp I told them to invite the old man and the lad to have a feed with them when they were having their own grub: the strangers didn't look as though they had much with them. They did that, and then after the meal the old fellow again took up his position under the same tree where he could watch me. After a while he came over, greeted me politely, and indicated that he had something to say. As he looked a decent old soul I pushed across the box I use as a footrest and invited him to be seated. But he said he would sit on the ground. He looked very steadily at me for a spell and then commenced to speak.

He asked me if it wasn't a fact that I had been shooting in that other district some two or three years previously. I replied that it was quite true, and what about it. He asked me if I remembered caring for an aged woman when I was there. I said that I'd forgotten the incident, but now that he reminded me of it I remembered. And what of it? Anyone else would have done as much.

"Oh, no, *Bwana,*" he corrected me. "Another white man would merely have ordered his boys to go out and see what was the matter. But you, a white man, went out yourself in the wet and cold and helped the old woman back to her hut. You ordered your cook to warm up some of your own food, and yourself fed her with a spoon. You had them bring a blanket from your own bed, and yourself wrapped it around her. You saw that they built a good fire and left wood close to her hand. You yourself stretched her hand out so that she could feel the wood and know just where it was. You thought to leave her a can to beat should she need anything during the night, and you had your men bring food and water daily, and generally cared for her as her own people should have done."

"Well," I asked again, "and what of it?"

"Just this, *Bwana,*" he replied slowly. "That old woman was my

---

* A conical thatched roof on stilts. If there's a wall it won't be more than two to three feet high. We use such places as dining room and sitting room generally in the hotter districts to get the benefit of any breeze that blows.

mother. I was her youngest child. I was away working in Rhodesia for several years and returned only recently. My mother herself told me what you had done for her. She is dead now. But to you who cared for her I, her youngest son, have brought my youngest son: to serve you and care for you as you served and cared for her, my mother. This is he. His name is A-ubi. He will accept no pay from you but will serve you faithfully and well. I have spoken."

And well and truly did that youngster serve me. A slave? Of course he was a slave. But he was as happy as the day is long, and actually proud of being a slave! Far from being ashamed of his status, he made a point of telling everyone and anyone who he reckoned might not have heard. He begged and implored me to take him with me when I went off to World War II, and I would have liked to do so, but he was too young. (We whites in the East Africa Command were not only allowed to have servants—it was compulsory.)

I'm not suggesting that African servants and employees be pampered —they don't want to be pampered, anyway. But surely they can be treated as human beings. What kind of "trusteeship" is it that permits a first-class cookboy to be paid the equivalent of three dollars or perhaps four dollars a month, plus fifty cents (yes, fifty *cents!*) a *month* for food? And not permitted to eat any of the leftovers or scraps from the kitchen? It might encourage him to cook more than is necessary for the boss so that he can feed himself well! I have personally, with shame and disgust, seen the "Missis" or "Memsahib" herself supervise the throwing of leftovers into the ash bin so the cookboy and houseboys couldn't have them. Gratitude! Maybe I am a Negrophile; that sort of thing is calculated to make any decent man take the Negro's part.

By the way, it might be of interest to say something about the Masai method of spearing lion. You will doubtless have seen it in motion pictures, or at least heard or read of it, but there are one or two little points that seem to be missed by most writers on the subject: points that frequently caused me to wonder until I got among the Masai and made friends with them. For instance, you probably have heard that the man who gets in the first spear thrust and he who first gets hold of the lion's tail share between them the mane to be made into headdresses. Maybe you'll have figured, as I used to do, that it's the height of folly to get hold of a wounded and savage lion by the tail, and that the fellow who does it won't live long enough to wear his share of the mane. It was the Masai themselves who taught me different. You know yourself that if you get hold of your Aunt Martha's pet cat by the tail it will *always* try to pull away from you. Well, a lion is just a big cat and will do exactly the same. That's the fellow's chance to drive his spear in through the ribs and up toward the lungs and heart.

The Masai form themselves into clans and age groups and are very good to one another. They aren't jealous. They will always give some fellow who hasn't yet won his share of a mane the place of honor when closing a lion, so that he'll have a fair chance of doing so this time. A charge is a practical certainty every time they tackle a lion, and the man immediately in front of him is the one who'll have to receive it. He does this by crouching down behind his buffalo-hide shield, with the butt of his spear stuck in the ground behind him, the haft clasped between forearm and side, and the point of the long narrow blade directed toward the lion. When the lion impales himself on the spear, the force of his rush brings him on and the man allows himself to go down under the lion, his legs drawn up under the edge of his shield if possible. He knows perfectly well that his companions will instantly rush in and drive their spears through the lion from both sides. The lion in his frenzy will frequently claw aside the shield and to a greater or lesser extent maul the man beneath; yet sometimes the fellow is uninjured. (Incidentally, it's a never-ending source of wonder to medicos and others how easily and quickly these men recover from such maulings—blood poisoning is almost unknown among them.)

I have a boundless admiration for the Masai and was able to do for a party of them what they evidently considered a really good turn at one time during the recent war when I was around those parts. I became good friends with them, two of them in particular, and had the almost unprecedented tribute of being made an honorary member of two age groups or clans, and blood brother of the two with whom I was so friendly. This meant that if at any time I required help, provided I could get word to them, both of those clans would turn out, in force if necessary, and come to my assistance.

Incidentally, if a rhino shows signs of being a nuisance on Masai grazing grounds, they will tail him as they do a lion, and drive their spears through the ribs and forward into the lungs and heart.

But I seem to have wandered from what I was saying.

I've had occasion to remark so many times that you can safely meet lion face to face when you are unarmed, and they will not interfere with you provided you don't do something stupid, that perhaps an actual experience or two of my own may be of interest.

I was hunting for camp meat one day and carrying a Mauser in front of my gunbearer who, as usual, had my heavier rifle in case we encountered buffalo. We were passing through rather open palmetto scrub with a fair amount of four-foot grass about. Six or eight of my men were straggling along behind to act as butchers and bring in any meat I shot. I stepped past a clump of grass and suddenly froze on seeing a movement immediately in front of me. There was a fine dark-maned lion looking at me, and I instantly realized that the low deep purring growl I now heard was coming from him. He was about eight or nine paces away. He'd just jumped to his feet from where he'd been lying in the shade of a small tree that grew out of the top of a small anthill. One's range of vision widens amazingly under such circumstances. At the same time as I caught sight of him I saw out of the corner of my eye two other lion on my left, about five or six yards away, two females on my right even closer, and another very big lioness so close that without stooping I could have touched her hindquarters with my outstretched finger tips. It had been her movement that had first caught my eye. She'd been lying just beside that clump of grass I'd passed through, and if she hadn't got to her feet when the lion growled I'd have stumbled over her. Curiously enough, however, neither she nor the others had yet seen me. They were all looking toward the big lion as though asking him what had bitten him. He had been the only one facing in my direction and I had, of course, been moving silently.

My gunbearer froze the instant he saw me stop, as he knew I must have seen something. He'd heard the soft growl but didn't realize what had made it. The other men sank down on one knee, for they knew it would be more than their life was worth to move and perhaps scare what it was I'd seen. The grass prevented their seeing the lion.

How long we all stood with more conscious rigidity than the actors in a "living picture" I cannot say—but the dark-maned lion finally realized what I was, spun around with another deep growl, and bounded back of the anthill. Still the other members of his party didn't see me. They just stood there wondering what had upset the big fellow and caused him to break up the party. Then one of those on my left looked over my way, saw me, and loped after the lion, his companion going with him but without knowing why. At the same time yet another lion (which up to now I hadn't seen) standing beyond them also went off, but quite unhurriedly. The females gazed after the males in amazement. Then the farthest of the three glanced over her sister's shoulder and looked straight into my eyes. For a long moment she gazed at me, then with a low purr she also loped after the others—long slow bounds. There was no indication of panic. The one she'd been standing beside looked around, saw me, and off she went too in exactly the same way. And still that all-too-close lioness right beside me stood there without movement. I was so close that she couldn't see me without turning her head around and looking back along her shoulder. I was beginning to chuckle inwardly as I pictured her surprise when she eventually *did* see me. For what seemed a very long time she continued to stand looking after her companions, and I could almost hear her wondering what on earth had caused them to leave the meeting. Slowly she looked first to her right and then, equally slowly, to her left. And it was only then that something must have caught her eye—possibly the sun glinting on a brass shell in my bandoleer as it moved with my chest as I breathed. Anyway, her head came around and she looked right through me. I'm quite certain she didn't see me at first. Then perhaps she caught the glint of my teeth through my beard as I grinned—I simply couldn't help it—and her eyes lifted to mine.

Her beautiful golden eyes, the most beautiful eyes possessed by any animal on earth, looked straight into mine. Gradually I saw recognition dawn in them: it was in the sudden dilation of the pupils. But there was no fear, no animosity, no threat; there was mild, bland curiosity and nothing else. It was for all the world as though she were saying, "So that's what it was! Holy maverick! And the fella must have been standing there right along! Say, this is a mite too close. Wait till I focus."

She turned her head away from me and took a long slow bound and then another not quite so long. Here she turned broadside-on, perhaps twice her own length away from me, and once more gazed at me. For long and long she stood there. Then with a slight shake of her head, she loosed a low purr, not a growl, and *walked* slowly and deliberately after her companions without another backward glance.

That lioness knew perfectly well that I wasn't inimical. She must have realized eventually that I'd been standing there right alongside her left hip all this time, yet hadn't attacked her. I'd made no threatening move even when she finally saw me, and I within arm's reach of her. She had no ill will toward me since I very obviously hadn't any toward her.

It's true I had a rifle on my shoulder, but it would have been of no more use to me than a walking stick had any of those lion turned nasty. But I knew they wouldn't. Just as I knew it on a previous occasion when I had nothing but a stick in my hand. I wasn't hunting. I was trekking from one place to another along a small native footpath. I was well ahead of my porters and my thoughts were ten thousand miles away when I suddenly saw a fine lion, accompanied by a lioness, step out of the grass on the left side of the path, see me, turn to face me, and then deliberately sit down to study me at his leisure. His mate stood beside him. Whether or not there was an easily climbable tree close by I don't know—I'm not in the habit of looking for trees to climb. It wouldn't have interested me if there had been. As I have said, it's asking for trouble to make a dive for a tree in such circumstances as so many men say they do or did. I just stood there and gazed back at the two lion until their curiosity was satisfied. When it was, they continued across the path and disappeared in the grass on the other side. And I went on my way.

Talking about trees: I've recently been reading a book in which the author would seem to have spent his life looking for ones that he could climb easily when tackling buffalo. Apparently he didn't care about tackling them if there were no such trees around. He claims a very big bag of buffalo, but I have no hesitation in declaring that no man will make a big bag of anything if he spends his time climbing trees—unless it's birds' eggs he's hunting.

Once again: no normal animal will wantonly attack man. It matters not if it's lion, tiger, or leopard you encounter, provided you don't do something stupid that the creature interprets as a hostile or threatening gesture, or startle it unduly. For the past eighteen months I have been living in the open day and night. I haven't a tent or a bed. Lion, leopard, and hippo sing lullabies nightly and elephant have been coming around regularly. The only things that have worried me have been earwigs, which persist in crawling into my typewriter and getting squashed when I run in a fresh sheet of paper. How does that read compared with accounts of writers who would have us believe their rifles scarcely ever cool down, they are so constantly saving their lives from unprovoked attacks of various beasts?

I have referred earlier to the inner premonition that so often has saved me from blundering unaware into danger. It's worth noting that I've never once felt any such warning prior to encountering lion—by which I mean ordinary hunting lion, not man-eaters. Does that not speak for itself? Does it not uphold my contention that I was not in danger? And does it not show the stupidity of those who get terror-stricken just because they meet a lion when they are unarmed?

When I was on my way to shoot those wounded man-killing buffalo to which I have referred in a previous chapter I was canoeing through the Lupata Gorge. This gorge, through which the Zambezi hurls itself, is a most impressive spectacle as you enter it—especially if you're in a small canoe, as I was. There's always a strong current in the Zambezi, and it's considerably more than doubled in the narrow upper entrance to the gorge. When the river is low during the dry season there is a rough path beside it which natives follow to save clambering up and down the hills through which the river cuts its way; but when the river rises that path disappears, and it's then necessary to take the hill path if you're walking. Apart from the light canoe in which I was traveling I also had a big freight canoe following me. It wasn't until I was halfway through the gorge that I heard of the man-eater. There was a small sandy beach there in a backwater below a big outjut of cliff, and a native fisherman shouted asking me to come and help because a lion was causing terror in the small deep valley. I shouted back that I'd return overland by the hill path within the next day or two, as soon as I'd dumped this kit of mine in the place for which I was making. I reached my destination next morning and, leaving my boatmen to look after things, I, along with my gunbearer, cook, and three or four porters who carried food and bedding, returned by the hill path to the valley where the man-eater was. There was too much water in the gorge for us to follow the path that ran through it.

The hill path runs steeply up and down, and the valley for which we were making was the only one that deserved that name: the others were merely ravines, more or less densely wooded and bushed. I'd been along this way before, and knew the valley in question, and also knew that there was a bad old rhino living in it. Native travelers were always glad when they had passed the section because of this animal's evil reputation. He had the whole of Africa from which to select a domicile, but for some reason best known to himself he had chosen this small valley and objected to anyone's entering it. Even at that, there was no reason why he should habitually have stuck close to the path—no reason, that is, except sheer cussedness.

It was a pleasant little valley, about a third of a mile across at its widest part, quite open but with clumps of bush here and there. A small creek ran through the center of it. The hills on both sides were heavily bushed. As we dropped down the last of the seemingly endless succession of steep hills and for the first time struck level ground we were still traveling through bush, though there were small clear patches here and there. I was, of course, carrying a loaded rifle, both because I'd come in search of a man-eating lion and also because of this bad rhino.

Suddenly I heard a snort and a crash about thirty yards away on my half-right front. It was followed by a yell, a yell that rapidly rose to a high scream of agony, choked, and shuddered down to a series of long sobbing moans. It was all too clear that the rhino had claimed a victim. I snicked forward my safety catch and hastened through the bush to a small clearing; and there on the far side of it, about fifteen paces from me, stood the bad rhino with his horn and the whole side of his face plastered with blood and gore. He was eying something that lay huddled on the ground between him and me, shaking his head slowly from side to side as though wondering whether or not to come at it again. I threw up my rifle and shot him dead where he stood.

The pitiful huddled thing on the ground, lying in a pool of its own blood, resolved itself into a gray-bearded old man who hadn't had the agility to save himself when the rhino charged. I'm not going to harrow your feelings by describing his condition. Had I been my father, acknowledged one of the five greatest surgeons of his day, and armed with the most modern of implements and drugs, I could not have saved the old man's life. He was beyond speech and, mercifully, was scarcely conscious. I'm glad to say he did not suffer long.

We now pushed on down the valley to the kraal where the fisherman lived. This was situated where the valley opened out a bit more near the river. There were three or four small kraals scattered about here. In a clear place under a big shady tree my cook got a fire going and quickly had a pot of tea ready for me. The local villagers came around while I was drinking this, and I told them about the old man's death and gave instructions about the dead rhino. My men could take what they needed of the meat for themselves, and the villagers could have a generous ration of the remainder, but I did not want it all taken away. They must leave plenty because I hoped it would be bait for the man-eater. If he spent most of his time in this valley, as they'd already told me, he'd soon get to know of this free feed. On the great open plains of British East where rhino are shot to a much greater extent than they are here in the bushveld, and where lion are much more numerous, I knew that a dead rhino was the best of all baits for lion—a sure draw. Here, the position was rather different and not quite so sure, because lion seldom get a feed of rhino. Still, the valley was so small the man-eater could scarcely fail to find the rhino remains.

It wasn't necessary to wander about looking for spoor so that I could identify the man-eater; the locals assured me there was only the one lion in the valley and that he was a big old male with quite a fair-sized mane. They had seen him several times. The last kill in this vicinity had taken place the day prior to the fisherman's calling to me as I passed in my canoe. Afterward, according to his usual custom, the lion had disappeared and probably had wandered to the top end of the valley, or possibly into one of the neighboring valleys. This is quite usual with man-eaters and is one of the things that make the hunting of them so difficult. They seldom return to a human kill because they know the relatives of the victim will usually find his remains and remove them. Moreover, they soon learn that the other villagers will double their precautions after each kill, and it will be extremely difficult to secure another in that locality, until the scare has had time to die down a bit. After several days, the African being what he is, precautions are gradually relaxed and by the time the man-eater returns he will usually have no particular difficulty in finding someone foolish again. It is only after man-eaters have been scourging a district for a considerable time that a genuine reign of terror sets in and the natives remain in their huts until the sun is well up and shut themselves in again long before sundown (sunup and sundown being the two most dangerous times of day where man-eating lion are concerned).

The villagers had placed a clean hut at our disposal, so I told my men to shut themselves into it when I left. I intended to sit up over the remains of the rhino, and my men had fixed a small platform—"machan" they call it in India—in a convenient tree about twenty yards from what was left of the beast. The fact that the carcass had been partially butchered should help, as the smell of blood and fresh meat would carry farther and better than would the smell of a freshly killed beast that hadn't been cut up. About half the animal had been left.

The moon was a day off the full and I knew I'd have it until almost daybreak. Both jackals and hyenas put in an appearance early in the evening and had the time of their lives; but the lion didn't show up. So as night gave place to day I climbed down from my perch and returned to camp, where I gave orders that the remains of the rhino should be covered with bushes to keep off the vultures. Since I had no knowledge of the lion's whereabouts and since one place was as good as another in which to wait for him to come around, and this place better than most right now because of the big pile of bait we were lucky enough to have, there was nothing to do except have a bath, some breakfast, and then later in the day lie down in order to make up for the sleep I'd lost and to prepare myself for another night of sitting up. So that was my program.

Had we been almost anywhere else we would probably have received some word of the lion, because most kraals are situated near paths, or rather the paths lead from kraal to kraal, and there are always natives wandering around the country along these paths. Each of these travelers is his own broadcasting station, and they stop and pass the time of day and any news they may have with everyone they meet. But here we were somewhat isolated, being at the end of the little path that merely ran down to the river. There would be no occasion for passing travelers to drift down this way.

Again shortly before sundown I took up my position in the tree. I had already had the branches that covered the bait removed. Again my vigil was fruitless. This did not depress or discourage me. It was all part of the game. If it were not for the hardships and disappointments which make success doubly satisfying when at last it comes your way, big-game hunting would be too easy and would soon lose its appeal.

This day followed the same course as the previous one, and an hour or so before sundown I was once more seated on my machan. The moon wouldn't rise until about an hour and ten minutes after dark, and as I had no batteries for my shooting lamp I determined, if the lion arrived early, to hold my fire until the moon gave me sufficient light to make a certain shot. It's a great mistake to be in a hurry and shoot too soon, and with all this free meat he wouldn't be in any hurry to depart. I felt pretty confident of getting a shot this night. The lion was due again in the locality if he kept to his normal habits, and there didn't seem to be any very good reason why he should have altered them. In addition the bait was in just about the best possible place it could have been—on the eastern edge of the valley, which ran roughly north-south. What breeze there was almost invariably blew up the river from the east, which meant that the smell of the dead rhino would be carried right across the valley. The carcass was beginning to tell the world of its existence, and lion like their meat high.

After the sun had been down some twenty minutes and the light had gone I heard a lion moan about half a mile away up the valley. Without doubt this was my quarry arriving in his own time. And I wasn't the only one who heard him. The hyenas, which had arrived as soon as it was dark, ceased gulping meat for a moment and also listened. Then, realizing that the lion was still some distance away, they returned to their stolen feed with redoubled energy as though to get as much down them as possible before the lion arrived. I sat on. Perhaps twenty minutes after I had heard the lion's moan I suddenly realized that the hyenas had gone. I hadn't been taking any notice of them as I had been concentrating on listening. The fact that they had gone could only mean that the lion had arrived; yet I hadn't heard a sound. I sat as motionless as the dead. The lion was here somewhere and must be under cover weighing possibilities. I wasn't afraid of his decamping without approaching the bait. It wasn't as though he'd had others sit up for him over a bait and take shots at him. Hunting lion don't look up in treetops as leopard are apt to do, because lion don't climb trees and hence aren't interested in anything up there. So long as I sat still there was no reason why the lion should spot me and therefore no reason why he should not approach the bait. He must have seen the hyenas on it and should therefore know that there was no other lion around whose kill it might have been.

And then a darker shadow than the surrounding gloom moved out from directly below me and advanced toward the bait. I continued to sit still. After prowling around the carcass to examine it from all sides and, perhaps, to figure how many days it would last, his tail waving from side to side in joyful anticipation, the lion started in to feed. And still I did nothing. The moon hadn't yet risen, and although I could see the lion I couldn't see the sights on my rifle. It would have been plain foolishness to fire. And what was more, I knew I'd have to wait until the moon had been up at least an hour, possibly more, before its light would reach us down here in the valley. I might well have to wait a couple of hours for my shot. It was quite likely that the lion would have a feed now, but not a full feed, and then wander off for a drink. After that he'd probably return and remain in the vicinity of the bait until daybreak if I didn't get my shot before then—though it was more than likely that I'd be able to shoot after he returned, supposing he left at all. From my experience I expected him to go for a drink unless, of course, he'd already had a bellyful of water.

As I listened to him feeding I noticed that the night was becoming less dark. The moon was rising on the far side of the hills to the east of me. Gradually objects became more distinct. I could now see the lion quite clearly, where previously he had been only another shadow among shadows. But before it was sufficiently light to see my sights he ceased feeding, drew back a bit from the bait, lay down and commenced licking his paws. He'd had enough for the time being. Now what would he do? There are men I know who would have risked a shot at this stage of the proceedings; but I'm not one of them. A little more patience now and I could bank on a clean kill, a certain kill. The lion hadn't the slightest suspicion of danger. Then why risk muffing things by shooting before I could see my sights clearly? I waited.

Presently the lion, having completed his toilet, stretched himself like the big cat he was, yawned hugely, and began to roar. But his roars were obviously for his own enjoyment and edification. He didn't throw out the full volume of sound he was capable of. Nobody could doubt it was a lion roaring, but that is about all you could say for it. When he'd finished he didn't seem to know just what to do. From the way he looked down the valley toward the river and then back at the remains of the rhino it was clearly to be seen that he was debating with himself whether it would be wise to leave all this meat and go have a drink, or whether it would be wiser to remain. And then he suddenly must have remembered the little creek that ran through the valley. He gave a low grunt and started off toward where the path crossed the stream two or three hundred yards away. Just momentarily I had a qualm as I watched him move into the bush surrounding the open space in which the bait lay: What a fool I'd feel if he didn't come back! And yet I was quite certain I'd acted wisely and as a genuine hunter should in not firing until I was certain of a kill. He was practically certain to return. Anyway, there was nothing I could do about it now except wait.

I needn't have worried, if that momentary qualm could be called worry. He was back again in less than fifteen minutes. And now I determined that nothing would tempt me to squeeze the trigger until I was positive. It must have been almost eleven o'clock before I took the shot. There was no doubt about it, either, though I put in the left barrel also just to make doubly sure.

Destiny, kismet, fate, call it what you like—when you come to look around the big-game hunting world and see the things that happen, you are compelled to the conclusion that there is no such thing as chance. You will come to believe, as I came to believe many years ago, that when your bell rings, you go; and that until it rings it doesn't matter what you do—you *won't* go. Let me give you a few instances in support of that contention.

Salmon, of the elephant control staff of Uganda, was twice grabbed by wounded elephant, yet so far as I know is still alive. The first time the elephant took his head in its trunk and gave it a twist; then years afterward another wounded elephant got hold of him and used him as a flail to beat down the tough grass, then tried to bash the life out of him with a solitary tusk. Salmon's head gunbearer sacrificed his life in a gallant attempt to save his master, and then his second gunbearer drove the elephant away by firing a bullet into his ribs. Salmon wasn't seriously injured on either occasion.

A German hunter in Tanganyika was grabbed by a wounded elephant and tossed high into the air, but instead of falling close by where the elephant was waiting with the obvious intention of trampling the life out of him, he fell into a river and managed to swim clear.

The late Fletcher Jamieson of Rhodesia said in a letter written to me immediately before his death that he'd just returned from a short safari after elephant during which he'd killed six good bulls, and out of seven shots at elephant had experienced no less than four misfires. Yet it wasn't an elephant that got him, as you might have expected—he was accidentally electrocuted when working down in his own well! Had he continued after elephant it would doubtless have been one of them that settled his hash; but his number wasn't yet up, though on its way. By the time he got home and went down his well, it was.

Then take the time Jim Corbett killed the man-eating tigress of Chowgarh. Had he been carrying the heavy rifle he ought to have been carrying, which in other circumstances he almost certainly would have been carrying, it's improbable that he would ever have written his absorbing book. Just picture the position: He was standing in a deep depression, a dry watercourse; immediately behind him there was a steep rock face down which he had just glissaded; there was another tall, almost vertical slab of rock on his immediate right; in his left hand he was holding two bird's eggs which he'd picked up and wanted to keep; his men pushed his light rifle into his right hand and told him they had just heard a tiger growl; he glanced back over his right shoulder—and there was the man-eater crouching on the other side of that vertical slab of rock and, as afterward measured, just eight *feet* away from him, with, as he describes it himself, a smile on her face like that you see on the face of a dog welcoming his master back after a long absence.

I'm not going to spoil the book by saying how he got himself out of that predicament; but he tells how all the factors which would seem to be fighting against him were actually on his side, weighing the scales in his favor: the light rifle, the fact that the tigress was a man-eater, even the eggs in his left hand! Chance? The long arm of coincidence will stand a lot of stretching, but it would dislocate it to hang all that on the end of it.

Once upon a time, when I was camped in that remote and lonely valley which I've previously mentioned, my little cookboy was sleeping by himself. He was withdrawn from the others, who were in a fairly compact circle. Some time in the middle of the night the lad woke up— at least partially woke up—for no reason that he could give, and decided he would join the circle where the others were sleeping. I saw him pick up his sleeping mat and sheet by one corner so that they dragged along the ground behind him and, heavy with sleep, walk slowly over to the others, drop his mat, let himself drop down on it, kick the sheet over himself, and instantly go off to sleep again. Next day I found the pug marks of a man-eating lion within a foot of where the lad's head had been before he shifted his position. It was one of a party of three man-eaters, two of which I shot the next morning at about ten o'clock, and the third the following night. The other two members of the party had stood in the center of the road watching the one that approached so close to where that lad had been sleeping.

Then there was a Colonel Glasfurd who was swept over a cliff in the embrace of a sloth bear in India. He and the bear were wrapped in each other's arms as they fell through the air. But some fifteen feet down was a small tree growing out of the side of the cliff. Glasfurd struck that, and the shock was enough to tear him and the bear apart. The bear continued the fall, but Glasfurd managed to wrap his arms and legs around the little tree and hang on. This tree, of remarkable flexibility and known locally as *Bhiria,* was the *only* piece of growth on the face of the precipice; yet there it was, in exactly the right place to catch Glasfurd, and in addition had the necessary flexibility to break his fall without also breaking his back and to prevent its being torn from its precarious root hold in the little fissure. Chance!

The Arabs will tell you that every man's fate is written on his brow. Or as old man Omar put it:

The first Morning of Creation wrote
What the last Dawn of Reckoning shall read.

Finally: what rifle to use for lion? See to it that you have plenty of power. The lion's tenacity to life is something you can't possibly appreciate until you have had actual evidence of it. You can drill him through and through, right through the heart, lungs, liver, and intestines, and *still he'll come on.* Your rifle must have a sufficiently powerful punch to ensure its knocking him down during a charge. You may shoot many lion without being charged; but sooner or later you'll have to face one. I consider it the acme of foolishness to tackle lion with a low-powered rifle. If the lion are out in the open a small-bore will kill provided you place your little slugs in the right spot; but the trouble is that an exceptionally good mane may tempt you into taking a doubtful shot. And where a heavier bullet might have been able to plow through into the boiler room to kill, it will happen all too often that the little light slug thrown by the small-bore will not get beyond the paunch. The lion will clear off and you will have to follow—an extremely dangerous and unpleasant job. Even if you decide to wait until the next day, it probably won't help. A bullet in the belly certainly won't kill within a mere twenty-four hours. The lion will still be able to kill you first. It's happened many and many a time. The British seem to have a mania for featherweight small-bores throughout Africa, and when I hear or read of one of them getting killed or mauled, I just can't shed a tear.

I strongly recommend that you carry a good handgun, loaded, in a sensible type of open-topped holster when hunting lion. If anything goes wrong when you're facing a charge and the lion gets "home," you can save yourself a bad mauling or even death itself if you have a handgun as a stand-by. When a lion gets you down he seems to lose his head. Instead of just taking you by the throat and shaking you, he will chew an arm or a leg for a long time and appear to be quite satisfied with that. Men have tried to get hold of the lion's tongue only to have their hands crushed to pulp, or to gouge out his eyes. Had they had a handgun on their belt they could have blown out the animal's brains a few seconds after being brought down.

11:   LEOPARD

Curiously enough, although I have always looked upon the leopard as one of the most dangerous animals, potentially, in Africa, there is surprisingly little to say about him. This is without doubt due to the fact that he's so seldom seen in daylight. If you do catch sight of him by day, all you will generally glimpse is a yellowish-tawny streak as he disappears. The unfailing discrimination he shows in his choice of lying-up places enables him to slip away into thick cover without your knowing he was there at all. This trait is so pronounced that you might be excused for believing the leopard must be nearing extermination due to the extent to which he has been hunted. Nothing could be farther from the truth. I've never heard of any other hunter's concentrating on leopard, apart from myself for a period. And leopard are found throughout Africa from the Cape to the Sudan, and from the Indian to the Atlantic oceans. I'm certain I won't be contradicted when I declare there must be many more leopard than lion in Africa. But the leopard is a solitary creature, whereas the lion likes the company of his pals. Even pairs of leopard are rare and, I think, are only to be seen during the actual mating or when a female has a cub or two at heel.

It's sheer luck, as I indicate above, if you get a shot at a leopard by day—except in just one or two districts known to me. The animal is far more essentially nocturnal than the lion. But you do occasionally spot one when hunting something else—one that's dawdled over his feed or killed close to daybreak. And I remember shooting one around ten o'clock in the morning—a female. She was apparently returning to have a second feed on the carcass of a klipspringer (a small buck) she'd left lying not far away. She was heading toward it when I spotted her.

That was very unusual, and it was also unusual for a leopard to leave a kill lying like that. I think a possible explanation might be that she had very young cubs concealed somewhere, had taken them some of the meat, and that when I spotted her she was either returning to get them some more or to hide her kill. The usual habit is to lug the remains of the kill up a tree and wedge it by means of the head and horns into a fork perhaps twenty or thirty feet from the ground. This, of course, is to save it from hyenas and jackals. However, it is no safeguard from vultures—though, in a tree, vultures might not spot it so readily as they would if it were on the ground. Indeed, I can't remember ever seeing vultures on a kill so placed.

It's amazing the weight a leopard can lug up a tall tree. I've heard it suggested that two or more leopard must help one another; but I can't support that view. The leopard is much too solitary to rely upon help. During the mating season, if male and female happened to be together, they *might* help each other in that way, but I cannot believe they'd do so otherwise. The question is then asked, "How can a leopard climb a tree with a buck as big as if not bigger than himself in his mouth?" The answer to that, after careful examination of the spoor and the carcasses of many buck on many different occasions, is that the leopard takes the carcass by the back of the neck, slides his own shoulder under the buck's shoulder, and climbs the tree with the buck hanging down his back and so out of his way.

Speaking of this, you will sometimes hear or read of how a lion has broken into a cattle kraal, killed a full-grown beast, and *thrown* him clear over the wall of the kraal. Occasionally he is said to have jumped over the wall with the ox in his mouth like a cat with a mouse. I don't for one instant believe that any lion ever *threw* an ox anywhere—how on earth could he? And the same doubt applies to the statement that he jumped over the wall, perhaps ten or twelve feet high, "with the ox in his mouth like a cat with a mouse." He'd inevitably trip over the beast, even supposing he could lift a full-grown ox right off the ground. Again from my own observations, and I have had a lot of experience with cattle-killing lion, I say the lion does exactly as the leopard does: he takes the ox by the back of the neck, slides his own shoulder under that of the kill so as to get it on his back, and *then* jumps and clambers over the wall. That explanation brings the story into the realm of possibility —though maybe it's not so picturesque.

Here's the sort of thing that exasperates me when I see it in print:

Up in the northern frontier province of Kenya a large lone lion, after killing a big zebra, not only carried it two hundred yards up the steep

slope of a stony hill, but landed it over the top of a high boulder stand-
ing twelve feet sheer from the ground and dropped it inside an enclosure
formed by that boulder and three others.

That was written by an experienced hunter, and, frankly, I find it
completely unbelievable. He doesn't tell us *why* the lion performed this
magical feat—the explanation, I guess, would have been too much even
for his imagination. A lion will frequently drag a kill into a shady place
before commencing to feed; but why on earth should he carry it up a
steep hill and then perform the prodigious feat of slinging it over a
twelve-foot rock? It isn't as though he had killed in a densely populated
locality and wanted to make sure he wouldn't be disturbed. The northern
frontier province of Kenya is but one degree removed from desert. It's
a great pity that men so often allow their imaginations to run away with
them when writing about big game.

A variation of the leopard's hiding the remains of his kill is his
concealing it under grass and bushes. This is better than sticking it up a
tree because it will definitely keep it safe from vultures. It is quite a
common habit, though not as frequent as the tree larder. Perhaps the
type of country dictates the method used.

Going back to that period I mentioned in which I concentrated on
leopard for a spell: I had originally come to the district in question for
elephant and had shot several. I was out hunting for camp meat one day,
but game was very scarce. This forced me to take a somewhat doubtful
shot at a waterbuck bull. I knew I had hit him hard and also knew I
couldn't expect to kill him outright. Normally I don't take such shots,
but the need of meat for my men overrode my own inclinations. The bull
dashed away, and we proceeded to follow him. He swam across a deep
pool and then plunged into the thick bush that grew on the far side of it.
It was forest rather than bush, though there wasn't very much of it. We
followed, and I was amazed to see a really big leopard directly in front of
me when I turned a corner around a clump of undergrowth. He also was
following the fresh blood spoor. He wasn't more than fifteen to twenty
feet ahead, but his appearance was so totally unexpected that he was gone
before I could get my sights on him. I killed the buck, and we all
returned to camp. However, when the butchers went out to cut up the
meat and carry it in, they found a large leopard feeding on the carcass.
Since that was about eleven o'clock in the morning it was certainly most
extraordinary. But it was part and parcel of the equally remarkable sight
of a leopard hunting at the time I was following the wounded buck—in
fact, it must be the same animal.

I thought no more of it, beyond making a note of it in my diary. But

I was really amazed the next time I had occasion to shoot for the pot and the butchers *again* told me they had found a big leopard having a feed on our buck when they got there. Since this buck had been shot many miles from where the other one had there was no reason to suppose this was the same leopard. Accordingly, if the habit of hunting by day was customary with leopard in this locality I might be able to make something of it. I had recently received a letter from a big firm in New Zealand offering very attractive prices for good skins. Besides, the price of ivory had dropped to next to nothing. So the next time I shot a buck for my men I climbed up a suitable tree with a convenient fork about ten to twelve feet from the ground. This was not for safety but to give me a better field of fire. As usual, my stouthearted gunbearer refused to leave me, so I sent the other men back to camp to fetch their companions to cut up the meat. They were little more than out of sight when a fine leopard appeared out of nowhere and made toward the carcass of the buck. I waited until he reached it and then dropped him with a bullet from my .350 Rigby-Magnum—a very effective weapon.

Saduko—my gunbearer—and I then set to and skinned the leopard, afterward making for camp. We met the butchers coming out and had a joke with them about their meeting another leopard when they got there. To anyone who knows leopard my feelings can be better imagined than described when they told me later that they did in fact find another leopard there. I took it at first as a continuation of my little joke and laughed politely, since they had been good enough to laugh when I made the joke in the first instance. But they assured me it was not a joke. It seemed almost unbelievable; but I had been in the bush long enough to know better than to spurn information about game from members of the hunting tribes.

So next day I dropped the elephant hunting entirely (they were not very numerous anyway) and decided to concentrate on leopard, taking elephant only when they came around asking to be shot. I got another waterbuck next morning not far from the one of the previous day and again sat up in a convenient tree. I told the men who had accompanied me not to return before midday. They left, and within little more than half an hour I had killed a leopard that had come to examine the dead buck. Saduko and I had a smoke but remained in the tree in case another came along. However, none did, and when our men came out at midday we left. The following morning I went in a different direction and shot a kudu. This time, since there wasn't a convenient tree anywhere near, my gunbearer and I squatted under a bush and had our men stick a few branches and some grass in front of us so we would not be too conspicuous. Again I bagged a leopard before midday! It seemed he materialized out of thin air. The forest was open, there was practically no grass and very little bush; yet one moment there was not a living thing in sight and the next a leopard was approaching from a mere thirty yards away. It's true there was one tiny little bush, and he slipped out from behind it. But what I'd like to know is how he got to that little bush without either of us spotting him. I let him approach the carcass, and then dropped him with a bullet through the shoulder.

I was to see more of this extraordinary power of the leopard to render himself invisible. Having traded the surplus meat to neighboring natives for such things as meal, we moved on another ten miles or so, since we could not expect to find an unlimited supply of leopard in one locality. There I went through the same performance. It really seemed as though the leopard knew exactly what the sound of a rifle meant: that if they came quickly they stood a good chance of a free meal. Time after time throughout the five or six months I remained in that district I shot my leopard within an hour or less of killing the buck or other beast that served as bait. There were several occasions when I shot two during the course of the morning. That, however, seemed the limit. Several times I tried remaining over the bait all day and it did no good.

I shot quite a few elephant from time to time here and there throughout the area; but the leopard didn't seem to realize they could get a feed from an elephant carcass. I would have my men cut off the trunk immediately so that there would be a good smell of freshly killed meat, but only twice did I shoot a leopard when sitting up over a dead elephant. And it didn't look to me as though the leopard on either occasion had intended to feed. I had the impression they had merely drifted up out of curiosity at the strange mixture of scents in the air: elephant and freshly spilled blood.

Although buck were scarce—scarce, that is, for Africa—there were plenty of bush pig and wart hog around, and they made splendid bait. Saduko and I were sitting over a wart hog one day—sitting again under a little bush—when once more a leopard appeared just beside me. He was certainly not more than eight or nine paces away on my half-left front. There was a small tuft of grass there, and he really seemed to have materialized out of it somehow. There wasn't a scrap of cover anywhere near it; yet, again, neither of us had seen him approach it. He didn't see us. His attention was concentrated entirely on the dead wart hog. He was so close that I didn't dare bring the rifle around to bear on him—he would have spotted the movement and fled. I just nudged my companion and indicated with a lift of my chin where to look in case he hadn't seen the leopard and might make some movement which would reveal our presence.

The leopard was staring fixedly at the bait. He was so motionless that he might have been an exhibit in a museum. (So might we, for that matter!) Then he suddenly swept forward, belly to earth, so swiftly and smoothly that he flowed over the ground. It's no good saying I wish I'd had a small movie camera because the whir of the mechanism would have spoiled things. He halted when he reached the bait and started waving his tail in joyful anticipation. But my rifle put an end to him. He dropped dead in his tracks, and I reloaded.

It was perhaps an hour later when my companion nudged me and looked over to his right. Sure enough, there was another leopard coming. But he was taking his time. I guessed it was the sight of the first dead leopard at the kill that made him pause so often in indecision: from what I've seen of leopard they're not given to sharing their kills—for that matter neither are lion, except with their own pals. Well, the second leopard came on in short stages, slipping along from one tiny scrap of cover to another until he was about twenty-five yards from the kill. Then he lay down beside a tuft of grass with a dead bush growing out of it. There was only a small stick or two, no thicker than a man's thumb, and some stems of grass; yet if you looked away and then looked back that leopard merged so perfectly into his background and surroundings that you could look clean through him. I was tempted to shoot, but the angle wasn't too good; besides I wanted to see his reaction to the dead leopard when he eventually closed in on the bait. I knew that lion think nothing of eating a dead companion—all reports concerning the species' nobility notwithstanding—though sometimes they just ignore a dead fellow. Well, the leopard merely gave the carcass a casual sniff, to satisfy himself that it was indeed dead, and then turned his attention to the bait: it was much more to his liking. But he didn't get a chance to enjoy it.

I found leopard hunting an intensely interesting break from elephant hunting—quite aside from its being easy and profitable. It was so utterly different from other kinds of hunting I'd tried and so strangely different from all usual kinds of leopard hunting that, as I have said, I spent half a year at it. I quit then because fashions changed and the skin buyers informed me they would be unable to keep on with the prices they had given me thus far. So that was that.

Incidentally, except for that one half-year I have never interfered with the ordinary hunting leopard—any more than with the hunting lion: he does no harm and never interferes with man. Ever since that time (and it was many years ago) the only leopard I've hunted and shot have been man-eaters and man-maulers.

Most men describe leopard as cowardly, slinking brutes and express hatred for them. I wonder why. Sure, the leopard slinks around and has far too much intelligence to pick a fight without having a very good reason for doing so, particularly when he doesn't see a fair chance of winning. But I certainly can't agree that he's a coward. If you are trying to drive a leopard toward a spot where a gun is waiting for him, he will break back far more readily than will a lion or tiger; and what's more, whereas a lion will try to slink between two beaters, the leopard will almost invariably attack one or both of them. He won't necessarily kill but will claw savagely. Since he'll use all four feet (a lion uses only his forepaws to grab while he bites) the leopard can do appalling damage in a matter of seconds. His claws are like razors, and he can cut a man to shreds. It's worth mentioning, perhaps, that a leopard's claws do not appear to be so septic as a lion's or tiger's. Men who die as a result of a lion's mauling mostly die of blood poisoning—and, if they don't die, they may lose an arm or a leg if they can't get to a surgeon in time—but although I know a number of men who have been mauled by leopard I cannot think of one who suffered badly from blood poisoning. The answer? Your guess is as good as mine. The leopard's claws are also hollow, like a lion's or a tiger's. There it is. I might also mention here, once more, the African's remarkable ability to recover from maulings by lion, buffalo, or anything else—maulings that would inevitably kill a white man. The native does not seem nearly so susceptible to blood poisoning, and his vitality approaches that of the African game.

If you have wounded a leopard and are following up, you can be quite sure of a charge. I think a wounded leopard is more certain to attack than either lion or tiger. That, too, doesn't bear out the accusation of cowardice. Then, leopard sometimes develop a curious habit of man-killing or, rather, man-mauling—it's usually this rather than man-eating, though I've also known man-eating leopard. When they take to this habit they will attack man, woman, or child without the slightest provocation. There will be a sudden rush, a man goes down, the leopard mauls him badly and decamps. There doesn't seem to be any reason for it. Blaney Percival states that in his opinion there are many more natives mauled and killed by leopard than by lion—which means a great many. Does that look like cowardice? Mind you, the man-mauling or man-eating leopard is definitely the exception throughout most of Africa—always excepting certain parts of West Africa where there are no lion but numerous leopard. I've written elsewhere of a very bad man-eating leopard I knew and hunted down the lower Zambezi. This brute wasn't satisfied merely to kill for food, but did so for the sheer fun of it. He so terrorized a district that it was evacuated by all the natives with the exception of two families. That was shortly before the outbreak of World War II.

I sometimes wonder if this man-mauling could be a form of rabies or something akin to it. But I'm afraid I'm not qualified to express an opinion on such a subject, and besides, I do not know of mauled victims who subsequently developed the disease.

Corbett tells us that it can be taken as a general rule in India—a rule to which he has known no exceptions—that all human kills which take place by day are those of tiger and all those which take place by night are those of leopard.

This does not hold true of lion and leopard in Africa. Man-eating lion usually operate at night and just around dawn and twilight, rarely by day, though I've known them to do so when they have created such a reign of terror that the villagers do not move about until long after sunup and lock themselves into their huts long before sundown. But this is exceptional.

Man-eating leopard are comparatively rare in both continents. Corbett says that the man-eating leopard in India never loses his fear of man no matter how many he may have killed, and that the people go about their daily tasks as though no terror exists until shortly before sundown. My experience with man-eating leopard in Africa is that irrespective of whether it's actual man-eating or mere man-mauling (incidentally, I am interested to note that Corbett makes no reference to mauling by leopard in India) the leopard loses all his natural fear of man and becomes positively contemptuous of him. He will sit up in a tree by day where he has a clear view along a path frequented by natives, and when he sees some coming he usually drops down and ambushes them from behind a small bush or tuft of grass at the foot of the tree or close to it. As in the case of the lion, he tackles the inevitable straggler.

Indian fauna would seem to be a good deal more vocal than African fauna, which is of great assistance to the hunter. Most African game will just stand and gaze at lion or leopard that happens to pass. Lesser kudu, however, will usually bark at a lion, and bushbuck at a leopard, while baboons will always tell the world if they spot a leopard, their most hated enemy. Their night vision must be extraordinarily good: even on a dirty wet night, almost pitch-dark, they seem to have no difficulty in spotting a leopard. But generally speaking the hunter does not get a great deal of assistance from other game in the bushveld.

I was greatly surprised at one incident which occurred when Corbett was hunting down the notorious Rudraprayag leopard. He had been sitting up for him on the ground, hoping to get a shot before the light failed; but he also carried a flashlight, in case the leopard should be late arriving. Rain coming on made his position on the ground too dangerous, since he would be unable to hear the leopard approaching. Accordingly he got to his feet and started off to cover the five hundred yards or thereabouts that separated him from his camp. He had every reason to believe that the leopard was close, and probably following him—actually following him, as the spoor showed next morning. But what surprised me was that Corbett says he was afraid to use the flashlight to see where he was going since it might attract the leopard. He had a most unpleasant time struggling along over wet boulders and mud in the pitch-dark, not knowing but that every minute might be his last. What I can't understand is why he didn't think to use his flashlight to see if the leopard were close. If he picked up the animal's eyes in the beam of the torch, he would have been able to kill it without difficulty. That is the method we employ in Africa for leopard as well as for lion.

It makes no difference whether a leopard is stalking you or has slipped ahead and is lying in ambush: no matter what he's doing he'll take mighty good care to keep you in sight so that you won't be able to slip away unbeknown to him. Consequently, no matter how well he's concealed himself, when you turn your flashlight toward him you will inevitably pick up his eyes. He won't know that you've spotted him, any more than, in a car approaching at night, you can see the driver. You can only see the headlights. This is what makes the night shooting of the animals so easy when you finally manage to find them.

I consider leopard far more intelligent than either lion or tiger. I have no hesitation in saying that if leopard were as big as lion they would be ten times more dangerous. They are much bolder than lion at night; human habitations hold no terrors for them. They will enter a house through an open door or window and prowl right through it—not excepting the room in which you're sleeping—in the hope of finding a dog, which the leopard prefers to all other food. But if he is not a man-eater the leopard won't touch you even though he is in the same room with you—you won't know of his visit until the next morning. No single dog, of course, has a chance against a leopard. There are men who have boasted that their dog killed a leopard singlehanded, but I have never come across an authenticated case. Yes, the ordinary leopard is as bold and as cunning as a bad man-eating lion, but when he takes to man-eating his boldness and cunning develop even more. He can reason, and reason well. Moreover, his ability to climb trees and such is a tremendous asset.

Personally, I have a genuine admiration for the leopard. He is the real hunter and bushman, the fellow who never overlooks a bet, who never acts like a fool and forgets his bushcraft, who always, always,

always has a good line of retreat. But curiously enough, his intelligence stops short of traps. Little care is necessary in setting traps for leopard. I can't even pretend to explain that—unless a poor sense of smell is in some way responsible.

The reason I describe leopard as potentially the most dangerous game in Africa is because they are so much smaller than any of the other dangerous beasts; because they are by far the best camouflaged; because the leopard's charge is so incredibly quick; and because of the appalling damage leopard can do in a short space of time, owing, as noted above, to their custom of using all four sets of claws as well as teeth. But of course you will understand that I consider leopard dangerous only when they are considered as a hunter's quarry—not otherwise.

If you are following up a wounded leopard and are armed with a rifle, let nothing persuade you to fire until he is practically on you. You can bet you won't see him until he is actually under way. He's inclined to come with a bit of a swerve, as though hoping to dodge the bullet he knows is waiting for him. And a shot, even if it misses him, will often cause him to swerve still more, so that he may leave you and make for one of your men. You can be quite sure that *someone* is going to be hurt if you fail to kill a charging leopard. For following up a wounded leopard I'd strongly advise a shotgun loaded with buckshot. One and a quarter or one and a half ounces of British SSG is just the medicine for him. There is a much larger margin of permissible error with the slugs than with a single bullet.

By the way, if you're out after leopard with a shotgun at night when the grass is burned off, and you shine an animal's eyes while still too far away for a certain shot, you'll find that he won't stand gazing at you for anything like as long as a lion will. Lion are very accommodating and will often allow you to close in over a considerable distance; the leopard is more wary. But if he turns his head away and disappears, don't be discouraged. Wait a few minutes, turn around, and walk slowly back the way you came. You will not infrequently find that the leopard has made a detour to get behind you and back of the light and is now coming toward you from the opposite direction. I have on several occasions bagged my leopard in this manner.

12: SOME DON'TS

I've mentioned quite a few "don'ts" here and there in the foregoing chapters, either directly or indirectly; some of these might be elaborated upon and discussed, and there are still a few more that deserve mention.

Don't allow your imagination to run away with you and scare you stiff with thoughts of all the horrible things that *might* happen. They probably won't. And even if they do, you won't be helping yourself by worrying about them in camp before you ever go out. For example, I remember reading of a sportsman who was very eager to shoot a buffalo. He eventually encountered three bulls at some unspecified distance, though from his description of the country they could scarcely have been less than fifty or sixty yards away. He tells us how the big beasts snorted angrily and tossed their heads. (Why do the inexperienced always assume that any sound an animal makes when looking toward them indicates anger? Buff do not snort when angry.) He then goes on to describe how with great presence of mind he moved slowly and steadily backward, away from the bulls. He tells us of his thoughts and how he felt wondering what would happen if they all three charged together. There are no convenient trees near, we are told; and the sportsman and his followers are so encumbered with food and water bottles and ammunition and what-have-you that they are in no condition for sprinting. His rifle is raised, ready for instant use; but he doesn't want to fire while they are so "threatening." He spins out the tension for a page or two and evidently believes he was looking death fairly between the eyes. Finally, after he had taken several steps backward, the three buffalo took a few paces toward him and then stopped again. He came to the conclusion that this was the end, and as the center one of the three started slowly toward him once more he fired. But he was apparently so nervous his bullet only nicked the big animal, which turned and cleared off accompanied by its companions.

Do you have the picture? The fellow had scared himself with the notion that buffalo invariably attack at sight and without any provocation. When they stood up in front of him and snorted and blew, he instantly jumped to the conclusion that their snorts were those of rage. As a matter of fact they were snorts of consternation and curiosity.

If that fellow hadn't swallowed so many notions about buffalo he wouldn't have frightened himself into impotence and would probably have succeeded in bagging his coveted trophy. It's true he was writing about Asiatic buffalo, but do unwounded Asiatic buffalo attack at sight? I've never come across a genuinely authenticated case of their doing so. I know many men who are equally afraid of African buffalo and have the same notion that they will invariably attack at sight without being in any way provoked. That's all bunk. That fellow's "tense moments" may have been tense enough to him at the time, and whenever he subsequently spoke or wrote about them, but they were entirely unnecessary. American outdoor magazines nowadays are full of similar accounts written by visiting journalists and tourist hunters. Every buffalo's snort is an angry snort; if he takes a step or two toward a man, it's a threatening step; if he shakes his head, it's threateningly. The step or two the buff takes toward you is merely an attempt to focus better to see if you are really a man or just a tree stump that appeared to move. . . . An angry buffalo does not snort—you'll be in no doubt at all about his feelings and his attitude when you hear the sound a really angry buff makes!

Then this writer speaks of running. There's another "don't" for you— as I have said several times before.

Don't imagine for a moment that you can outrun any animal that's coming for you. You can't. You may occasionally dodge a rhino, whose charge is generally a blind rush; and if you are very lucky you may now and then be able to dodge downwind of a charging elephant, and so get clear. But you certainly won't be able to run from a charging buffalo, lion, or leopard and get away with it. *Stand your ground and shoot.* If you turn your back on a charging animal you can do nothing. So long as you face him you have at least a hope. You have your rifle, and you ought to have a good *sharp* sheath knife and, for lion or leopard, a handgun. Even if your rifle jams and all you have is a spear you've grabbed from a fleeing follower—well, it's a whole lot better than nothing, isn't it? Many a lion has been killed with a spear. There was a little native youngster of not more than thirteen or fourteen who killed a lion and lioness with a short spear he picked up when the lion pulled down his father. Instead of shinning up a tree like the other men the lad advanced on the lion until he provoked a charge. He then dropped on one knee, as he had seen older men do, planted the butt of the spear in the ground behind him and directed the point of the spear toward the lion, so that the brute impaled himself on it. And the boy was cool enough to withdraw the spear from the dead lion and turn to face the lioness, which came for him the instant she realized her mate was down. He killed her in the same way. A pretty courageous effort! That took place within about one hundred and fifty yards of where I was camped.

Blaney Percival, who probably had more experience hunting lion on horseback than anyone, frequently refers to the astonishing speed of a lion's first rush. He states that the lion hasn't been born that can catch a horse once that horse is into his stride; but, by the same token, the horse hasn't yet been foaled that a lion can't catch within a hundred yards, giving the horse a fifty-yard lead—if it's from a standing start. This is because a lion starts off right away in high with both throttles wide open. He's like a rocket-boosted plane getting away with the added impetus of a catapult from a warship's deck. Percival says that on one occasion when he was astride his favorite pony, the fastest mount he'd ever ridden and one thoroughly accustomed to this game, he was some thirty yards from an angry lioness which suddenly came for him, roaring, after he foolishly took a shot at her with his revolver. Since the pony knew what those roars meant he legged it from that spot as fast as he could lay hoof to the ground. Yet fast as he was, Percival states that before he'd covered another thirty yards the lioness was alongside. Well, since you know you couldn't run from a galloping horse, what hope would you have trying to run from a charging lion that can cover two yards for every one the horse covers?

Yet time and again someone says that he "took to his heels." Here's one, writing about a wounded tigress:

> *Before we had gone two hundred yards the tigress charged. My comrades displayed the greatest agility in making for the treetops. I fired one shot and turned to run, but fortunately the tigress had turned and disappeared.*

I'll say it was fortunate.

And then there's the fellow who lets his imagination play with his experiences after they've happened until he fancies all sorts of things that never took place. Whoever originally started the myth that animals' eyes glow in the dark has a lot to answer for. Perhaps I should say the eyes of Carnivora. Right back to my nursery days I can remember pictures of wolves in Siberia and the far north of Canada with their green eyes glowing around the camp. Even Fitzpatrick in his charming *Jock of the Bushveld* falls for this. He describes a pair of mysterious eyes glowing from out of the center of a bush and instructs or allows his illustrator, Caldwell, to show a full-page drawing of the scene. And the late Sir Malcolm Campbell, the British speed racer, when out in South Africa looking for a suitable pan on which to break some speed record, had a forced landing in his plane and was persuaded by some paper or magazine to write his experiences of the night he spent out on the veld. Presumably he felt duty-bound to give his readers something of what they expected, because he mentions a leopard's coming up close to have a look at him and speaks of its green eyes glowing at him out of the dark. Even

Paterson unthinkingly says something of the sort when describing a night in which he and two companions sat up in an empty boxcar hoping for a shot at the famous man-eaters of Tsavo. When Paterson was on watch he noticed two very large, very steady glowflies or glowworms, but thought nothing of them. Yet later when he was writing his description of that night and came to where he'd been relieved by a companion (who must have fallen asleep at his post) and one of the man-eaters sprang into the boxcar and carried off an occupant, Paterson refers again to these glowworms and says they must actually have been the man-eater's eyes all the time. Yet surely a little thought would have shown him how absurd the notion was. When he tells of another night, when he sat on a plank tied to four sticks only ten feet above ground, in the hope that the man-eater would come back for another feed on a donkey he'd killed, he found the lion stalking him instead. He had a very unpleasant time as the lion circled around, because his perch was very unstable and he was unable to keep turning to face the lion. Yet there's no mention of the lion's eyes glowing. Paterson's difficulty was trying to see where the brute was at all.

There were many occasions when Jim Corbett would have been grateful if the eyes of his man-eaters had glowed in the dark! How is it that we don't get these ridiculous reports from India? There is far more sitting up for tiger and leopard in India than there is for lion and leopard in Africa. Lion and tiger almost certainly descend from the same original parent stock; while there's no difference between African and Indian leopard. Why then should the eyes of lion glow and tiger not, and the eyes of Africa's leopard do so while those of India's don't?

No animal has phosphorescent eyes. Accordingly, the eyes *can't* glow unless a strong spotlight is directly toward them. And then it's not the eye that glows, but merely the reflection of the spotlight which you see— exactly like the red reflectors fitted on road signs: they glow only when the headlights of an approaching car strike them. The analogy is exact. The eyes of all animals have a myriad of tiny mirrors or reflectors which catch all available light, thus enabling them to see in what we call the dark; the human eye doesn't have these reflectors. Why in heaven's name should nature, which has endowed the Carnivora with every necessary attribute to assist them to secure their prey, turn around and fit them with signal lamps to warn all beasts that they are coming? How could they hope to stalk or ambush their quarry if their eyes glowed a warning?

No, if you read that some fellow saw eyes glowing in the dark when he had no flashlight turned toward them, you can chuck the book through the window.

It annoys me when I read rubbish from the pen of a self-styled hunter of vast experience. Such twaddle, moreover, is apt to mislead the inexperienced. For instance, I recall the story of a hunter who had wounded a man-eating tiger in India one night. Next morning he set off after the animal on an elephant. He tells how, on coming to a deep nullah, or dry watercourse, he dismounted and slid down to the bottom of it. Here he sees a drop of blood on a leaf and on glancing up finds himself looking right at the wounded tiger, which had been watching him. He says that he later measured the distance between them and found it was fourteen paces. But instead of shooting, he merely stared at the tiger and backed slowly away. When halfway to the top of the nullah he turned around and scrambled to the top! He says if he had fired and only wounded again, nothing could have saved him from certain death.

After reading a thing like that it's a little difficult to know just where to start criticizing it. Perhaps the best thing is merely to wonder what more the hunter wanted than a shot at a motionless tiger a bare fourteen paces away.

But I have known more than one beginner who got hold of a book like that by some amateur and thought he was learning the correct way to do things. There are many amateurs who are real hunters and whose advice is well worth following; but that doesn't mean they're all like that—any more than it means that all pseudo-professionals are sound in the advice they give and the yarns they spin. You need to be very careful whose advice you follow.

It's a little difficult to understand how some of these men's minds work. Take this one:

> *More by instinct than by deliberation, I pointed my rifle toward her and let go. She emitted a deep, full-throated grunt and fell to the ground with a thud—a mass of impotent fury. I found afterward that I had broken her back. She got up and retreated toward the covert. Hardly had she gone ten yards, and I had just time to reload, when she changed her mind and charged again.*

That's about a tigress. She seems to be doing pretty well with a broken back.

A visiting American sportsman had a safari in Kenya not long ago and when he got back home he wrote an account of some of his adventures for one of the outdoor magazines. In the course of this account he described his difficulty in stopping a charging buffalo. I forget the distance over which the buff was supposed to have charged, either thirty or sixty yards, but it really doesn't matter. This sportsman stated that he had to fire seven shots from his double .470 into that charging buff before he succeeded in stopping him just a few feet away. Now, since a buff charges at between twenty and twenty-five miles per hour, it won't take him very long to cover even the longer distance, sixty yards; but it takes quite a while to fire and reload a double rifle often enough to get off seven shots. So all one can assume is that it must have been a leisurely "charge."

There was another visiting American hunter who recently wrote in a letter that when he was charged by a buffalo from thirty yards or so he fired no less than eleven shots from his .375 Magnum and even then had to take over his .475 No. 2 with which to kill the animal at a range of a few feet. He stated that all those shots were placed in the vital spots: head, neck, chest, and on both shoulders. Now I ask you, what kind of charge was that? Did the buffalo stop for a rest or a feed en route? A .375 Magnum holds only four shells in its magazine and a magazine rifle takes quite a time to recharge; yet this fellow must have recharged his no less than three times and still had time to take over his heavy rifle. Moreover, the buff must have been practicing figures of eight like an ice skater if the sportsman was able to shoot him in the neck and on both shoulders during his so-called charge. Do you see now what I mean when I suggest you shouldn't allow your imagination to run away with you later when describing your hunting adventures?

There was a fellow who came down through Africa, or said he did, who fetched up in Salisbury in Southern Rhodesia when I happened to be there. He told the newspapers a whale of a yarn about the hardships he'd experienced, and how he'd been compelled to live on nothing but crocs' tongues for several weeks when making his way through the swamps of the upper Nile. The papers gave him a big write-up, and I remember thinking to myself that he must have been mighty hungry after several weeks of that diet and nothing else. You see, a croc has no tongue—not a vestige of one. Rhodesia is in Africa, you might call it South Central Africa, and there are crocs in practically every river, stream, and creek. Yet those Rhodesians made a big song and dance about this poor fellow's "revolting diet," and decided they must get up a collection to help him on his way, so that he wouldn't be able to say he'd had nothing better than crocs' tongues in Rhodesia. When they asked me to subscribe I told them that if the fellow had merely spoken about having a rough passage, well and good, but I considered it an insult to ask me to believe the yarns he was telling and I'd be damned if I'd give anything. They got up another collection for him in Bulawayo, a rival town, and he pulled a lot more fancy yarns there. Perhaps that will substantiate what I've said about the scarcity of hunters in Africa nowadays. If such yarns had been told in Europe there would be excuse for this being believed; but I could hardly credit my eyes when I saw the write-up Rhodesian papers gave him, and the things they swallowed.

I feel compelled to say something here about the White Hunter racket, in the hope that it may save American visitors from sorry disappointments.

Just as after World War I, there is a spate of advertisements appearing in outdoor magazines: calling themselves professional hunters and offering their services as guides and mentors for big-game hunts. As in the past, some of the men have had little or no experience. Some of them are not qualified to be their own gunbearers. I know of one who threw his rifle away and fled, leaving an American woman unsupported to face a charging elephant. I know another in Tanganyika who has never killed an elephant in his life, though he's wounded several. I know another in Kenya about whom the same may be said. Then there was still another in Nyasaland who had killed just two elephant—a cow and a little pup with teeth like toothpicks or cigarette holders—yet who advertised his services to visitors for elephant hunts in Portuguese East Africa and wound up his statement with the words, *"ivory guaranteed"!*

Now it's a serious thing to lead inexperienced sportsmen, and women, up close to dangerous game; but it's a little difficult to know how to prevent it. All one can do is warn prospective visitors not to take advertising at its face value unless the advertiser's name is known or they have friends or acquaintances whom he has escorted and who can vouch for him.

To give you more idea of the racket I'll transcribe a conversation I actually overheard. I heard it not once but several times, and it varied little. There was nothing secret about it: a bunch of men were sitting in some hotel bar or pub tossing poker dice for drinks, and one of the party was very much in the dumps. He had been telling the world that his farm or plantation or whatever was just about bankrupt and would certainly be so by the end of the year.

Said one of his companions:

"Well, what are you worrying about? Why don't you turn professional?"

"Professional? Professional what?"

"Why, professional hunter, of course. What other professionals are there in these parts?"

"But I don't know anything about hunting."

"What the hell does that matter? Look at So-and-so. He's got a fine reputation nowadays, always seems to have a party of American millionaires in tow. He's been doing damn well out of it."

"Yes, but then he's been at it all his life."

"That's what he tells folks; but I remember him when he was just the same as you: And it's not so long ago either. He came out here, took up a plantation, went broke, sold everything he had, bought himself a couple of rifles, stuck advertisements in various sporting magazines and clicked with a wealthy American party who, fortunately for him, were genuine sportsmen who really could shoot. The result was that he never fired his rifle at all on that first safari. The visitors did all the shooting. This fellow saw his first big game on this first trip. The only game he'd ever seen or shot before were the buck he'd knocked over to feed his labor when running the farm. But those Americans gave him fine testimonials and were mighty generous to him. The result was that he was set up as a well-recommended professional right away. Why can't you do the same?"

"But damn it, I don't know the first thing about it."

"You don't have to, boy. The niggers do all the tracking and hunting and know where the game is likely to be found. The visitors will be so pleased when they kill something they will be generous to the trackers. *You* don't have to be. The coons will do their damnedest for the Americans because they know they'll be well paid for it. Try to get them always to come out together so that there will be several guns blazing away. Since they all carry the finest rifles that money can buy, they are pretty sure to kill without any help from you. You'll be gaining experience all the time, and naturally will always talk big about the experience you've had. It's easy."

What do you think of that? Maybe you'll say I've rather overdone it. I wish for your own sake I had.

This racket was so bad back during the twenties and thirties that a self-styled East African White Hunters' Association was formed with the entirely laudable intention of putting a stop to it. Before a man could advertise himself a professional hunter he had to satisfy the association that he was a member and was a safe and reliable person to take inexperienced sportsmen around. But in a place like Kenya, where you are nobody unless you've a handle to your name or stick a captain or major or colonel or something in front of it, the association's first high-sounding principles soon fell off. Men who couldn't or wouldn't be bothered with titles and ranks to which they weren't entitled were not wanted, no matter how fine they were as hunters, while others were welcomed irrespective of their hunting ability.

I think the association is now defunct. But the very fact that it was deemed necessary to form it may show you that I've not been exaggerating.

Don't use cheap rifles or ammunition.

Don't fire both barrels of a double rifle simultaneously. That may sound like an insult to your intelligence but just take note of the number of times you will see "he curled two fingers around his triggers" in some book or other.

Don't believe all you hear or read by those who are obviously catering to the lovers of thrills.

Don't use an automatic safety on a double rifle. This is a vitally important rule, hence the italics. For the benefit of readers unfamiliar with firearms I shall try to explain. Most men are unfamiliar with such devices since the average safety catch on the average rifle does not lock automatically. (It is only the double-barreled rifle which is ever fitted with such a catch.) Therefore, in the excitement of facing a charging animal, it is all too easy for the hunter to overlook the unaccustomed automatic safety. After reloading his rifle he might forget to move the catch forward, would find himself unable to fire, and by the time he had remembered what was wrong and rectified matters it would probably be too late to do anything. That is why I advise a safety catch that is not automatic—and the automatic sort can easily be converted.

3

A DIFFERENT
KIND OF GAME

13: NON-DANGEROUS ANIMALS

Although the elephant hunter (poacher or otherwise) naturally concentrates on the big fellows, since he generally has many mouths to fill he must from time to time shoot for the pot—particularly when he's trekking from one district to another. Whenever possible I shoot buffalo for my men, not only because of the quantity of meat they provide, but also because they can hit back. However, there are districts where there are no buffalo to be had and in those localities one has to shoot non-dangerous animals. Once upon a time I used to despise this kind of hunting, looking on it—very foolishly—as beneath a hunter of elephant. It was just a necessary chore to be got through as speedily as possible. It was the use of really suitable rifles for the job that opened my eyes to its possibilities and made me realize what fine sport it was.

GIRAFFE are the biggest of the nondangerous game. When you first encounter them your eye is naturally absorbed by their height and incredibly long necks. A mature bull will stand better than seventeen feet from the ground to the top of his almost air-borne head. It's only when you get one down that you appreciate the immense size of his quarters— truly gigantic. Owing to the giraffe's height, and the fact that he relies upon his eyes to warn him of danger (and at least one if not several of the troop will be perpetually gazing, gazing, ever gazing), some very pretty stalking is usually called for before you can get within what I call comfortable range of the animals. Other game relax their own precautions almost entirely if there are giraffe close by: they are satisfied that no danger can approach without those long-necked sentries' spotting it. This is especially noticeable around a water hole. Normally the different species take a long while to work up enough courage to approach water, as they know it's a favorite place for a lion to be lying in wait. But if there are giraffe around the water the other species will approach quite unconcernedly, without hesitation.

It takes a giraffe a long time to get his drink because he has to stretch his forelegs wide apart so as to reach down to the water, and then sort of crouch by bending his hocks. He stays down a good while and has a long, long drink since he knows there is no danger in the immediate vicinity—he took darn good care of that before lowering his head. After a spell to get his breath, he may go down for a second long draught. I cannot remember ever seeing more than one giraffe drinking at the same time. They politely wait for one another to finish. Possibly others who have sat over water holes with their cameras watching the giraffe for longer spells could tell a different tale; I can only say what I've seen myself.

I don't think you are likely to get permission to shoot giraffe anywhere in Africa nowadays. They are very strictly protected. They do no damage —now that the telegraph companies have bowed to necessity and fitted much taller poles throughout giraffe country, since the game department informed them they could not find means of shortening giraffes' necks. Incidentally, giraffe are said to be the only animals that can't make a sound of any sort. Or perhaps I should say that this is the notion that has been current almost since the first one was seen. But if you are very close you *will* occasionally hear a very soft call that can come only from a giraffe's throat—that is, if there is nothing else around. I've heard it on a couple of occasions, and Percival mentions hearing a similar softly made sound. Furthermore, there was a letter in the British *Field* some years ago in which a close observer stated he also had heard some sound which he had to attribute to giraffe.

If you can persuade some museum that it badly needs a new specimen, then you *may* be able to wangle a special governor's permit to shoot one of these weird creatures. But don't try it with a small-bore. And see to it that the bullet is one that won't break up too soon. A giraffe is far more heavily boned than you might imagine. And talking about bones—oh boy, wait till you get those marrowbones of his on a dish in front of you! You'll need a dish, not a mere plate. The flesh of a mature bull is too coarse and strong for the average white; but there's nothing wrong with the marrowbones—unless their owner was a patriarch, for the marrowbones of a very old specimen close up almost entirely and you may not get more than a pencil-sized strip of marrow.

By the way: if you're shooting a museum specimen it will cause your men some grief. They value giraffe hide above everything for sandals— even above buffalo hide. It seems to be tougher and better wearing.

I haven't shot many giraffe. But there were times when, trekking from one district to another on poaching raids, I needed meat for my men and there were no buffalo in the vicinity. Then, if I encountered giraffe, one of them would have to serve. I remember one that I shot with a soft-nose split bullet from a .465 at a range of about a hundred and twenty paces. He was knocked backward onto his bottom and just rolled over and died. His heart was blown to rags—and a giraffe's heart is a pretty big organ.

In some parts favored by giraffe there is little cover except for low bushes which afford the hunter small concealment from the tall creatures; but there are other parts with quite good clumps of bush containing tall trees. These make a close approach much simpler. However, you need to have your eyes very much about you. Almost invariably there will be one beast gazing steadily at you over the *top* of some tree. You must remember this and search the tops of the trees and not merely under them as you would with other game.

During World War II, at least during the early stages of it, long convoys of trucks and troop carriers drove north and south through East Africa, passing through the northwestern fringe of the southern game reserve in Kenya and so into Tanganyika. There was one stretch along there, north of Arusha in Tanganyika, in which the giraffe were very numerous and became very tame. They became so much accustomed to cars that they disdained to stampede and just stood there gazing at the long convoys in mild curiosity. From behind some of the larger clumps of bush they even developed a habit of playing that infuriating game beloved of domestic fowl: "Last Across the Road." In the case of giraffe, however, it was the motorist who was in danger.

Incidentally, native women in Africa are as bad as hens in this respect. If you are motoring and there are women walking along the side of the road in front of you, with baskets and such on their heads, when you sound your horn they will invariably grab at their bundles and make a dive for the opposite side of the road. It does not matter on which side they may be, as soon as they hear you the opposite side appears irresistibly attractive. They never dream of looking to see how close you may be—there is just a sudden wild rush and scramble. The men are better in this respect; they will at least look around first.

ELAND are the biggest of all antelope. A full-grown male will run from fifteen hundredweight to close to a ton on the hoof. I'm not sure that a really big bull would not turn the scale at a full ton. They are huge creatures, and normally as inoffensive as giraffe. Time and again I've seen one brought down, and dying, just turn his head away when the man closed in to cut his throat. Other beasts will swing their heads and horns and put up some sort of fight; but I've never seen an eland do so. Yet such is their strength and weight that if they did get in a thrust with those horns of theirs no man would last a second. Exceptions to this rule *do* sometimes occur. Percival mentions one occasion on which he was charged by an eland he'd wounded when he closed in to finish it off. The attack was so utterly unexpected that he and his pony were nearly caught. Blunt also mentions some fellow's being treed by a wounded eland. So you see, it doesn't do to make dogmatic statements about wild animals. Nevertheless, such attacks by the great buck are very, very rare.

Although the eland doesn't usually put up a fight once he's down that doesn't mean you will do all right with some pet .22-caliber rifle when you are out after him. The eland has the characteristic toughness of all African game. You can riddle him and still lose him. He puts up plenty of fight against going down—it's only after he's down that he cries enough. Moreover, eland are always on the alert, especially if they have the slightest suspicion of danger. And they seem to remain suspicious and take longer to settle down again after alarm than do lesser critters. For this reason, your average shots at eland will be a mite longer than at other of the commoner species. By this adjective I don't mean that eland are as common as lesser kudu or waterbuck, for instance. But there are some districts in which they are quite numerous, wandering around in troops of from ten or twelve to forty or fifty or even more. And if they get a taste for cotton bolls or learn to chew tobacco they become something of a nuisance. (By the way, elephant also get a taste for tobacco and soon make a mess of some unfortunate native's little plot, as they will return night after night for a chew.)

The eland pace is the trot. They, particularly the cows, can keep up a long swinging trot for many miles. They like the more open types of bush and forest, with plenty of clear spaces and short grass. If they've stampeded from you, either because you've fired or they have winded you, you might as well give them best for that day. No matter how hard you try, you will be very, very lucky if you get another chance. You may make long detours to try to get across wind from them—they usually clear off downwind—and then stalk most carefully to where you are sure they must be, only to find they aren't there at all but are some distance away interestedly watching you all the time. Their alertness and the open bush they favor means that there are keen eyes looking in all directions all the time. It's not so difficult for your first shot or two, provided you were hunting with your eyes open so that you spotted them before they spotted you. Of course, if you are well off the usual safari tracks, the eland, like all other species, will offer easy shots, not having yet learned that man is inimical. But it doesn't take the big fellows long to learn their lesson. Moreover, they seem to have a better memory than most other species of buck. I remember hunting a herd one time, a big herd that must have numbered over sixty head. I knew for a fact that no other hunter had worked that district for at least ten years—and that fellow had been there for a very few weeks, not more than five at the most (though he must have shot up this herd on at least one occasion). Anyway, I spotted them when they were about a hundred and seventy yards away and immediately started to close in. Had I known what was in store I would have opened fire right away; but I was freshly come to the place and hadn't as yet tackled this herd, so naturally I assumed I'd have no particular difficulty in getting a good deal closer. I moved slightly to one side so as to get a clump of bush between me and the herd, and then started stalking. I naturally made no attempt to keep them in view (do I need to suggest to you that you must not keep your eyes on your quarry when actually stalking? They seem to sense you even more easily than you will sense somebody staring at you in a hotel lounge—and how often you have suddenly turned around and found a stranger staring at you). I made a good stalk; but there was no herd there when I cautiously peered through a bush at the fringe of the clump behind which I'd approached. Still, I'd hunted plenty of eland before so, running at a crouch in order to keep my head down, I made for another clump of bush across wind and very carefully parted the branches to enable me to see through. Sure enough, there were the eland fully two hundred yards away. The majority of them seemed to be quite unconcerned, but there were two or three gazing back over the way they'd come. They weren't looking toward me, but toward where I'd left my men. They must have spotted some slight movement back there where we'd first spotted them, and that had been enough. Although I might have risked a shot now I knew they were on the alert; and even as I brought forward my rifle they wheeled around and broke into their long swinging trot. I let them go, gave them an hour in which to settle down, and then started after them again. But it was no use. When I sighted them, they sighted me at the same instant. Just one look they gave me, at about two hundred and fifty yards, and made for the next county. (No, we don't have counties out here.) Several times I sighted them during the next couple of months, but they never gave me a chance until I was about to leave the district—and then I got among them by means of a trick.

Some natives who had been out looking for wild honey reported they'd sighted the herd and offered to guide me to it. When we were within about half a mile of the herd we halted and I had a conference with my gunbearer. I decided to make my way around alone to the far side of the place indicated, leaving my gunbearer here with the guides and my revolver. He was to give me plenty of time to get into position and was then to fire a shot or two—better, two or three—and then come straight across to where I was supposed to be. Since I was the only hunter in the district I hoped those eland would figure that the shooter was me and would have their attention directed toward their rear when they moved off, as they certainly would when they heard the shots. I calculated that their looking behind them would give me the chance I wanted since I would be either down- or acrosswind from them as they came (their habit was to retreat downwind). It worked nicely. I'd seen no sign of anything when getting into position, nor for some considerable time afterward. Then there came three shots from a sixgun. For a little while nothing happened; then I saw several eland coming toward me to pass about forty to fifty yards upwind of where I was squatting behind a little bush close to the foot of a tree. They weren't running, but coming at a good fast walk. They would have known that the shots had not been fired at them, had been much too far away, but thought it advisable to make for a healthier locality. More and more of them came into view, until I had the whole herd in sight. As is usual with eland, the biggest bull was acting as rear-guard. Later on he would doubtless go to the head and act as leader, but with danger in the offing somewhere in the rear his place was back there. The whole herd halted when they were some forty to sixty yards away and swung around to look back the way they'd come. I took a long shot past the main body of the herd to drop that mighty bull and then drove my left barrel through the shoulder of another big fellow about thirty paces closer. The first bull received the shot behind his right shoulder. The bullet raked forward slightly to pass through his heart and come up against the inside of his opposite shoulder. He lurched badly, but just didn't fall. He then staggered around drunkenly for a few moments before going down. The second one dropped stone-dead in his tracks on receiving the bullet.

Big old bulls, when you get them on their own, are comparatively easy money. They are so fat that they almost waddle, and an agile man can run them down easily. The flesh of the eland is excellent, even from a big bull, and you cannot get better cooking fat. The marrowbones are delicious. But the hump is my choice—hot or cold. There's nothing like it in the African bushveld. By the way: except for the buffalo, eland are about the only animals on the veld that carry fat worth speaking about. An occasional old elephant bull will have fat; and, of course, hippo. But their fat is essentially used for cooking. If you're fond of bread and drippings, spread eland and buffalo drippings thickly on your bread. As a matter of fact, when we've shot large numbers of buffalo my cookboy renders down a batch of marrow fat so that I can eat it that way, like butter.

In spite of his bulk, which does not promise athletic ability, the eland's agility is remarkable. If you hit one somewhere behind the shoulder it will often leap straight up into the air for four and a half to five feet before clearing off. They have been known to clear five-foot fences in the most matter-of-fact way. Most game make a tremendous job of getting through a fence, or under it; but the eland, led by a big bull, take just one look at the top strand, lollop gently along, rise easily, and clear the top with inches to spare, one after the other in single file. Nothing looks easier: they seem just to take it in stride.

There are two varieties of eland, the ordinary and the tufted. Unless I'm mistaken, the latter is also known as Lord Derby's eland—though it may be that the photograph I saw of a fine tufted specimen with the caption "Lord Derby's Eland" was merely a fine specimen shot by Lord Derby. At any rate, this variety has a thick tuft of black hair growing on top of his head between the butts of his horns. Each time I shoot a big bull of either kind I feel certain his particular variety is the bigger. Actually, they are both huge.

At certain seasons mature bulls shed their hair, like the greater kudu bull, which gives them the peculiar blue-gray appearance of a freshly clipped horse. The tufted fellow, however, retains his characteristic tuft.

Eland are very easily tamed, and it seems extraordinary that only halfhearted attempts have been made to domesticate them. Their weight, strength, and docility are such that they would be most useful for farm work, while a pair of cows (bearing in mind their long tireless trot) would make a splendid team for a buggy. Another point in their favor is that, like goats, they are always in good condition since they browse as well as graze. Moreover, tsetse flies, the bane and killers of all domestic animals, don't affect the eland.

The OKAPI and BONGO, though entirely different species, have very similar habits in that they both like dense forest and bush—or perhaps I should say heavy forest with plenty of undergrowth. The okapi is a denizen of the great Ituri forest system in the Congo; the bongo is found in the forests of Kenya. For a long time the okapi was considered a myth, as well he might be: he looks like a cross between a giraffe and a mule. That is to say, he has a disproportionately long neck and small stubs instead of real horns, while his hindquarters are somewhat mulelike in shape though with lateral white stripes. He's one of the few species I've never shot; and this applies also to the bongo. This fellow's looks are somewhere between those of a lesser kudu and a bushbuck. (For descriptions see later on in this chapter.) We don't get him around my part of the country. He likes higher altitudes than I do.

ORYX are, so far as I know, rarely seen south of the Equator. They're the fellows with the long, thin, straight horns. They are quite plentiful in the northern frontier province of Kenya. Like the big Grevy ZEBRA, among which they're found, they like open dry country. These biggest of all zebra are also dwellers in the equatorial belt and seem to prefer the northern side of the line. From what I know of it there's little real sport in the hunting of either of these animals, and I don't care for their very open country for hunting. I prefer the bushveld in which so much of my life has been spent. To me it seems to afford infinitely finer sport.

WILDEBEEST are a queer-looking breed with horns not unlike those of a buffalo cow, long faces like HARTEBEEST (see below), black manes, shoulders resembling those of a buffalo, and hindquarters like a mule's. They are found in countless thousands on the open plains in Kenya and Tanganyika. During some of their seasonal migrations they will steadily pass a given spot, day and night, for several days, in hundreds of thousands. They're about the size of a good mule. They have been known to attack quite savagely if wounded—the hunter should not close in too carelessly to finish them off. If you have a good rifle they're not difficult to kill. As with any other beast, drive your bullet through the shoulder and you'll have no further trouble. Wildebeest post sentries around the herd when they're grazing and relieve one another at intervals. Those sentries do their stuff, too.

HARTEBEEST, the *kongoni* of East Africa, are also incredibly numerous on the great open plains of Kenya and Tanganyika. They too set sentries, keep decidedly on the alert during their tour of duty. However, there are times when they fall from grace and the careful hunter can sneak up within easy range of the main body of the herd. (After he has opened fire and the first stampede is over it needs little imagination to picture the indignation with which the others berate the erring sentry!) There are numerous varieties of hartebeest in Africa. I don't pretend to be able to distinguish them all. But there's no getting away from that characteristic long, thin, very foolish-looking face. However, they are by no means all fools. Those I've just been speaking about certainly aren't. But there's another variety which is mostly found in groups of about half a dozen and seems to prefer fairly open, lightly bushed veld to the open plains; and they are the most abject idiots. If you drop one of them in its tracks, as you should endeavor to drop every animal at which you fire, his companions will just cluster around and look at him. It doesn't seem to occur to them

hat there's danger in the offing and they'd better clear. You could wipe
»ut the entire party if you wanted to.

All hartebeest are good eating, but they carry disappointingly little
meat if you're shooting for your men. Their quite disproportionately long
aces tend to catch your eye and deceive you into thinking they're much
»igger than they really are.

The HUNTER'S ANTELOPE, found, so far as I know, only within about
hree miles of the Tana River in Kenya, is a small variety of hartebeest
iaving horns much longer and less tightly crumpled than those usually
issociated with hartebeest. He's a solitary animal.

Hartebeest all seem to be a bit crazy, like hens. They will be standing
loing nothing, gazing blankly into infinity, and then suddenly without the
lightest warning will put down their heads, throw up their tails, and go
;alloping clumsily around in a circle. Equally suddenly they will pull up
.gain and stand gawking at one another with those long foolish faces,
.or all the world as though asking, "What the heck?" Because of the way
hey shake their heads during these gyrations, the natives say it's maggots
»iting them that set them off. (Practically all hartebeest carry fat white
naggots somewhere up inside their heads, which come out of their
iostrils when they're dead.) Maybe the maggots are a contributing factor,
»ut it must not be forgotten that most elephant also have maggots inside
heir heads which can be seen coming out of the trunks after death. And
 can't remember ever seeing elephant acting in the crazy way hartebeest
lo.

The hartebeest is very thin-skinned and lightly boned and, I think,
.ather more easily killed than the general run of African game. That,
iowever, doesn't excuse your using little featherweight copper-pointed
»ullets on him. I simply can't understand the mania there has always been
n British Africa for these totally unsuitable slugs: they are responsible
.or an immense number of wounded animals' getting away, possibly to
lie miserably days later, or, even worse, to be pulled down and literally
:aten alive by hyenas and other varmits which would be unable to kill
hem otherwise. I consider such shooting the very essence of unsportsman-
ike behavior.

The GREATER KUDU is a coveted trophy. His magnificent corkscrew-shaped
iorns make any sportsman's mouth water. He's a big beast, far bigger than
.ny of the other buck except eland. He's very rare in Kenya, where most
risiting sportsmen go, and takes a lot of hard hunting there as he is
rery much on the alert. But in Portuguese East Africa he's by no means

so uncommon and is comparatively easy to bag—provided you know where to look for him. The bulls and cows separate for the greater part of the year, and you will sometimes find four or five of the magnificent males together. In my experience, they aren't usually on the alert, at least in this country, when they are without their harems. Moreover, if there are just two or three of them and you drop one, the others (as happens with most parties of males) will stampede a short distance and then pull up for a backward look to see what's happening. This generally brings them broadside-on to you and so gives you a excellent chance for your second barrel. I'm a firm believer in the double-barrel rifle for this kind of big game hunting.

I've never known a kudu to attack, wounded or unwounded, but be very careful of those horns of his when you close in. If you were to get one of those four-and-a-half- or five-foot corkscrews through you it would do more than unsettle your digestion.

SABLE ANTELOPE are among the finest looking of Africa's game. When young, they are red, with characteristic white belly and white markings on the face. The cows remain like that, but as the bulls reach maturity they gradually turn black where they have been red. Their magnificent scimitar-shaped horns sweep back over their withers and give them a superbly proud look, particularly when they adopt their favorite attitude: forefeet on some slight rise and hind feet stretched out behind, tail slightly raised. They look for all the world like prize hackney or trotting ponies posed to be photographed or to catch the judge's eye in the show ring. They like open forest with plenty of clear patches and not much in the way of scrub or bush. The youngsters are very lively, and you will see them galloping at speed, fifteen or twenty of them, in single file around and around in a circle, in the center of which their elders are feeding. On account of the undulating country they favor you will usually get your shot at about seventy yards. The big old bulls are usually alone; but you will not infrequently encounter perhaps four or five of them together. These, however, will not be the really big ones.

Sable seem to like altitudes of between two thousand and four thousand feet. (Possibly this varies in different latitudes.) You don't usually find them in the low veld in the tropics, though you will find them much lower down than their cousins the ROAN ANTELOPE. I've shot sable at little more than three hundred feet above sea level but have never yet seen the roan lower than about two thousand to twenty-five hundred feet. The roan, as their name implies, are strawberry roan in color. Their horns are shaped much like the sable's but are not nearly so long. The roan is heavier than the sable and very sturdy. He likes the light open forest with plenty of clear places and *dambos* such as you find in the high veld.

But where you may encounter as many as two or three dozen sable together (such a troop will almost always have a number of youngsters in it), the roan seem to be much more solitary. I've never seen a large party of them. They are numerous, for all that. There are some parts known to me where you will find one or two in every *dambo* you come to, and others along the fringes of the light forest between.

Sable are excellent eating, about the best of the antelope next to eland. That is not the case with the roan. They seem to be almost poisonous to some men. I once ate roan and suffered badly afterward, but as I soon came down with dysentery it may have been the onset of that which was responsible. When I ate roan again it may have been my imagination but certainly didn't enjoy it and ever afterward tried to get something else to fill my own pot. Needless to say, the African wallops into it with relish.

But sable, as I say, can be strongly recommended.

WATERBUCK are among the commonest game in Africa. Wherever you get water in any quantity, there you will almost certainly find them. There are two general types, the common one and Crawshay's, much less widely distributed. The principal difference between the two is that the common variety has a white ring around his buttocks while Crawshay's has a white patch on his rump. Otherwise there's little to distinguish between them.

The waterbuck is strong, tough, and is covered with long coarse hair which smells as though he'd spent his life in a public urinal without bathing. He's a powerful swimmer and takes readily to water if it happens to lie across his path when he is hunted. I suppose most beginners in Central Africa start their shooting career on waterbuck and lesser kudu.

As a table beast the waterbuck can only be described as foul. His flesh is coarse and tough and strongly flavored, but by far the most objectionable feature is his fat. He doesn't carry much but that little is quite sufficient to put any normal man off eating him. Although it may seem all right on your plate the instant you get it into your mouth it congeals and sticks in the most unpleasant and determined way to your teeth and the roof of your mouth. It takes a lot of removing. Hot tea is probably the easiest method, but the flavor of the tea is not improved. My advice is to leave the waterbuck alone unless you are really hungry and have nothing else to eat.

Although the waterbuck cannot be recommended as food he can most certainly be classed as a good game animal. There are times when he offers some very pretty stalking. But use a bullet of generous weight: he can

take a lot of punishment and if he gets into long grass—there's usuall'
plenty of that around his haunts—you'll have your work cut out to finisl
him off.

Waterbuck are very numerous throughout Central Africa. They seen
to be everywhere and are the great stand-by for your men's pots. Sure, the
men would appreciate something else if they had any choice, but yo'
won't find the African turning his nose up at anything in the meat line. Be
sides, most of it will go in trade to the local natives for meal and they nor
mally get so little meat that they will jump at anything. Unless there's a'
absolute famine in the district you'll never go short of meal for your me'
so long as you've a shell left for any of your rifles and any meat into
which to drive the bullet.

Waterbuck are usually found in small parties consisting of perhap
six to a dozen, with several old bulls on their own somewhere in the vicinity; but you also find them in quite sizable herds in certain districts where
conditions are favorable. There may be anywhere from fifty to perhaps on'
hundred fifty in such herds.

For the shooting of all these general African game animals, and the
ranges at which they're usually shot, there's no need to think in terms oi
high velocity—which can only be obtained at the expense of bullet weight
You will get better results from a bullet of generous weight driven a'
moderate speed. Such bullets are far more reliable in their action, don'
break up, and have much deeper penetration. It's all wrong to use light
high-speed bullets for these species. I can give you an example: I was
using a copper-pointed bullet of the kind that expands very rapidly. I
wanted to see for myself exactly how it behaved. I got a shot at a waterbuck bull at about forty yards' range. It wasn't an easy shot owing to the
length of the grass, which practically concealed him. But I was able to
see his horns and the general outline of his back. I let drive for the spo'
I figured his shoulder must be, and he dropped instantly. Quite sure I had
killed him, I descended the anthill from which I had fired and started toward him. My men rushed ahead of me, so when the brute suddenly scrambled to his feet and made off I was unable to get a shot; besides, I was
too low to see him properly. There was plenty of excuse for my men because for a long time past I had been using such perfect weapons and bullets that if I fired at all they knew there would be meat for them. It took
me a full hour to get another shot at this bull, and I used another rifle
for the job. I then found that the copper-pointed bullet thrown by the first
rifle must have touched something like a dead twig, which started it opening just before it hit the buck. The twig was probably no thicker than
your little finger and was hidden in the grass, so I could be excused for
not seeing it. The point is that the bullet hit the buck at a slight angle,

opened up instantly, and instead of driving straight in through the shoulder glanced along it and then down along his ribs. (He hadn't been quite broadside-on to me.) It had pretty well opened up his entire side, and I found minute particles of the envelope scattered throughout his innards, and tiny shreds of the lead core. There wasn't a single bit the size of the head of a match.

I had a somewhat similar experience when using another rifle some time afterward, and another of those wretched copper-pointed bullets. I hadn't had the slightest intention of using it on waterbuck when I started out: I had hoped to knock over a couple of reedbuck, for which it would have been satisfactory. However, game was scarce and wild, having been much shot up by men who were apparently content merely to wound, and when a waterbuck bull offered himself at about a forty-yard range I fired, placing my bullet well up on his hip as he was quartering away from me. When he dropped I naturally imagined I'd broken his hip and spine—a decent bullet would have done so. But his hip and spine weren't broken. When I eventually managed to kill him I found that the bullet had simply disintegrated. It had opened up on the hip, skidded along the sloping bone—causing a dreadful surface wound and blowing all the meat off the hip—and had then blown itself to pieces against the spine, causing an appalling mess of shredded meat over an extent of perhaps nine or ten inches. I certainly felt sorry for that wretched buck and vowed I'd never again find myself loaded with *any* copper-pointed high-velocity bullets if there were the slightest chance of encountering an animal bigger than a goat.

LESSER KUDU must be just as common as waterbuck if not even more. You find them around nearly all old native lands. They seem to like to be in close proximity to human dwellings and gardens. They're apt to be an infernal nuisance if you're trying to raise a few precious vegetables, and the natives complain they eat all the bolls of their cotton. The bulls have corkscrew-shaped horns like those of the greater kudu but, naturally, smaller. I know several districts in which both varieties are plentiful, but they don't mix. The lordly big fellow seems to look down his nose at his smaller relatives as he stalks grandly past. The smaller variety actually seem to have a look of envy as they gaze at the great horns and shaggy manes of the big fellows.

Both varieties are excellent eating, with dark meat and a rich fine flavor.

Next to the howl of the hyena and, in certain districts, the bark of the bushbuck, the gruff bark of the lesser kudu bull is one of the commonest sounds in the African bushveld: almost ubiquitous. By far the best time to hunt for them (around the nearest old native lands) is between daybreak and sunup and maybe again shortly before sundown and between then and dark. If there are any about you'll be unlucky if you don't spot them; and provided they haven't been shot up too badly recently you ought to be able to get a by-no-means difficult shot. You need to use a fair measure of caution during your stalk, especially if there are cows among them—the bulls seem so pleased with their appearance that they are not normally as much on the alert as the cows.

Americans, I think, would find this hunting pleasant. There are not swarms of other hunters around scaring the game. Indeed, you may hunt not merely for weeks or months but literally for years, if you choose, without seeing another hunter or hearing a gun fired. Probably millions of African game animals have never heard a rifle in the whole course of their lives. Moreover, the local tribesmen know exactly where the different species of their own districts are likely to be and will willingly guide you there in return for a feed of meat. (It's they who really do the hunting for you until you gain experience and knowledge of the districts and localities and types of bush favored by different species.) They will take you through the bush by the easiest ways, lead you up to the game, and then point toward them before slipping behind you out of the way. The rest is up to you. If you only wound, it's they again who will do most of the spooring until you get your chance to finish off the animal. You'll find it easy.

I've frequently had occasion to remark how strange it is that when wild animals are captured and tamed they seem to lose all fear of man and become friendlier and more intimate than domestic beasts—with the exception of dogs, cats, and, very occasionally, horses. Prior to the advent of the automobile there used to be many tame buck and antelope wandering around the township of Tete on the Zambezi. There were a couple of big eland bulls; a number of lesser kudu, bulls and cows; and several smaller buck. The eland and kudu, particularly the latter, would without fail take a stroll right along the main street every morning and evening during the hours when they knew the populace would be sitting, continental fashion, at little tables on the sidewalk or on the open verandas just back from the sidewalks, drinking beer and wine and enjoying little snacks with their drinks. The kudu and the majestic eland would come stepping daintily up to each table in turn and greet the people sitting there. They were exceptionally good mannered. They did not make a nuisance of themselves. If you had some bit of food and handed it to them, they would lip it daintily out of your fingers, nuzzle you in thanks, and then move on to someone else. They never stood begging too long, they never asked you for a second helping, and if you gave something to one, he others did not come pestering you—they moved on to someone else or o a different table. They were a most attractive feature of life in an otherwise rather unattractive place. They *never* attempted to help themselves rom an unoccupied table. The big eland bulls were inclined to be a mite standoffish from time to time, but the kudu were always friendly and liked you to make much of them and scratch them behind the ears.

There was a fellow down-river who had a mighty buffalo bull which he had captured years before when it was a youngster; and it was quite a sight to see the little pickaninny who looked after him scrambling up on his back and twisting his tail to make him walk faster. I declare that great bull loved his little keeper: when the boy came to look for him sometimes, and called him, he would low softly in welcome and come walking o meet him. The child was very proud of his magnificent charge and used o send the big bull almost into ecstasies by rubbing him behind the ears.

LECHWE and SITATUNGA are quite different creatures although I bracket them together. I do so because they're always associated in one's mind if one has ever hunted around the swamps of Lake Bangweulu in Northern Rhodesia. I expect they're found elsewhere too, but that's the only place I ever saw them, and it's undoubtedly *the* place for them. Lechwe, judging from their habitat, must belong to the waterbuck family; but they're lighter and much prettier and more graceful, and they don't have the long coarse hair of the waterbuck. There are said to be two varieties of lechwe, the red and the black, but I sometimes wonder if the darkening of the latter isn't due to age, as in the case of the sable antelope. Lechwe are found in immense numbers around Lake Bangweulu, and if you wanted to you could doubtless make a big bag with an aperture- or scope-sighted magazine rifle: as with so many kinds of buck found in large herds, they seem to lose their heads completely when several quick shots have been fired close to them. They run helter-skelter in all directions without apparent aim, just blindly dashing around. It frequently takes them quite a while to make up their minds to get to hell out of it. I never shot more than two or three at a sitting but could have dropped many more. The sitatunga live actually in the sudd of the swamps and can be called semi-amphibious. To enable them to get along over the sudd their hooves grow out to an enormous extent—I've seen them nearly nine inches long—and turn up in front. This prevents their feet from sinking through. It's quite hopeless to attempt to hunt them in the sudd. As you try to get along in it you'll find it billows up into great waves in front of you and when you endeavor to scramble over that it sinks until you find yourself waist-deep in water with the wave now behind you and another of equal height in front of you. You can do nothing. The going is so difficult and noisy that you will rarely be able to get any closer than you were when you first spotted the sitatunga. The only way to get a shot at them is to be out on the firmer ground around the edge of the swamp at first crack of dawn in the hope that you might sight them feeding. There will be no cover at all —you'll just have to shoot from wherever you happen to be. Because of the bad light and the mist that almost always rises from the swamps at this hour you will find a low-powered scope sight a real help.

You won't make a big bag of sitatunga. I've only once or twice seen a head hanging on some fellow's wall, and know several keen hunters who have tried in vain to bag one. The going is generally considered too tough. You have to be really keen to stick at it long enough to ensure success. I've shot only two myself; but then, as a tent-dweller I'm not looking for trophies. I just wanted to be able to say I'd succeeded in bagging one of the weird creatures that had defeated so many men, and see for myself if it were really as difficult as I'd heard. Well, I can assure you it isn't easy.

The SASSABY, closely related to the hartebeest, has somewhat similar, small crumpled horns and is much the same size though darker in color. He is frequently mentioned in the books of old-timers writing mostly about southern Africa; but I doubt if you'll see many nowadays. Sassaby must have been common in South Africa before the Boers got busy with their Martinis and Mausers and, in their customary way, blotted out everything they could reach on horseback. I've a notion that there are just a few still left in Northern Rhodesia. I was returning from an elephant-poaching raid one time, and way across an open plain I spotted what I instantly put down as a sassaby. But he was a long way off, and since I had a considerable string of porters all laden with ivory I didn't feel like delaying long enough to make sure. Had I been mounted, well and good; but I was, of course, on foot. However, if that was indeed a sassaby then there must have been more of them somewhere.

The sassaby had the name of being the fastest of all antelope in Africa, if not in the world.

Of the smaller buck that the hunter usually shoots for his own pot— which, of course, means the pots also of his cookboy and personal staff and, if he's a decent fellow, his gunbearers—the REEDBUCK is the biggest and many men say the best and tastiest. He's true venison. As his name implies, he spends his life in the reeds and tough longish grass of the *dambos*. Not the ten- to twelve-foot elephant grass, but the stuff that grows in wetter places and mostly runs from three to four feet or thereabouts. Hunting him isn't difficult, but the shot frequently is. When the

edbuck stampede they almost always loose a shrill whistle, presumably
a warning, sometimes repeated several times. There has been considerable
controversy as to how this whistle is produced. Many men firmly believe
that it is somehow related to the little depressions the animal has high up
on the inside of his thighs. It's really extraordinary the notions that enter
some men's heads. The simplest explanation never seems to suffice; there
must be some more difficult answer. Personally I see no reason to suppose
that the reedbuck does not produce his whistle as any other animal produces his pet noise, either through mouth or nose or both combined. I've
never heard anyone suggest that the bushbuck produced his characteristic bark from any place but his mouth. At any rate, the whistle of the
reedbuck is well known, and many a man has used it to advantage, blowing a shrill whistle himself when the buck stampedes which frequently
causes the animal to stop and look back, giving the hunter a second shot.
I think I first read that in *Jock of the Bushveld* long before I set foot in
Africa, and I've used the trick many a time; but as I've never learned to
blow a shrill whistle from between my lips or teeth, as so many men and
all Africans can, I carry a referee's whistle and use that. Just the one short
sharp shrill blast. Although I have met many men who have practiced this
trick on reedbuck, curiously enough I've never heard of anyone's trying
it on other species—anyone else that is. But I've done so with the greatest
success on practically all species from elephant down, not excluding the
usually wary eland. So successful have I found it that right up to the present day I carry that whistle of mine on a thong around my neck. The
procedure is to let the game, whatever they may be, run twenty to thirty
yards after the first shot, and then blow just that one short sharp blast.
You will often find that they'll instantly pull up and look back, turning
broadside-on to you to do so. That is the chance for your left barrel, if
you've already spotted the beast you want. If they don't stop at the first
blast it's no use trying again; you can blow your head off and they'll take
no notice of you. Naturally this trick doesn't always work, even with reedbuck; but I've bagged many a second beast with the aid of my whistle
that I wouldn't have got without it. There are, of course, many times when
the game will pull up anyway and look back—and many more when
they won't. But even if your whistle doesn't trick them into doing so it
won't do any harm and is well worth trying; and provided you don't pro-
long the blast unduly, you can pretty well bet on success with it with
reedbuck. Your best plan is to listen to reedbuck themselves whistling and
try to imitate that. If you're camped anywhere near a *dambo* containing
the beasts you will often hear them whistling around sundown—and after,
if they happen to be disturbed by a leopard. That will give you all the
instruction you need.

Reedbuck generally live alone even though there may be quite a number in the *dambo*.

It's for all these smaller animals, from reedbuck down, that you'll get the best results from lighter bullets. All-too-many men shoot carelessly at these little fellows. Since the target is so much smaller than those they are accustomed to they should take even greater care to place their bullets accurately.

Reedbuck, owing to the grass they live in, are usually shot at under a hundred yards' range. Just occasionally, if the *dambo* has an appreciable dip in the center and you spot one of the buck on the far side of the dip, you may be called upon to take a somewhat longer shot. Normally their only enemies are leopard and occasional lion, so they are not unduly timid and you can usually take your time over the shot as they don't look for danger from any distance away.

You can have quite good sport shooting them with bow and arrows, though it depends entirely on the kind of *dambo* in which you find them whether or not you can get such a shot. The conditions sometimes make it impossible to come close enough without scaring them. A rifle is then called for.

BUSHBUCK, as their name implies, like dense bush and scrub jungles. They are generally smaller than the reedbuck and red in color with white spots. Their bark is heard at all hours of the day and night, but mostly during the morning and evening. They have been known to charge savagely when wounded and the hunter closes in carelessly to finish them off. They make good eating, being typical venison. In some areas they're very numerous, but they live solitary except during the mating season, when they may be found in pairs. You will rarely get a shot at one in daylight until the grass is burned off; then you may stalk carefully around during the early morning and late evening and spot them coming out for a feed.

Probably most bushbuck are killed with buckshot from a 12-bore at night with the aid of a flashlight or shooting lamp. There's absolutely no sport attached to such shooting, but it's a convenient way of keeping your pot filled if you've nothing to eat in camp. You'll find bushbuck in astonishing numbers around your camp at night. And, if you're trying to raise a few vegetables, you are entitled to discourage the little animals from raiding them.

I've known hunters who took only their elephant rifles out with them and relied entirely upon a long-chambered 12-bore to fill their pot. Naturally, they did this 12-bore shooting at night. The method is usually condemned by the thoughtless as sheer slaughter, but a little consideration will show that it isn't. The elephant hunter won't knock over more than one, or at the very most two, at a time. And since he'll be hunting mostly where there are no other hunters, and nobody at all to interfere with the little buck, and will seldom be spending more than a night or two in any one place, and probably won't be shooting for the pot more than once or twice a week, the number he kills will have no material effect on the population. Besides, if the small animals are to be shot for the pot anyway, does it matter in the least to them whether they're shot by day or by night? You have only to wander around after dark with a flashlight, after the grass has been burned off, to marvel at the numbers of these little buck there must be: whichever way you turn your light you will see their eyes. It's an easy way to collect fresh meat, and the elephant hunter gets all the walking any man in his right mind could want.

There's one thing about this method of shooting that's very much in its favor: that is, that unless you attempt quite needlessly to shoot at fantastic ranges, you should kill clean every time you squeeze your trigger—there should be no wounded beasts running around to die miserably. Night ranges generally run from fifteen to twenty-five yards. There is no need for snap shots—you can take your own time over aiming. The buck will stand gazing at the light, generally with only one eye, for a long time. You can walk up quietly as close as you like. If you keep quite still, the little fellow will recommence grazing and you may be not more than ten paces away. He'll nibble daintily at this and that, looking up occasionally at the light and wondering what it is. You could kill him with a handgun if you liked, but I always recommend the shotgun—you won't get as close to a leopard as you will to a small buck, but I've shot leopard at night with a shotgun and cannot remember ever having to fire a second shot.

IMPALA are, in my opinion, the most beautiful and graceful of all African game—always excepting the leopard. They are about the size of goats and are mostly found in more or less large parties in mopani* forest; they seem to consider the conditions ideal there. Where they aren't interfered with they become remarkably tame; and even if they are shot up occasionally they remain faithful to the same locality. Usually they offer very pretty stalking. The kind of forest they prefer has little or no grass in it but contains open spaces with just the kind of feeding they like. There will be small clumps of bush here and there, while the ground will be mostly undulating with flatter stretches in parts. You will see from this that the conditions are favorable for the hunter. Still, despite this and the

* The mopani is a tree which grows in very poor soil—i.e., on land unfit for cultivation. It has small leaves that turn as the sun moves across the heavens, so that at no time do they throw any shade to speak of.

animal's tameness, the impala is a buck, has mighty good eyes, and knows well how to use them.

Impala have some exquisite traits and some that can be described very differently. For instance, they seem to have a queer aversion to setting foot on a road: they much prefer to jump it. And it's a familiar sight to see a beautiful living arch of these little creatures sailing about six feet high over a motor road. They will be head to tail in single file, all in identical attitudes and all at exactly the same height—until occasionally a young buck, extra-full of energy, will soar up perhaps a couple of feet above the remainder of the arch. Their lovely soft fawn-colored hide glistens and gleams in the sun. And you will appreciate that if there are anything from eighty or ninety to a hundred and fifty or more in the party this lovely living arch is there in front of you for a considerable time. Impala, by the way, will often leap around, high over any bush or over nothing at all, when you fire. They seem to have powerful springs in their legs.

Another of their traits, as I say, is by no means so attractive to the hunter. They are apparently obsessed with the notion that they have been chosen by the gods to be everybody's sentries. If you are trying to stalk some wary eland or kudu, but especially eland, you will be driven almost crazy by the impala if there are any in the immediate vicinity. They can't let well enough alone, or merely clear off as they would normally do if you happened to be stalking them and let them spot you. They know perfectly well that you're after those big fellows and will come sweeping across your front, whistling and snorting and blowing, not more than fifty to eighty yards away, and then stop and stare in what can only be described as an impertinent manner. If you just continue your stalk pretending you haven't noticed them or don't care, they will sweep back across your front again and do it several times as you advance until they eventually sweep over the rise in front of you and stampede the game you were hoping to bag. How I've cursed them. Several times they've lost me what should have been an easy shot at eland.

And they're the cockiest little devils. I remember I was returning to camp one afternoon after a buffalo hunt. It was around three-thirty and raging hot. I'd been chasing the buff since shortly after daybreak—I left them when they literally flung themselves into the only water hole in the vicinity, instantly converting it into a wallow. They had been panting and foaming at the mouth and were obviously suffering badly from the heat and all that galloping around. Well, so were we. We'd been gulping in dust and ashes of burned grass all morning and I'm sure that had I tried to spit what I produced would have resembled a piece of dirty cotton wool. Many a time have I envied my Africans their apparently inexhaustible flow of saliva. Even on an occasion like this my gunbearer could eject a strong squirt of gin-clear saliva from between his teeth with a mere flick of his tongue. (I almost wished I had the courage to ask him to squirt it into my parched mouth instead of wasting it on the ground.) I was making for a small water hole I knew of a couple of miles away from where I'd left the buffalo, where I guessed we'd at least be able to rinse our mouths; and as we approached the water hole, which was in a bit of a dip slightly sheltered by bush, I saw a small troop of impala. They were staring intently toward it and didn't see us until we were quite close. That told me there was some big creature at the water. Suddenly one of them looked around and saw us. Instantly he snorted, his pals looked around and did the same, and then as we continued to advance toward them they scampered to one side, pulled up again when not more than forty yards away, and created a considerable noise. If they weren't warning us, then what did they think they were doing? I advanced quietly until I could see down into the watering place, and there, sure enough, were three lion, a male and two females, slaking their thirst. Those little impala weren't the least bit scared of the lion, but they felt they simply *had* to warn somebody or something. Our arrival must have been a god-send to them. No longer making any noise now that we'd seen the lion, those little impala watched in curiosity as we continued to the water—and then whistled and snorted their congratulations when they saw the three lion give us the right of way. The impala knew perfectly well that we weren't after them and showed not the least fear of us. The lion also seemed to know it, because I had allowed them to drink their fill before we approached too close, and they must have realized I'd been watching them for some time before they saw me. But on such a mad-hot day the denizens of the wild aren't looking for trouble and a peace zone seems to exist around all water holes. It's true there was a thick green scum full of dead bees and such on top of the water, but you could brush that aside or blow through it and the water underneath was quite clear, if, on this occasion, pretty near boiling. Still, it was wet, and that's all that mattered. One trains oneself to go without water in these very hot districts: it's much better so. The more water one drinks the more one needs and the more one suffers when it's finished. All I really wanted was to rinse out my mouth and allow just one swallow to go down and clear the dust out of my throat. As for my men: well, how could anyone with a flow of saliva like theirs know even the meaning of the word thirst? All I ever carry is a bottle of tea with plenty of sugar and condensed milk in it; and that one bottle of sweetened tea does me and my gunbearer better than a gallon container of water: it's far more refreshing and, thanks to the sugar, far more sustaining.

But the impala, although intensely annoying at times, are grand little things and make very fine eating. Their flesh is more delicate and juicy than that of most other small buck, and I generally try to pick one for my own pot in preference to other species.

Like so many of these little beasts, impala frequent the same spots for dunging purposes. You'll see large circular areas in the forest simply covered with their droppings, showing that they have gone there for a very long time.

There's another little animal you find in some parts which seems to live on the fringe of the localities favored by impala, but isn't nearly so widely distributed. He's called the PUKU. He's redder than the impala and a mite heavier but not nearly so good looking or graceful. Neither is he so numerous. I don't even pretend to know the names of all these small buck—there are many varieties scattered about throughout Africa, some purely local. I have visited one place, for instance, where there are two small buck of a kind I've never seen elsewhere and which for all I know to the contrary may be new to science. But I have made no study of kinds of buck and know only the commoner varieties.

The KLIPSPRINGER is a funny little fellow, *green* in color. He's the only buck I know of anywhere of such a color: his hair is definitely green, with black and white tips. His coat is coarse, and he sheds it with the greatest ease—if you grab a handful of it it comes away in your hand. The natives say that this is to cushion him when he falls, but I wonder if a klipspringer ever does fall except when shot. His sure-footedness is astonishing. As his name—rock jumper—implies, he lives on rocky *kopjes* and jumps from rock to rock when disturbed. He gives a plump, round effect due to the way he likes to stand with all four feet close together on a little knob of rock. He's found in pairs and alone; but I've never seen him in troops even though there may be a number of klipspringer on the same *kopje*. He can give nice stalking, but he's not nearly so difficult to approach as a mountain goat or sheep.

All these small buck make excellent biltong, the Boer's great stand-by (meat cut in strips, salted and peppered, and hung—preferably in the shade—to dry). It's easily made and, provided you keep it dry, will last for months when properly prepared. If you're on a forced march a strip of it—a piece no bigger than a fat cigar—will keep you going comfortably for twenty-four hours. Under such conditions you use it like chewing tobacco; it's wonderfully sustaining. But if you're trekking through dry country see to it that your biltong's not too salty!

DUIKER are very numerous throughout South Central Africa. They are about the size of Irish terriers, or perhaps a little bigger, and they live alone. It is said they never drink, getting what moisture they need from the dew. I can't corroborate or deny that; but if they *do* drink they must do a great deal of trekking at certain seasons because you will find them on dry stony *kopjes* far from the nearest water.

Probably more duiker are killed with the shotgun at night than any other species. Toward the end of the dry season, if you take a stroll around the native lands after the usual fires have been through them, you'll see duiker's eyes all over the place as you swing the beam of your flashlight around. By day they lie up in clumps of grass, and if you have a well-trained shooting dog you can get some pretty sport with a 12-bore loaded with buckshot. Duiker are considered by most men to be the best of the small buck for the pot, but I still prefer impala: I find the flesh of duiker on the dry side when cooked as most men cook it—though if you live on Eastern curries to the extent I do, it doesn't really matter much which meat forms the base of it.

The STEINBOK is one of the smallest we get in this country—a good bit smaller than the terrier-sized duiker. He's a little red fellow who lives alone and lies up in a tuft of grass until you practically kick him out of it. Then there's a scrambling rush from right under your feet and away he goes, jinking from side to side at what seems a tremendous speed. Here again you'll get good sport with a scatter-gun and a good dog. You'll rarely get a shot with a rifle, and if you do you'll probably miss it.

The little creatures make good eating.

THOMPSON'S and GRANT'S GAZELLES, better known as "Tommies" and "Granties," are common stand-bys for the hunter's own pot in British East Africa. They are about the same size as impala. Their horns and markings, however, are different, and they are less graceful and agile. Moreover, while the impala is uniformly a soft fawn color, except for lighter belly, the Granty has a fairly broad horizontal black stripe along his side; and the Tommy may be instantly indentified even at a distance because his tail is never still. The little buck are very numerous on the open plains; you see them everywhere, with or without impala mixed in with them. There's nothing much I can say about them that hasn't already been said of their various cousins. Your shots of them, owing to lack of cover, may be at slightly long ranges, but even in the open—provided you have the patience that's an essential requirement of every good hunter—you should seldom have to press trigger at much more than a hundred and fifty yards. Most men I've seen in action are much too impatient, in too great a hurry to shoot. Don't let game affect you that way.

The gazelles have been there since the world began; they won't all evaporate within the next half hour.

If you have any difficulty getting a reasonably near shot on these open plains a good plan is to walk with your men slowly toward the game, but not *directly* toward them—go as though you intended to pass perhaps a hundred to a hundred and fifty yards away from them—and then when you've reached where you wanted to be, drop out yourself, squat down, and let your gunbearer and whatever other natives you are with continue as though nothing had happened. Provided you stay motionless the game may not notice you—they will be concerned with those men they see still moving and will keep turning around so as to remain facing them. In this way they will in due course give you a clear broadside shot. It's an old dodge but it still works.

Of course, if you're mounted things are very much easier: you merely dismount and walk slowly toward the game, keeping your pony as a blind between you and them until you're ready to shoot.

The GERENUK is a queer little beast who seems to be trying to ape the giraffe. He's a bit smaller than a goat, tawny in color, and he lives in the dry bush zones of the northern frontier province of Kenya and similar areas, where he browses rather than grazes. His neck has been getting longer and longer until it's now quite out of proportion to the rest of his body. He, like the duiker, is said never to drink, and that may be true, although perhaps he takes a drop after any rain there may be.

The DIK-DIK is the smallest of the buck, being little bigger than the well-known hare. I've never heard of him south of the equator, but his tiny footprints are a familiar sight in the north. If a breeze blows overnight, so as to smooth the fine dust of the desert regions, you'll see the dik-dik's exquisite little prints all over the place, showing that he must be far more numerous than is generally supposed.

He's fine on the table.

As I've mentioned before, I can discuss only the ordinary varieties of these little buck. There are many more. For instance, among the rarer ones there's that whitish desert fellow with the long straight horns that I've seen southeast of Malakal in the Sudan. I forget his name, but he must belong to the oryx family, although he is a bit smaller than the common oryx found in northern Kenya. Then there is that rare variety of GEMSBOK that so far as I know is found only in the desert country to the south of Mossamedes in Angola. The commoner variety is seen in Bechuanaland and neighboring parts. He's bigger and heavier than impala and with rather straight horns that curve only very slightly backward.

All gemsbok like fairly open short-grass country of the drier type. They are generally reddish-tawny in color with, as usual, lighter underparts. (The desert variety is light rather than reddish.)

AFRICAN WILD HUNTING DOGS. The African hunting dog or wild dog has a body much the size of an Alsatian but is shorter in the leg. He is variously marked with fairly large brown, black, gray, and white patches and invariably has a generous white flash on the end of his tail. His ears are large and rounded. He is almost universally condemned by hunters and naturalists as being the greatest of all foes to game. But is he?

Every hunter has had occasion to curse these animals from time to time, because it cannot be denied that when a pack of hunting dogs enters a district the game leaves it—if you hear that bell-like hunting call during the night it's of little use going out next morning to look for meat because the district will resemble Mother Hubbard's cupboard. It is ridiculous to suppose the dogs have eaten all the game. However, it appears that the canine family has the brand of Cain just as man has. A troop of lion can take up their abode in a district, kill three or four times a week, roar to their hearts' content, and other animals won't abandon the district. But as soon as game hear or see or smell wild dog, they go.

Although it's infuriating if you're short of meat, there's no need to worry. Since the game have gone the dogs must go too—there's now nothing left for them to hunt. The game know that perfectly well and usually start drifting back within twenty-four hours. A pack of hunting dogs must be continually on the move. Occasionally they will spend a couple of days in a district, in which case there will be little or no game to be found for another forty-eight hours; but as soon as the dogs have gone, back come the game with, frequently, a considerable addition in the way of fugitives from neighboring districts.

Now since there's no reason to suppose the dogs have not been in Africa as long as the game, and since it's known the bitches bring forth seven or eight pups in a litter, if the hunting dog were really such a menace he'd have eaten every animal long ago. He certainly hasn't succeeded in this up to the present; and in view of the centuries he's had it seems absurd to suggest he has suddenly developed new and devastating techniques coincident with the arrival of the white man.

The wild dog has few enemies. Since the bitch has her young whenever possible in a burrow (made by some other animal), the puppies are fairly safe. Driver ants may wipe out a few, heavy rain drown others by flooding, and leopard may reduce them slightly after they leave the burrow but are still too young to defend themselves. (However, I shouldn't think that many leopard risk the old lady's returning with, perhaps, some of her friends.) Eagles and vultures may also get away with a few pups when they're tiny, though the young animals are safe from them while they are still underground. All animals fear the wild dog. The wild dog fears nothing. All the same, there must be a heavy infant mortality or they would be as numerous as locusts by now.

The hunting dog has some fine characteristics which even his most ardent detractors should admire. For many years I thought he never hunted down the females among his quarry; but quite recently I had the dogs chase a bushbuck doe right into my camp and kill her a bare fifty yards away. However, since I've been living in the bushveld continuously for a good many years and have had wild dogs in most of the districts in which I've lived and roamed, and since that was the first and only time I've known them to chase and kill a female, I believe they will do so only if there isn't a male around and they are very hungry.

The leader of the pack picks out his quarry—almost invariably a male, as I say—gives tongue, and the remainder of the pack takes up his line. There's no confusion; the dogs will pass right through a herd without taking the slightest notice of any but the selected animals. Although a quick side jump might give a much easier kill, I've never seen it attempted. Moreover, the younger dogs, often a long way behind, never show the slightest inclination to break away from the line and try a hunt on their own from among the many animals they sometimes pass. Not being fools, they must realize, after it's happened several times, that by the time they arrive at the kill there will be little or nothing left for them; yet in spite of that they stick to the rules.

I have said wild dogs fear nothing. In proof of that the following incident may be of interest:

I was camped three or four hundred yards from a water hole. One night, or, rather, early morning, shortly before daybreak, we heard a lion roaring as he came down to drink. Suddenly there came the hunting call of a pack of wild dogs. The lion choked off his roar in the middle: I'd never heard such a thing before. He couldn't have known—yet—that the dogs had taken up his spoor, but he obviously decided hurriedly that it would be inadvisable to advertise his presence in the vicinity. The hunt rapidly approached, and presently there broke out the most appalling din. The grating snarls and roars of the lion were mingled with the yelps and worrying of the dogs. The instant it was light enough to see, my gunbearers and I went out. By the time we got there nothing was left of the lion except his head, one forepaw, and the tuft from the end of his tail. One of the dogs had had his skull crushed like an eggshell you'd trodden on; another had had his ribs smashed flat as though he'd been run over by a car; a third appeared to have had his back broken. There were two or three dogs just disappearing in the grass, apparently licking wounds. The main body of the pack had gone.

The African native, speaking generally, has a healthy respect for the wild dog, at least until he's been around with a hunter a while and learned there's no need to be scared. The dog doesn't fear man, but is intensely curious. He'll stand up on his hind legs if the grass interferes with his vision and then jump up and down in an effort to see better. A pack will close in until they are only a matter of feet away, and it's easily understandable that the uninitiated believe an attack is contemplated. But I've never yet come across an authentic report of their killing man.

Under these conditions, i.e., when a pack inquisitively closes in, it's possible to shoot a number of the dogs; the others don't show the slightest trace of gun-shyness but, on the contrary, crowd closer to see what it's all about. Personally, I don't waste ammunition on them, since I don't subscribe to the belief that they're a menace to game. I consider the hyena infinitely worse because he takes an immense toll from among the newly born: sometimes three or four youngsters a night.

I figure the hunting dog probably does much good clearing out many of those old bulls that keep the younger males away from the females. As I have said earlier, an old fellow collects a large harem which he cannot adequately serve and when he is killed younger sires divide up his females among themselves, their greater procreative powers ensuring an increase in the species in spite of, or possibly because of, fewer wives.

I certainly think the African hunting dog deserves a word said in his defense. It's the man with a magazine rifle who hunts from an automobile who is responsible for the diminution of game. And he must find a scapegoat to shoulder his iniquities. Thus it is that I discuss wild dogs here instead of in the next chapter, where most men would unhesitatingly put them, among the varmints. (By varmints I mean non-game animals, unpleasant and/or destructive.)

14: VARMINTS

The CROC is the curse and bane of all African rivers and lakes. You find more of the fish-eating variety in lakes—the one with the long narrow snout, in India called *gavial*—but there's nothing under the sun to prevent one of the others from getting in there unbeknown to you. It happens. I remember down on Lifumba, where the local natives assured me no one in the memory of the oldest graybeard had been attacked by a croc, and we all used to swim and dive for a certain nut that grew under water —at this very spot in one year no less than three children were killed within the space of ten days, and a big croc took up his residence at the ford where travelers used to cross a small creek that ran into the lake. There were several narrow escapes there before word got around.

Having taken the three youngsters from the lake itself, that croc disappeared and hasn't been seen since. Of course, the sudden appearance and disappearance were put down to witchcraft, and the father of the children, a very decent old fellow, was accused of transmogrifying himself into a croc so he could eat his own young. He was put to the poison ordeal; unhesitatingly he drank the dose as he protested his innocence. Three hours later he was dead—thereby conclusively proving his guilt. If further proof was needed, there was the indisputable fact that the croc had disappeared; so all—more especially the women—were satisfied.

The women, I find, are mostly to blame in these matters. It is a custom for the eldest son to take over all the old man's wives—except his own mother, of course—when his father dies. In this particular case some of the old fellow's women were young. He was grizzled; the son was a fine strong upstanding man. Q.E.D.

Nevertheless, sudden appearances like this are strange, so it is easy to see how superstition survives. I shall say more about that later.

Normally, when one speaks of a croc one refers to the broad-snouted kind. He's the flesh-eater, the man-eater. In some places he grows to immense size: there have been reports of a length exceeding twenty-seven feet—I heard of one exceeding thirty feet—but I don't know how authentic those stories were; I've killed them myself up to slightly more than twenty feet and have seen others which I'm convinced were a whole lot bigger than any I'd shot. The animals are unbelievably heavy for their size. I don't think I'd be far wrong if I suggested that big crocs may be the heaviest creatures in Africa, with elephant the sole exception. You get some very big ones in the lower Zambezi; but I think the rivers running between French Equatorial Africa and the Belgian Congo provide the biggest specimens you'll find anywhere — though at that the Nile is not to be sniffed at.

They're detestable brutes; but they're hunters, and as such one cannot help admiring their stealth, their cunning, and their inexhaustible patience. Life runs very calmly and easily for them with their slow-beating hearts—hearts which pulse for upward of half an hour after removal—and doubtless they live for two or three centuries. The female lays her eggs, forty or fifty of them, in a hole she scoops in the sand then covers over. She relies upon the sun to hatch them for her. Big water lizards make away with many of the eggs, and natives destroy a few more but taken all around many millions must hatch out annually throughout the continent. In view of this I tend to accept the belief that the mother returns when the hatch is expected and eats as many of the youngsters as she can catch. Were some such explanation not so by this time it would be impossible to launch a canoe in African rivers, they'd be so chockful of crocs. Even as it is, the number of crocodiles must be astronomical, and they must be responsible for the deaths of many thousands of natives every year.

I've seen a photograph, if memory serves me rightly, in the *National Geographic* magazine showing a native fisherman on Lake Victoria with only one arm, and a legend underneath to the effect that the other was "bitten off by a croc." I've frequently read of such things too; but it's clear that the writers have never examined a croc's teeth. As a matter of fact I happen to know that particular fisherman—or his twin brother—and his account of his loss is identical with the account I've had from many another African fisherman, and of what I've actually seen myself: the croc does *not* bite off the limb; he grabs it and pulls. If it's a big croc the owner of the limb goes along with his arm or leg; but if it's a comparatively small one he yells for assistance, his pals come around and grab him, and a tug of war ensues. The bone of the arm is frequently broken in these tussles, and the arm *pulled* off.

A croc's teeth are quite different from those of a shark. A shark's teeth are not only sharp-pointed, they are razor-keen along the edges, and mostly serrated as well. They are obviously designed for biting and are capable of shearing off a man's leg almost as cleanly as a bacon slicer cuts your breakfast rashers. But a croc's teeth are sharp only on the points; the edges are rounded. It seems clear that they are incapable of biting off a limb—all they can do is to grab and hold. For that they are perfectly designed, and the croc grabs his victim and then just allows his great weight to drag him under water and drown him. In the case of a heavy animal like a buffalo or an ox, the croc will also bring into play the tremendous leverage afforded by his tail.

I've been instrumental in rescuing two persons from crocs, and in neither case was the limb bitten off. One victim was an Englishman, the other a native woman; the man was grabbed by the arm, the woman by the leg. The man was one of those fools who won't listen to advice. He'd been visiting with an old friend of mine named Mac across the river from Tete, had had a few sundowners, and then said he was going to wade and swim across to the town. At that season there was comparatively little water in the river, and it was possible to wade the greater part of it; but there was still a deep channel about a third of the way across. This channel wasn't very broad, and it would have been safe by day—but not after sundown. Mac and I told the fellow not to be a fool, to take a boat. But he wouldn't listen. He started off, and we honestly thought he'd use a boat in spite of what he said. However, he didn't, and not long after he'd left we heard yells for help. We were camped on the riverbank and it took only a moment to grab a knobkerrie from a passing youth and race down and across the sand. I outdistanced Mac, who was older than I, and reached the source of the yells first. The fool was up to his waist when I first sighted him but had been dragged in to his armpits by the time I reached him. He was pulling back with all his might, but the croc was gradually winning. I splashed in beside him, took hold of his outstretched arm—the one the croc was pulling—and bashed downward with the ironwood knobkerrie, again and again. I felt it strike something solid and went on bashing. This served the purpose eventually and the croc let go. Mac had arrived by then, and between us we got the man back to camp and doped his arm. It had been terribly lacerated, with all the muscles and tendons torn.

As to the native woman, she was grabbed by the leg when she was drawing water. She had waded in almost to her knees to reach clean water. When she yelled I ran in, picked up the heavy clay pot she had dropped, and bashed the croc over the head with it. It broke the pot but so astonished the croc that he let go.

Now these were comparatively small crocs. Had they been big ones both persons would have been taken. Even as it was it's a safe bet they would have gone had assistance not been at hand.

If a big croc gets hold of you, you haven't a prayer—you'll be gone before you can do anything. A croc makes absolutely certain before it attacks, and the attack itself is utterly unexpected. In most rivers the animals are very shy and cautious, though there are some in which they are contemptuous of man. In the Zambezi, which is full of man-eaters, the natives load their dugouts until there is scarcely three inches of freeboard and the flat protruding portion overhanging the stern is flush with the water, so that it actually laps the bottom. I've sat there myself. And I have never heard of anyone's being pulled out of his canoe by a croc. When paddling down the river in that manner I have seen a big croc following on behind, about ten yards away; but he didn't attempt to approach closer, much less attack. (Yet when you pull in to the bank you must be very careful not to dangle a hand or foot over the side, if you don't want it grabbed by some croc.) I can't attempt to explain this because in the Ruvugwi, a tributary of the Zambezi, it would be madness to let anything protrude over the side when the canoe is under way, and the same applies to the Rufiji in Tanganyika. Nevertheless, I have never heard of an authentic case of crocs actually attacking a *canoe* in any part of Africa. I have many times read of such attacks—with crocs getting under the canoe and toppling it over with their backs—but frankly I don't believe the stories.

There's another inexplicable feature about the Zambezi croc: since the animal has no molars and no tongue it's generally accepted that he lodges his victim in an underwater cubbyhole, such as protruding roots of a tree, or a hollow where the water has swirled under the bank—you'll find many such in sandstone country—and there leave it until it's decomposed and so easily dismembered and eaten. This seems reasonable; but then, why will crocs take only live victims? There is no getting away from the fact that a number of persons have been drowned in the Zambezi at Tete, and their bodies have invariably been found untouched some two or three miles downstream. These men, I might mention, were all drowned by day when the constant traffic backward and forward across the river keeps it free from crocs in the vicinity of the crossing. This means the people were dead, merely floating when they got lower to where there are crocs at all hours. In the case of men or women falling overboard at *night* in the same place I cannot remember a single case in which the body was recovered: the assumption being that it was taken while still struggling—because the crocs close in as soon as the day's traffic slows at sundown. That stretch of the river is then just as dangerous as any other stretch.

In many places the man-eaters are so bad that the women have to draw water by means of a can or gourd tied to a long stick. Even then, the croc will sometimes grab the stick and jerk it out of the woman's hands in the hope of pulling her in also. They haunt a place where villagers come for water and seem to be fully aware of the native woman's henlike mentality. Patience is all that's necessary—and the croc has plenty of that. Sooner or later, some idiot woman will go down to the water's edge and give him his chance. I've shot many of these man-eaters.

It's easy. All you have to do is stroll along to the watering place with as many men as you like, all talking and laughing. When the croc hears he'll sneak along close to the bank and wait. You peer until you spot his head. It will almost invariably be immediately downstream of the place where the foolish descend to the water's edge, and facing upstream. (In all these "bad" places there will be a high bank with deep water immediately below it.) You can drive a bullet straight down through the top of his head without difficulty.

Men examining a croc's mouth for the first time, to see for themselves that he has indeed no vestige of a tongue, are sometimes mystified by a small flap at the entrance to his gullet and wonder what it's for. The answer is easy: it's a valve. When a croc opens his mouth that valve closes and prevents water or anything else from pouring in. His nostrils also close entirely when he submerges (so, incidentally, do a hippo's). When a croc is lying under water waiting for a feed of fish he is wise enough to know that if he were to keep his mouth closed he would go mighty hungry because by the time he opened it the fish would be gone. Conse- quently he lies with his mouth wide-open, and then has only to snap it shut to grab his fish. In the same way, if he's grabbed a buck by the nose and is dragging him under water, the valve is closed since the croc's mouth is open, and it takes a while to drown any animal.

If you're waiting for a shot at a croc, hoping he will come out on to a sandbank for his usual sunbath, don't be in too great a hurry to shoot or to crawl into a better position for your shot. Watch his mouth: so long as it's closed he's awake and probably looking around to be sure that all is well; but if you have patience you will see that presently it will gape open—that's your chance. He's asleep now and if you're careful you can sneak into a better position for your shot.

Did you know the croc is the only creature that can't look behind him? Maybe that was one of the reasons the old alchemists liked to have small stuffed ones hanging in their laboratories: indicating that science never looks back but always ahead.

Some nice marksmanship is generally called for if you want to re- cover your trophy. The crocodile's brain is about the size of a walnut and you've got to drive your bullet into that, or else break his neck, if you want his hide. On almost any other shot he will usually manage to get into deep water. Once there he'll sink like a rock, and it will be so long before he surfaces again that he'll be putrid. It's all bunk to say, as you so often hear it said, that a croc's hide is bulletproof—it's nothing of the sort. Sure, if you use some featherweight bullet it will almost certainly smash itself against his spine without doing any very great harm; but if you use a decent bullet it won't disintegrate. You can kill a croc by driving a good bullet from one of the modern Magnums through his shoulder: he gives a convulsive leap, his head and tail almost meet in the center of his back, then he flops on the sand and lies there trembling and quivering from head to tail tip—stone-dead. But you may not do it with one of the older low-velocity rifles. With them, as stated above, only the brain or neck shots will suffice. A croc has to give no more than one bound—and "bound" or "spring" is the word—and he's in deep water. He may be mortally wounded, but that won't help you to secure him: the trembling and quivering of his tail will send him scooting through the water. I remember shooting a very big man-eater in the Ruvugwi, driving my bullet straight down through the top of his head. I'd shot him in deep water and when he received the bullet he instantly submerged; but we were all astonished to see a large croc's head appear almost at once close to a steeply sloping sandbank in midstream and slide rapidly up it until the body was exposed halfway along its length. It lay there, and there could be no doubt that it was my kill, because there was a hole in the head. We could see the tail still trying to drive the body farther up the slope of the sandbank—still vibrating.

A croc gives the impression of being slow because he never exerts himself unless he has to. Don't let it deceive you. His speed is almost unbelievable when he cares to use it. I have vivid recollections of the first time I saw an exhibition of it. I was coming up the Zambezi in a big freight-carrying canoe with about three tons of stuff aboard. It was the dry season and where the water was shallow enough we all got out and waded, pushing the heavy canoe along. That was the easiest way. (The Zambezi's an unfriendly river—there's always a beast of a current to overcome when going upstream, and no respite from it.) The water just here was only up to our knees or a bit more. There were sandbanks on both sides of us, the one on our left about a hundred yards away, the others considerably farther away. I noticed a small croc, perhaps nine or ten feet long, on the sandbank on our left. He was fast asleep. But just before we came abreast of him he awoke, saw us, gave one mighty leap forward, which landed him with a splash in the water, and I then saw a white bubbling trail for all the world like the track of a torpedo streaking directly across our bow. And I declare it was faster than any torpedo in existence, with the sole exception of the Japanese kind—the fastest of all (though they don't leave those telltale streaks). I was truly astonished.

I once saw prints taken from a motion-picture film showing a rhino which had been grabbed by the hind leg by a big croc. The rhino was leaning forward, pulling with all his two-and-a-half- to three-ton weight; the croc appeared to be just grinning. Succeeding pictures showed the rhino pulled deeper and deeper into the water, until at the last only his upthrown head was visible. It was a remarkable and, I should think, unique series of photographs. The rhino, of course, was foolish: had he just pulled straight it's a moot point whether or not the croc would have won the tug of war. But from time to time he'd swung around to try to horn his attacker and had lost ground every time—that's probably why the croc was grinning! I forget in what paper I saw the pictures; I've a notion it was either *Field* or *Country Life:* such photographs could not be faked.

There are several inexplicable traits about crocs. When traveling on the Zambezi we invariably used to camp for the nights on sandbanks because we'd then be free of mosquitoes. Some of these banks were four or five feet high, others were only that many inches above the surface of the water. Our boats and canoes (often only the one small canoe) would be tied up broadside-on to the bank, bows facing upstream. We'd sleep within certainly not more than six feet of the water on occasions, though sometimes we might be three or four times that distance away. The point is that we slept with a feeling of complete security, and in all the years I've wandered in the Zambezi valley I've never heard of anybody's being attacked by crocs when so sleeping on sandbanks—though it might seem like deliberately using oneself as bait. It isn't that crocs never leave the water: they've been known to travel considerable distances overland during the night, moving from one stream or pool to another, or possibly just hunting. Dead crocs have been found miles from water in parts of East Africa—around Lake Rudolph, for instance. The natives said they'd been killed by lions; and certainly lions have been seen feeding on crocs on more than one occasion some distance from water. I myself have seen the indisputable spoor of crocs two or three miles from the nearest water, and my lad Aly last year encountered a croc on a motor road around midnight down Tete way on the Zambezi. He was perhaps half a mile from the river, between it and a deep pool which was much the same distance away. Yet despite all these peregrinations, on dry land the crocodile will not attack sleepers on shore.

You'll hear from time to time that crocs have round stones, the size of large gooseberries, in their stomachs—presumably to assist digestion. This is true. You'll also hear a yarn about a little bird that picks the croc's teeth as he lies basking in the sun with his mouth wide-open. It's true, too, not a figment of an inventive traveler's imagination. As you watch you expect momentarily to see the croc's jaws close with a snap. He seems to be grinning and merely waiting his chance; but apparently that's not so. I can't say if he appreciates the bird's attentions, though I doubt it; but he certainly doesn't seem to feel ill will toward the little fellow—I've never seen the croc make the slightest attempt to kill him or drive him away. And it isn't as though crocs won't eat birds: many times I've had occasion to swear at some croc that rose up and grabbed a duck or goose I'd shot which had fallen into the water. This is the great trouble with shooting wild fowl on African rivers and lakes. The goose and duck shooting is of the best, provided you know where and when to go; but you must be an optimist if you hope to recover your entire bag.

To return to the little croc bird. I'm not enough of an ornithologist to tell you to what species he belongs. I'm fond of birds, I like watching them, but I really know little about them. Anyway, the bird life of the lower Zambezi would afford many years' study to a trained ornithologist. I've been told by those who know far more about such matters than I do that there are many species there unknown to science, or at least as yet unclassified. I must say I should like to be retained by some bird-loving millionaire to make a full and detailed study and collection of the bird life of those parts. It would be a very pleasant and interesting existence drifting among the many reed-covered sandy islets on the lower river, especially during the dry season when the water is low. But such jobs don't seem to come my way.

Incidentally, crocs appear to turn darker and darker as they grow bigger and older. I've seen some pretty sizable ones with a yellowish-green color, but the really big ones are usually a dirty muddy brown: almost black, from a distance. The biggest I've ever seen was so dark (and so huge) that I was sure he was a dead tree trunk until he moved; and then it was too late for a shot because I'd just shot another somewhat smaller one that had been lying between me and what I thought was the dead tree. He also was a huge brute but nothing like the size of the one that got away. I know the "one that got away" is always biggest; but he really was this time.

Quite recently I had a close and interesting view of a crocs' conference or convention. It takes place in a deep still backwater on the Mandimba close to where it joins the Lugenda at the latter's source. I had crept quietly up to a thin clump of tall coarse swamp grass that still stood at the very edge of the backwater (most of the grass had been grazed short by hippo). The clump was thin enough to allow a clear view of the pool while affording me adequate concealment provided I kept still. It was hippo I'd come for, one of my scouts having informed me that a party of them visited the pool every evening. There were no hippo when I arrived, which didn't worry me since I had purposely come early. But as I sat down behind that clump of grass I noticed several crocs lying on a flat piece of mudbank immediately beside me and a couple of feet lower than I was. They were packed like sardines except that they were all facing the same way, with their noses just touching the water. They hadn't seen me, although I could have touched the nearest of them with the muzzle of my rifle had I wanted to. I had no such desire: it was hippo I wanted, not crocs.

As I sat quietly behind my clump of grass I could see perhaps a hundred and fifty to two hundred yards up the river. I watched a croc come into sight and drift down on the current. When he was opposite the backwater a flick of the tip of his tail sent him into it and he coasted slowly across toward his companions on the mudbank beside me. When he reached them he lay a few moments nose to nose with them and then turned around to lie pointing in the same direction as the others. He couldn't join them on the mudbank as it was already crowded. When I looked up again I saw another croc and then another and another all drifting down on the current in the same way. They kept on, a long line of them, and on reaching the backwater acted like the first comer except that subsequent arrivals didn't come right across to consult with the early ones. In turn each of them lined himself up alongside the one that had arrived immediately before him, forming spokes of an imaginary wheel with an as yet invisible hub. They came in scores! I would never have believed that the Mandimba, quite a small river, contained so many crocs throughout its entire length. Finally they had formed about three parts of a large circle, all in perfect alignment, but leaving the center empty. And there they lay without movement. It was obvious that they were waiting for something—but what? This was no ordinary gathering. There had been nothing unusual in finding a few of the brutes out on the mudbank: crocs like a snooze and a sun bath, and have favored places they use for such; but there was something so purposeful about them today, to say nothing of the great numbers that had clearly come from far upstream—for so many of them to have arrived they must have come from afar. I was fascinated.

And then, without the slightest warning, an enormous head appeared right in the center of the circle, facing directly toward me. It was so big that at first I thought it was a bull hippo. But almost immediately I saw that it lacked the hippo's little upstanding ears. It was a croc's head; and never have I seen anything remotely approaching it for size. Whereas the other crocs were on the surface, showing their full length right to the tips of their tails, this monster exposed only his head and a few inches of neck. All was still: there wasn't a movement or a sound. For how long the giant remained visible I don't know, but without warning or the slightest ripple of the water he submerged. Still the others did nothing. For about as long as he'd been on the surface the big croc remained invisible; then again, there he was in the same place, his head just appearing without the slightest disturbance of the water. It now seemed clear that the animals must be communicating in some manner. Either the monster—surely the Father of all Crocs—was hearing reports and news, or else imparting the wisdom of his many, many years. Crocs must, I decided, have some means of communicating that is outside the range of human hearing — because no one seeing this performance could doubt that it was a conference. Several times that enormous head appeared and lay there in the center of the motionless circle, and each time, at regular intervals, it slowly submerged again. I was so much interested in all this that I completely forgot about the hippo until I heard one approaching from behind me along a deep-worn track overgrown with swamp grass. But a whiff of wind from me to him sent him off and I knew he wouldn't return before dark. Well, I didn't care; I considered my evening by no means wasted. I wouldn't have missed that croc conference for a dozen hippo. I couldn't help thinking of the old croc (Mugger) in one of Kipling's jungle books, though I hadn't read it since I was a kid.

The light was failing now and there was no chance of the hippo's offering me a shot so, since I had some miles to go to reach my camp, I stood up. What a commotion! And how those crocs must have sworn at me for breaking up their session! I've often wondered what the old boy had to say about their lack of a sentry.

I suppose I ought to have shot the big one to see just what size he was; but the more I hunt the less I like shooting anything that isn't interfering with man. Oh, I don't doubt that the brute would take a man if he got the chance; but the Mandimba is small and is mostly crossed by means of trees that have fallen from bank to bank.

The locals tell me that when the river's down during the dry season they have often seen an immense croc *without a tail*. I have a hunch that that is probably my chairman. Not having a tail, he wouldn't seem so very big to their eyes when out on a sandbank; but I wonder how many centuries he has seen pass to have such a gigantic head.

The HYENA is another detestable brute. It's my firm belief, as I say, that he's infinitely more of a menace to game than the wild hunting dog. The hunting dog is a sure-enough hunter, and a good one. The hyena is merely a scavenger. He's much too cowardly to attack anything but the newborn or the sick-unto-death; and he must kill an incredible number of newly dropped buck every year throughout the continent. I can't think of a single point in his favor. He must be very numerous; you'll hear his mournful howl nightly wherever you camp in Africa, bush forest, high veld or low veld, or open plains. You'll hear him down on the coast; you'll hear him high up on the slopes of Mounts Kenya and Kilimanjaro.

His howl is not unlike the Australian bushman's *Coo-e-e-e-e*, rising up sharply toward the end. You hear of the laughing hyena, though many men who have hunted for years will say they've never heard anything remotely approaching a laugh, and that they believe the hyena's mournful howl is his only call. Well, I can assure you that he does have another sound, though "laugh" is perhaps not the happiest description. Still, it's difficult to find another word to fit it. It's an infinitely more hideous sound than the customary howl. How can I describe it? It's the ghastly maniacal chattering laughter that might have issued from a torture chamber of the bad old days as some poor wretch was driven insane by unspeakable torments. It's the horrible soulless laughter you might imagine the chief torturer's giving vent to as he inflicted new atrocities on his victim. It's an unspeakably horrible noise, quite capable, if it's close by, of making your hair stand on end. You hear it only when the hyenas are sitting around waiting for a lion to finish with his kill and they fear he won't leave enough for them: I've never heard it except when there has been some sickening disappointment, or expectation of it. Which would indicate that it does not connote happiness. What's more, it seems it is only the leader of the band that produces it. When hyenas are prowling to see what they can find they howl to one another, presumably broadcasting the news. When a feed or prospective feed is discovered by one of them he'll howl to his comrades to come join him. But if it's a sizable feed, the band won't start on it until the chief himself arrives. The leader is a much bigger animal than the others, with an unmistakable voice— much deeper and more powerful than his followers'. When he arrives you'll hear them tell him the news. They don't howl when he's among them but have a horrible series of sounds that can only be described as conversation. It's little wonder the natives throughout Africa are afraid of hyenas and attribute to them many strange qualities.

By the way: I've heard a hyena give a perfect imitation of a lion's roar. It wasn't so powerful, of course, but it was just like a lion some distance away, downwind, and possibly facing in the opposite direction. The hyena I speak of did this several times, for all the world as though practicing, and completely deceived about half the men in camp—they were certain it was a lion. The others were equally sure it was a hyena, and I agreed with them; but the debate became so furious and prolonged that at daybreak the entire camp went out to see what spoor they could find. There was only that of a big hyena. I've heard hyenas do this on several occasions. I've a hunch they deliberately practice it in the hope of scaring lesser beasts and possibly getting themselves a feed that way.

Hyenas have extraordinarily powerful jaws and teeth which can crunch bones that even lion won't touch. There is just one loud crunch, hat's all; they don't gnaw at a bone as a dog will. I've had one of them teal a frying pan at night from my grass kitchen. When we recovered it next morning we found the heavy iron crumpled as you might crumple an envelope. The brute without doubt smelled the buffalo drippings in which my last meal had been cooked and then ruined a perfectly good pan in his rage and disappointment. Only a couple of weeks ago another of the brutes took a heavy-gauge aluminum saucepan full of drippings. Next morning we found that, having cleaned out all the fat, he had wantonly destroyed the pot. He hadn't been content simply to crumple it (we could have straightened it out, since it was aluminum); he had literally torn it to rags, making it quite useless.

Hyenas are extraordinarily bold. Houses hold no terrors for them if there's an open door. They will sneak into your tent in the same way, even though you're sleeping there. This makes it very easy to catch them: you don't have to worry about leaving the smell of man after making and setting a trap. (They're such foul-smelling brutes themselves that it's doubtful they could detect the smell of man anyway.) They wander at night through the streets and alleys of the towns in many parts of Africa to see what they can find in the way of dogs or fowl or anything else in the eatable line—which, of course, includes hide or skin as well as bones.

There are parts of eastern Africa, Kenya, for instance, where the hyenas are not merely bold but also dangerous. This has come about because of the habits of tribes such as the Kikuyu, which don't inter their dead but leave them out for hyenas to "bury." Toward the end of the last century and early part of this one epidemics swept these people. They died by the thousands; and with all those bodies laid out nicely for them it goes without saying that hyenas literally swarmed. Moreover, the people didn't always wait until someone was actually dead before putting him out. The result was that the hyenas learned how helpless a sick or sleeping man was; and when the number of corpses dropped they took to sneaking up to where the people were sleeping around their fires in the kraals and grabbing a feed here and there. With a hyena, there's just the one bite and the piece is gone—whether it's a hand or foot or half the sleeper's face. There were and still are some dreadfully disfigured natives wandering around those parts; and there are white men bitten like that, too, in parts of East Africa, but they will almost invariably tell you they were mauled by lion or leopard—they apparently consider it derogatory to admit having been damaged by the foul and cowardly hyena. For a while it was not uncommon for a woman to awaken and find her infant had been taken during the night. Things are rather better up there nowadays, however. I'm told that thousands of the hyenas were killed off with the aid of poison; and the government takes steps now to prevent or check devastating epidemics. But in view of the fact that hyenas have been the repository for their dead for thousands of years it's not to be wondered at that Wakikuyu won't even touch a dead hyena.

Wherever ostrich farming is practiced, the hyena is Public Enemy Number 1. He eats eggs and young birds with equal impartiality. Ostrich farmers bitterly curse him and all his breed—with good reason. I believe the hyena, more than anything else, is responsible for the comparative scarcity of wild ostrich. In true hyena spirit he'll tackle anything that can't hit back.

How I remember swearing at him one year! I'd been fattening up half-a-dozen Muscovy ducks. Then one night a leopard broke into the pen and killed some of them. In accordance with his custom he stuck the carcasses up in the forks of tall trees. I was hoping to collect the ducks that escaped next morning. Alas for my hopes! A hyena had been following the leopard and had killed and eaten what ducks the big cat had missed. Knowing the leopard would come around the following night to collect the carcasses he had, as he thought, hidden, I set a trap gun for him, baiting it with one of the dead ducks. It worked and I killed him. I at once set it again in the hope of bagging the hyena also. Again it worked; I killed him too. So I had at least that satisfaction, but it was poor consolation for the loss of our feast.

The trap gun, properly set, is a simple engine of destruction. Any gun will do. You merely prop it horizontally on two forked sticks driven into the ground. Tie the bait around the muzzle, seeing to it that the string is fastened to the front of the trigger guard (otherwise hyenas have been known somehow to get the bait off the muzzle without firing the gun). You then run another cord from the trigger to anything firm, such as a convenient tree. All that's necessary besides is to set a few bushes in the ground around the trap, leaving an opening so that your intended victim will approach from the front. When he takes the bait in his mouth and draws away with it, he fires the gun and gets the bullet or slugs down his throat. The trap usually blows the back of his head off, though if not properly set it may merely blow a hole in his cheek, break his jaw, or wound him in the shoulder. If you are after a leopard, you will have a nasty customer to follow up next morning. But there's little chance of the trap's not killing, unless you were careless in setting it.

Daly is the only man I know who has tried to say a good word for the hyena. He reports that when hyenas are feeding one of them will carefully put aside the liver, stomach, and such organs for his mate if she is nursing pups, and the other hyenas will respect the gesture and not attempt to touch the delicacy. He doesn't tell us how he's so certain of all this, but even supposing it's so I don't see that it's much to make a song and dance about. I would reckon it more of a virtue if hyenas ate their young.

JACKALS are very numerous in some parts of Africa. I've never previously seen so many as there are right here where I'm typing this book. They are by no means strictly nocturnal. Many a time I've seen them hunting guinea fowl by day. They're very cunning: one or two will slowly creep toward a flock so as not to scare them into flight but just get them bunched together and walking slowly toward where the other jackals are lying in ambush downwind of them. That gives the pack a much better chance of making a big killing than if the birds were separated.

Curiously enough, jackals show little or no fear of man when encountered by day: I expect they know we wouldn't be hunting them and so don't bother about us.

CHEETAH are to be found in the bushveld as well as on the open plains, though you don't often see them. They are also an infernal nuisance when they learn that you have fowl around your camp. It's this habit they have of raiding the potential larder that makes me class them as varmints.

They are said to be the fastest animals alive, but they have little staying power. If they fail to connect with an intended victim on the first rush they usually give up and hunt around for something else. All the same, that first rush is so terrifically fast that I don't suppose they have many failures. Their lack of staying power makes it easy to ride them down on horseback. There was a Dutchman in either Kenya or Tanganyika who with his two sons made quite a good thing out of capturing cheetah to sell to one of the Indian princes who kept a stable of them for hunting black buck in India. They are very easily tamed and have never been known to attack even when being captured.

The procedure for capturing them is to gallop a cheetah to a standstill; as soon as his breath is gone he just lies down. The horseman then throws himself off his horse and drops a sack over the cheetah's head and fore-paws. He bundles the animal into the sack and ties the mouth of it, then hoists it over his saddle, mounts, and, holding the cheetah more or less on his thighs, rides back to camp. That's all there is to it. A piece of fencing wire is stretched between two trees and the cheetah attached loosely to that by means of a dog collar with a large ring on it. This allows a certain amount of freedom. If kindly treated the cheetah quickly becomes tame and very affectionate, but curiously enough can't take punishment—even a stern reprimand upsets him badly.

But it's difficult to capture the animals in the bushveld.

BABOONS are unlovely creatures. There are few parts of Africa where you don't find them. I think those of the far south are the biggest—I've seen some enormous ones in the Cape province. Taken by and large they must do millions of dollars' worth of damage every year throughout the length and breadth of the continent. Farmers and planters detest them.

Your best safeguard against baboons is to leave plenty of leopard around. The leopard prefers baboons to anything else and the baboons certainly look upon him as their greatest enemy. If you bring a leopard skin anywhere near a captive baboon he'll almost have hysterics. A cruel trick I have several times heard of being played on baboons in southern Africa was to catch one, sew him up in a leopard skin, and then turn him loose to try and rejoin his companions. They would tear him to pieces.

Baboons have wonderful night vision. As I have said before, it's astonishing how they can spot a leopard even on a dark night. And how they then rend the silence with yells and barks as they hurl abuse at the hated enemy! If he manages to kill one, the others nearly go crazy. They cluster around on the rocks or trees, screaming and yelling, doing everything in their power to drive the leopard away from his kill, in spite of their fear and hatred of him. However, I have never seen them make an attempt to throw stones, as one so often reads of their doing.

In spite of this fear of leopard it's surprising how old baboons will sometimes settle themselves for the night in comfortable tree forks scarcely ten or twelve feet from the ground. Such are easy money for a prowler. I remember one's being taken close to where I was camped. We had no idea there were baboons anywhere near us but around midnight an appalling uproar suddenly commenced. Everything seemed to happen at once: a hyena, after strips of hippo hide hung on a rickety overhead contraption for storing peanuts and meal out of the way of fowl, pulled the entire outfit down on top of himself. As he fled with a surprised howl he got himself inextricably tangled in a long net that some near-by fisherfolk had hung up. Just at this moment baboons started an uproar as a big leopard grabbed an old-man baboon out of a low tree fork. Needless to say it was a pitch-dark night with rain falling steadily—it always is on such occasions. You would think the confusion was now complete. Far from it! The leopard, which had killed the baboon scarcely more than twenty paces from camp, apparently experienced his share of confusion when the hyena started things up so close. Anyway, he bolted, momentarily without sense of direction, and next thing we knew he had entangled himself in the same net as the hyena. The two of them thrashed around and crashed into another overhead platform bringing it tumbling to the ground, half of it falling on the roof of the nearest hut. The occupants thought a man-eater must be trying to tear his way in and started yelling their heads off. That started the rest of the village doing likewise. You never heard such a din! Men, women, children, baboons, all yelling and screaming, barking and howling at the tops of their voices, with the grunts, growls, snarls, yells, and howls of the leopard and hyena thrown in! My heroes were also yelling, they didn't know about what—but they always yell on such occasions. My gunbearer seemed the only sensible one among them. He, as usual, shared my tent.

Hearing the baboons I guessed a leopard was responsible for it all, so I grabbed my Paradox, which had a load of buckshot in the right barrel and a bullet in the left. I had a flashlight clamped to the barrels, so out I went.

At first it was difficult to make out exactly what had happened. All I could see was a confused mass enveloped in the net. It was extremely lively, rolling around with furious grunts and snarls. Finally something raised its head and looked toward me, and I caught the unmistakable flash of a leopard's eyes in my flashlight beam. I fired instantly, using the buckshot, and waited for further developments. But there weren't any. It was only when we cleared the leopard's body from the net that we found a dead hyena under him. I guess the leopard had just finished killing him when he looked up at me; doubtless he figured that the hyena was in some way responsible for everything—as indeed he was.

At the sound of the shot the baboons ceased their rumpus. As we drew the dead leopard from the net I could *feel* them watching us, wild with curiosity to see if we'd killed him. When it was clear he was truly dead there came one deep congratulatory bark from the forest, and then silence and peace for the rest of the night.

There's a widespread belief, among whites as well as blacks, that big baboons will attack native women to rape them. I don't believe it for one instant. I've questioned countless natives about it, and have never heard of an authentic case. Yes, they all believe it—especially the women!—but they can't point to a single one who has ever been so threatened. It's all hearsay. African women, like many of their white sisters, seem imbued with the notion that every male, human or animal, wanders around with but one intent, one aim and object, one thought in mind: rape. It's the most fantastic conceit but there it is. What's more, if you suggest to a woman that it isn't so she immediately feels slighted.

There have certainly been cases of big baboons' attacking youngsters on the outskirts of the "lands." But the attacks never developed beyond the stage of a bite or two. The youngsters were mostly little girls; but the baboons bit them merely as a bad-tempered dog might do. Baboons show complete contempt for native women in the lands. They'll come raiding the crops at any hour of the day, when the women are pounding grain, say, or grinding it into meal. They'll approach quite close and will pull faces; but that's all. They know perfectly well the women are un-armed and can't throw sticks and stones like the menfolk. But let a man, or even a youth, show himself on the edge of the cultivated patch and every baboon will clear off instantly to a respectful distance.

They make quite amusing pets when they are young and become very affectionate toward their owner. They know very well which one among those by whom they are surrounded is likely to extend the most sympathy. When they've been up to some mischief or broken something they will immediately make a beeline for this person, jump up on his shoulder, and pretend to be busily engaged searching for fleas in his hair or beard. If the aggrieved owner of the broken article comes around vowing vengeance the culprit will throw his arms around his boss's neck and cuddle up to him, seeking—and knowing darned well that he'll get it—protection. Baboons never make a mistake in this direction. Their instinct here is re-markable. But they are too mischievous to be allowed to run loose.

I've heard it said that baboons turn bad-tempered when older. I'm inclined to think that is only because of the teasing to which they are inevitably subjected by the thoughtless. I don't know how some people can derive pleasure from teasing animals, but you will see it wherever you go—I've even observed adults trying to poke sticks and umbrellas into a caged lion's eyes in London and Dublin zoos. There's something wrong with such men and women.

If a baboon has been in captivity it's no use thinking you can let him go and rejoin his companions, even if you see or hear them quite close. He won't do it. He seems to know that, having been in close association with man, he now has a brand on him and is no fit companion for the free denizens of the wild. They'd turn him out and refuse to have any-thing to do with him.

You can do good work shooting baboons with a scope-sighted .22-bore rifle, even a rim-fire; but I consider a scope sight essential. It's a pathetic sight to see a wounded baboon or monkey pulling his own guts out after receiving a badly placed bullet, trying to find the thing that's hurting him. He may be a varmint, yes, but that doesn't relieve you of the obligation as a sportsman to kill him with the minimum infliction of pain and suffering. A .22 Hornet would be a much better weapon be-cause of its flatter trajectory. So long as you are close you can kill with the rim-fire, and it won't scare the others as would a weapon that makes more noise; but as soon as they realize there's danger around you won't find it too easy to get within certain rim-fire range again. With a properly sighted Hornet, however, you could continue shooting up to two hundred yards. And you would certainly have them guessing at that range. A scope-sighted Swift, of course, would be an almost ideal weapon for the job.

The BUSH PIG is a reddish-colored fellow with a dirty cream-colored mane running back along his spine. In some districts he's very numerous, while in others he's scarce. He's strictly nocturnal.

Lion are very fond of pork, preferring it to everything except porcupine and zebra. Consequently, if you're trying to raise things and are worried by the depredations of hogs, don't be so foolish as to exterminate all the lion in the locality. You'll regret it if you do, for the lion will keep their numbers down far better and more certainly than you will.

Generally speaking, you don't get these fellows by day, but where they are at all numerous you can bag plenty at night. I can find little to say about them: they're not considered game in the accepted sense of the term; most men consider them excellent pork; so far as I know they're clean feeders; they carry little or no fat.

The WART HOG is an entirely different proposition. With the exception of certain incredible deep-sea fish—which look more like nightmares than living creatures—the wart hog must be the world's ugliest beast. But he has a stout heart back of that horrible dial. Though he never looks for trouble he's ready and willing if you want a fight. He's a hog, sure; but that isn't his fault. Neither is his ugliness his fault. And I'll give him his due: he's a sportsman. Maybe he isn't much to shoot with a high-power rifle but he can give you some nice stalking if you go about it the right way.

He doesn't raid your precious vegetable plot to the same extent as the bush pig, though I must admit that, being a hog, he does occasionally come around. Most of the time, however, he seems content to collect his grub elsewhere. You'll find where he has been rooting all over the veld. He must be very numerous. He's by no means so nocturnal as the bush pig — you'll have no difficulty in seeing him by day, particularly when the grass is burned.

He seems to live mostly in ant-bear holes and similar excavations. And it's rather amusing to see him make full speed for one of these holes and then, just when you expect a dirty dive, watch him suddenly swing around and *back* into the hole. Obviously, this is to enable him to face the entrance with those dangerous tusks of his. But sometimes he tries to back down a hole occupied by a brother. When this happens he shoots out again at speed! Wart hogs are ungenerous to their fellows in such emergencies. I'll never forget the expression I once saw on the face of one of these hogs when he tried to back down a hole too small for him. I wasn't hunting him, had no intention of interfering with him at all, but of course he couldn't know that.

When dogs chase one of these hogs and have him at bay the hog waits his chance, then makes a rush for the nearest dog and—bites off his tail! This he apparently considers adequate punishment for the indignity of being hustled around. Having inflicted the punishment he's quite willing to call it a day. If he's left alone he'll just trot off contentedly with his tail in the air. And since the cur that lost his tail will yelp and go for his life, the other curs nine times in ten will leave the old hog alone. I've seen a number of Kaffir dogs minus their tails as a result of encounters with wart hogs. For that matter, I've both seen and shot many wart hogs without tails — just short stumps. I used to think that lion or leopard had been responsible, but subsequent observation leads me to the belief that other hogs were the biters. Nevertheless, I once shot a wart hog that *had* been mauled the previous night by either lion or leopard. He had deep claw marks on his rump—and was without a tail. But, although the stump of the tail was ripped, I have a notion the original loss had taken place some time before.

If you only wound and the hog gets to cover—watch out! He can, and often will, make a most savage and determined charge if you close in too carelessly to finish him off. Those long curved tusks of his can disembowel you as effectively as any tulwar. They've disemboweled many a horse.

Mention of horses in connection with wart hog brings up memories of what I've always considered a grand sport—one, too, that shows the wart hog of Africa to be one of the bravest creatures on earth, fully the equal of any Indian wild boar. I refer to pigsticking from horseback, the rider being armed with a short hog spear: that ancient but, when properly used, very deadly weapon. You can be certain of a rousing gallop—the wart hog is much faster than you might imagine—with a fine fighting foe in front. He'll jink as smartly as any hog on earth, keep you guessing just as long as he likes, and then, when he thinks you are close enough, or when he's had enough for the present, he'll wheel around and charge straight home. There's nothing halfhearted about his charge—he fully means it. You've asked for it; okay, here it comes! "Never take a pig's charge standing" is a time-honored maxim. If you do it will probably cost you a good horse. There was one occasion when a grand old hog unhorsed no less than five men, and remained victor. He stood looking for a time, in no way scared, for all the world as though he were saying: "Well, had enough? If you want any more, I'm ready; if not, let's call it a day." As there wasn't a horse fit to ride, nobody accepted his challenge. So presently he just trotted away, his mane erect and his tail sticking straight up. He isn't the least bit vindictive, doesn't bear grudges. You can't help liking the old warrior.

The sow is just as brave as the boar in defense of her young. She'll face up to anything. But she is really too brave and jackals and, I suspect, hyenas are clever enough to exploit the trait. What they do is have one of their number make several short rushes toward her or one of her youngsters, until they provoke her into giving chase. As soon as she's a safe distance away the others rush in and grab a youngster or two. They will then go for their lives because the sow will quit the useless chase the moment she hears her youngsters squeal and return full of vengeance. But she'll now be too late. She'll gather the remainder of her family around her and go, leaving the dead one or two on the ground. There must be a considerable death rate among young wart hogs because the old girl normally brings forth five, but you seldom see more than two well-grown youngsters with her later in the season.

On the first shot at one of a group of wart hogs the remainder will run a little way and then pull up and stand motionless. They will generally be broadside-on to you, watching you out of the corner of one eye, piglike, without seeming to do so at all. (Incidentally, be careful of cow elephant that don't seem to be watching you after the first shot has been fired. I've had cows that seemed to be looking in the opposite direction suddenly wheel around and charge without the slightest warning. There is something very piglike about elephant—and young pigs in the grass look exactly like elephant, tiny elephant, without trunks!)

Most men consider wart hog among the best, tastiest, and juiciest meat on the African veld; others find it little better than poison. There must be an allergy which affects some eaters and not others.

Apart from baboons we get several varieties of the little green, black-faced MONKEY. At least I call them varieties, but really I know little about such matters. They seem very similar except for size. Some of them are almost as big as baboons, others quite tiny. The very small ones live mostly in patches of heavy forest and cannot be considered varmints —though some of the big fellows can, even if they don't do so much damage as baboons. But not the tiny ones. They are nice little things and make affectionate pets. They are not nearly so mischievous as baboons—indeed, the smaller monkeys seem to fear making you angry and show every evidence of contrition if they've done wrong. Their little old men's faces wrinkle up as though they were going to cry, and they make pathetic efforts to be friends again—creeping quietly up to your shoulder

and when there whispering into your ear to tell you how sorry they are
and how it won't occur again. Then they throw their little arms around
your neck and hug you, quite sure they're forgiven. Children love them.
They're very good-mannered, too. They don't snatch food from your table as baboons will. They'll sit quietly on the arm of your chair—just occasionally reminding you that they're there—and wait for you to give them
something.

Although SNAKES are usually classed as varmints the vast majority of
them are nothing of the sort—any more than wart hogs are. As a matter of fact, snakes do vastly more good than harm.

Some men are scared stiff of snakes (I knew one who wouldn't sleep
in a hut if a snake had been killed or even seen in it) and must instantly kill every snake they see. They're too ignorant to tell whether
that particular snake is poisonous or not. In any case, no snake will
wantonly attack you—why on earth should he? He'll get out of your
way if he can. He'll feel the vibration of your footsteps and go. Mostly
you'll just notice a rustling in the grass and perhaps see him slithering
away. The PUFF ADDER is the principal exception. He's a sluggish fellow and can't be bothered moving. Moreover, he's more nocturnal than
most snakes. He's the one folks usually tread on at night. The resulting
bite is almost always on the foot or ankle. I've never heard of its proving fatal. A badly swollen leg results, which may lay you up for a week
or ten days, but that's all.

Bites from other snakes are rare in Africa as compared with India.
But then India is far more densely populated than Africa. COBRAS will
rear up and puff out their hoods at you but will glide away if you wait
a moment. There's a variety of cobra which spits his venom into your
eyes instead of biting you. He seems to be commoner in southern Africa than elsewhere. But he also will get out of your way if you let him.
He's a very accurate shot and the result is painful temporary blindness
which may last two or three weeks. The eyes will be sore and inflamed
for a time after that but the effect eventually wears off. I once had a
native working for me in the Transvaal who had been blinded in this
manner some little while previously. However, it's not very common.

The BLACK MAMBA is said to be the deadliest snake in the world.
He is also said to be one of the three snakes in the world that will attack man without provocation (the other two allegedly being the Indian
hamadryad and the South American fer-de-lance); but I don't agree with
that. I'm not qualified to discuss the other two but I'm entitled to my
opinion, and basing that opinion on my observations of the black mamba
—and other creatures often said to attack man without provocation—I

say that I don't believe any snake other than possibly the anaconda and some giant pythons, which can swallow a man, ever attack man without some kind of provocation. The provocation may not be intentional on your part; but the snake does not know that. After all, let's be reasonable: why on earth should a snake waste his poison? He needs it for his prey; he can see that man is far too big to swallow—so why the attack?

As I say, I don't believe the black mamba will attack without provocation. Admittedly I've had only three encounters with mambas during my thirty-three years of continuous living in the African bushveld. However, those three were all at very close quarters, and the smallest of the snakes was some nine and a half or ten and a half feet long, I forget which now; the others were all bigger (the black mamba grows to thirteen feet or thereabouts—about the same size as the hamadryad). I base my opinion on my observations of the snakes on these occasions—I'm not concerned with writing thrilling accounts of hairbreadth escapes at the expense of facts.

On one occasion I nearly trod on a black mamba, a pretty big one, early in the morning during the early part of the rains when the young grass was only about a foot high. Something made me look down and I saw I was about to place my foot squarely on a black mamba's back! I extended the length of that stride so as to step right over him without pausing. But the instant I'd done so I turned and signed to the youngster who was following me to halt. I was afraid that if I'd suddenly tried to draw back before completing my stride I would have lost my balance and the snake would have thought my dancing about with one foot raised was an impending attack. He would then certainly attack in self-defense —could you blame him? He was stretched out in the grass, which was dripping with dew, and was doubtless sluggish. However, it could scarcely have been a closer encounter without actually touching him.

Then, only a few weeks ago, when I was camped on the shore of Lake Namaramba, I saw a big mamba coming out of the sudd and aiming right for the center of camp. I was sitting on a mat in the shade typing letters and was almost directly in the snake's path. Had I been alone I would just have sat on and taken no notice except to watch him as a matter of interest—because I simply didn't believe that he would attack me if I didn't do something to alarm him. However, I had a number of men in camp and they were scattered about here and there and hadn't seen the snake. It would not have been fair not to warn them. So I called out and pointed to the mamba. Instantly all stopped what they were doing and looked. The snake seemed to have heard me call out and then, seeing everybody—except me—standing and looking toward him, he instantly raised his head some three and a half feet from the ground, in the black mamba's characteristic manner, and viewed the situation. Now a black mamba fears nothing because he knows very well that his deadliness causes everything to fear him. He certainly wasn't going to turn back, neither did he see any necessity for making a detour just because there happened to be a camp full of men in his path. So, keeping his head the same distance from the ground, he started forward on a route which would have brought him past me within a matter of three feet or so. Still I sat on. I just could not believe there was any danger so long as nobody interfered with him: I'm quite sure he would have passed close by me with no more than a cold look. However, one of my canoe men grabbed a twenty-foot bamboo pole we use for poling the canoe through the shallows and brought it down across the snake's back. He was easily finished then. Now, although it might have looked as though the snake was about to attack me, since he was seemingly coming straight for me as I just sat there on the mat, there didn't seem to me to be the slightest threat in his manner. It was as though he were saying: "Now listen, fellows, I'm going right through here whether you like it or not. I don't want trouble and there won't be any if you leave me alone; but if you want it, okay, come and get it." His whole attitude was a danger signal, a warning—but no more. It wasn't a threat.

I had a youth working for me one time who had the extremely unpleasant experience of watching his uncle die after being bitten by a black mamba. He was only a youngster at the time, and the experience so shocked and terrified him that ever afterward, up to the present day, he has been scared sick of snakes. One can scarcely blame him. He told me that the man bitten was dead within a matter of minutes. Violent convulsions followed the bite, then coma and death. You have little hope if you are bitten by a big mamba—you just haven't time to do anything. Moreover, the snake's habit of carrying his head so high, even when traveling at speed, means that his bite is high—usually in places where it is impossible to apply a tourniquet: the breast or shoulder or neck. The mamba is said to be the quickest snake of all, and I'm sure his strike is incredibly rapid; but I consider it bunk that he can outpace a galloping horse, as many men have tried to tell us. Apart from his color, you can always tell a black mamba from other snakes because he raises so much of his body off the ground when alarmed or on the alert or angry. The ordinary snake will raise only his head and neck. Cobras will raise much of their bodies when stationary, but even cobras lower themselves again when moving, especially when moving rapidly. The black mamba, however, will raise and keep raised at least one third of his body in addition to his head and neck, and no matter how rapidly he's traveling.

Mambas by all accounts are most dangerous during the mating season. If you kill one of them you are advised to be sure to kill its mate also. You are also warned not in any circumstances, unless you are armed with a shotgun, to get between a mamba and its hole at this season. These two bits of advice are, at any rate, often repeated; and it's perfectly true that natives have been known to kill a black mamba in the mating season and place the body under the bed of some fellow against whom they had a grievance. They knew that the second snake would come in the night looking for its mate and would probably kill the sleeper when he got out of bed. I say this is true; but that's not strictly accurate because no such case has come under my observation. I've heard of it and read of it but I don't *know*. To set strongly against it is the very true and real fact that Africans don't hold grudges—one speaks generally, of course, since there are bound to be exceptions even though but a few.

The GREEN MAMBA is another very poisonous snake but not so deadly as the black. It is most decidedly green, but I have seen red ones too. At least I pointed out a big snake to a fellow who claimed to know far more than I do about them, and he assured me that the green mamba tends to vary its color in accordance with the soil of the district in which it lives. This happened to be in red-soil country. In all other respects this snake was exactly like an ordinary green mamba. I remember encountering a very big one when passing through a kraal on my way down to the water hole for a bath one time. There was nobody in the kraal, the village all being out in the lands. As I walked past a hut the snake was coming toward me not more than six feet away. I halted and so did he. We watched each other for a few moments, each waiting for the other to do something. As nothing happened I drew back a step and noticed that the snake also started to draw back. In a few moments I moved forward again and found that it had gone. But you seldom see these big snakes in the kraals. It was the silence and lack of movement that tempted this one to pass through the center of the village; also the fact that the villagers hadn't bothered to hoe down the long grass that grew to the very edge of the settlement.

It was noticeable that this green variety did not raise its head more than an inch or so off the ground: a black mamba encountered at such close quarters would certainly have raised his at least three and a half feet off the ground. Moreover, a black one wouldn't have withdrawn and returned whence he came, as the green one did. When I drew back a step a black mamba would have continued on his way.

Bird shot from a shotgun is the best medicine for snakes if you want to kill them. There is no doubt about it provided you aren't too close:

remember that if you're only a few feet from the snake the shot charge will be traveling like a single projectile, since it won't have had time to start spreading.

PYTHONS are also sluggish and disinclined to get out of your way. But they'll usually bark or growl at you if they see you coming directly toward them. (The bark is not like a dog's bark—but I don't know how otherwise to describe the noise.) Sometimes, in some districts, they grow to an enormous size. I've never measured a really big one but have killed them up to seventeen feet in length with bodies thicker than my thigh. Portuguese Angoniland is a good place for big ones. Many a time when I've been elephant hunting up there I have come on them stretched out in the grass, sleeping off a big feed. The thing to do is just to step over them and continue on your way. Your men would be horrified if you attempted to kill one when you are hunting elephant. They firmly believe that if you do you won't kill an elephant that day and if you encounter elephant at all it's quite likely one of them will kill you instead. I myself don't believe in such things but invariably respect my men's faith in superstitions and try not to flout them too openly. I do this not so much for the sake of the men's feelings as for my own sake. The morale, the mental condition of the hunt, is a matter of the utmost importance. If for any reason your men have become disheartened or convinced, no matter how foolishly, that you won't find or shoot an elephant that day, and that continuing with the hunt is mere waste of time and energy, it's extraordinary how soon that feeling will commence to pervade you too. There may be no reason for it; but there it is. I've experienced it more than once. If, on the other hand, all are certain that you will kill, although there is equally no very good reason for that belief except that you're all feeling good, then that confidence quickly becomes yours also and you feel that you simply *can't* go wrong. And what's more, when you feel like that, it's remarkable how easy everything seems.

The python, belonging to the Boa group, is not poisonous. His strike is not to bite, but to stun. His head is like a rock hammer and he gives his victim a bunt with his nose (just as a prospector will rap an outcrop of rock with the hammer head of his little pick) and then coils around and crushes the victim to death.

Once upon a time I was riding around on horseback and heard a pickaninny screaming up on the side of a low *kopje*. I rode as high as I could, dismounted, climbed the rest of the way, and found the child being crushed by a python. I drew my revolver and killed the snake. What the youngster was doing so far out on his own like that I don't know. He wasn't badly hurt: the snake hadn't had time to break any bones.

It's amazing the size animal a big python can swallow after crushing the bones and smearing the body with saliva. The horns of a swallowed animal not infrequently come through the python's body later: it's this that gave rise to the rumor of a horned variety of python in Southern Rhodesia around Bulawayo. A prospector, given to hitting the bottle when in town, appeared one day with a wonderful account of meeting a horned python on a *kopje*. When asked why he didn't kill it and bring it in he frankly admitted he thought he was in for another go of "the rats" and was beginning to see things. However, when he later realized he wasn't quite as far gone as that, he knew he had indeed seen the horned snake. Somebody else went out and killed it, and sure enough, horns were sticking out of the snake's back—the horns of a buck which had been swallowed and had pierced through from the inside. I've seen this several times; once it was the horns of a half-grown sable, which gave the python a most peculiar appearance. These accidents don't seem to inconvenience the snake unduly.

There appear in British magazines and outdoor journals from time to time accounts of a crowing python. The call has been described several times by those who declared that it could have been made only by a python, as there was no sign of any other animal in the vicinity. It is usually said to have been heard from the top of low *kopjes* at evening, and all the writers said they had heard it in the Sudan. I myself have never heard a python give vent to any such sound, but only to the gruff bark-growl I've already mentioned when he thinks you haven't seen him and are going to blunder right over him. I don't think it's intended as a threat—it never sounded threatening to me—but just as a warning that he is there.

In the ordinary way I don't object to having a few snakes around, for they'll keep the rats down better than any cat; but if you're trying to rear a few fowl or duck you don't want pythons in the neighborhood.

Snakebite is something I've never worried about. The usual thing to do is to carry an empty cartridge shell full of potassium permanganate crystals, and I admit to having done so for a number of years. If you're bitten the procedure is to tie a tourniquet well above the bite, cut an X over each puncture with a sharp knife, and rub in permanganate crystals. But the permanganate can be of little real use unless it comes in contact with the venom, and it can do this only if applied immediately and then only in the case of those bites by snakes which inject their venom close to the surface. It would be of little or no use in the case of a bite from a black mamba, not only because he injects his venom deeply, but also because it is a nerve poison absorbed by the system with unusual rapidity. Probably the best thing with any snakebite is a tight tourniquet at once (to be loosened for a minute every fifteen or twenty minutes to avoid gangrene) and a series of cuts, beginning with a crosscut over each fang mark down to the bottom of the bite. Additional cuts are made at the edge of the swelling as the swelling progresses, and massage and suction are applied to squeeze out as much of the venom as possible. If you have no cuts in your mouth you can suck the venom out of a snakebite without being harmed.

Fitzsimmons, curator of the zoo in Port Elizabeth in South Africa, or at any rate of the snake house, has prepared an antivenin outfit which all travelers are advised to carry. Fitzsimmons doesn't guarantee it against every variety of venom, though he's experimenting continually to find a mixture that will prove useful against all African snake; nevertheless, it's unquestionably a good thing to have handy—though I've never had one myself. Personally, I rely upon pure carbolic acid. If applied as soon as possible it will work its way deep into the wound and neutralize the poison better than permanganate will. Incidentally, I also swear by pure carbolic acid for lion, leopard, and croc maulings, etc. Most men who lose their lives after being mauled don't die of the actual wounds but of the blood poisoning that almost invariably sets in afterward. There is nothing I know of quite so effective as pure carbolic acid. Just drop it straight into the wounds—don't bother about washing or dressing them or anything else. Permanganate, unless syringed into the wounds, won't be able to get way down into the apex of a deep puncture like that made by the long teeth at the corners of a lion's mouth—but carbolic acid will find its way down there and clear up what poison there may be.

I'm not alone in my belief in the efficacy of pure carbolic acid: Daly is also a firm believer in it. Then, do you remember that young Indian girl-wife who was so dreadfully mauled by the old man-eating tigress of Chowgarh? Corbett tells us about her and says a doctor friend of his had given him a little two-ounce bottle of some yellow fluid to carry with him always when tiger hunting. This he poured straight into the girl's wounds, with the result that they healed up perfectly in a remarkably short time. Corbett doesn't tell us what the fluid was and presumably didn't know but I suggest that it was pure carbolic acid, which is a reddish-yellow liquid and comes ordinarily in two-ounce bottles.

I have more than once read that some fellow purporting to be a hunter has denied that snakes hypnotize their victims. Such men are curiously unobservant. I've seen it on a number of occasions. I don't say that all snakes hypnotize their victims as a matter of course; but certainly some do. I remember an occasion in my early days. I was wandering around one evening with a rifle hoping for a shot at a klipspringer. I heard a persistent chattering from the top of a small lightly bushed hill and climbed up to see what it was. There were big boulders toward the top of the hill with trees growing among them. I came quietly through these until I got to the very top. Here there was a very big rock with two or three others jammed against it. The chattering was coming from the far side of the center rock. I slowly scrambled up and peeked over the top. Then I froze. There, on a little piece of level ground immediately in front of me and not more than ten or twelve feet away, was a red squirrel. He was crouching close to the ground, every hair standing on end and quivering and vibrating as he chattered and chattered unceasingly. His eyes were fixed on something in front of him and even as I sighted him, he took a grudging step forward toward it. I slowly turned my head to look to my half-left, and then froze again. There was a big snake. He was lying more or less stretched out with his head perhaps three or four inches off the ground, and staring straight toward the squirrel. As I watched he commenced to sway his head slowly from side to side, moving it about six or eight inches. At the same time the squirrel's head started to swing from side to side, as though there were an invisible steel rod connecting the two heads. He was plainly unable to tear his eyes away from the snake's. The chattering continued without a break. When the snake stopped swaying his head the squirrel's head also stopped moving; and as the snake stared fixedly at him, the wretched little squirrel again took that dragging step closer to the terror. Then again the snake started swaying his head from side to side. And so the performance was repeated. When I arrived there was perhaps six feet between them. The snake made no attempt to approach his victim: he was deliberately drawing it toward himself. It was truly a fascinating business to watch: the fixed beady intensity of the snake's eyes, the abject terror of the little squirrel, his utter inability to withdraw his gaze from the cold black eyes that held his, and the irresistible manner in which he was drawn forward against his will. Presently he was within less than three feet of the snake. Whether or not I would have waited for the final tragedy I can't say. But without warning the butt of my rifle knocked slightly against the rock. Instantly the snake's head turned toward me. He spotted me, stared for a second, then whipped around and was gone. The squirrel's chattering slowly died down and ceased. His trembling and vibrating abated at the same time, and his hair gradually settled back into place. It took some appreciable while for realization to sink in that the snake was gone. For quite a time the little creature continued to crouch motionless. I was close enough to be able to see comprehension dawn on him—to see his eyes lose their fixed glassy look and begin to focus again. And then he suddenly came to life. He shot straight up in the air—perhaps two and a half feet, turning around before he hit the ground again—and legged it from that accursed spot like a scalded cat. Or, rather, since he went in a series of jumps and not at all the way a squirrel usually covers the ground, I might have said like a scalded kangaroo.

I don't know what kind of snake it was. I've a notion it was a mamba: either a light-colored black one or a very dark green one. He was perhaps eight feet long.

But don't let the thought of snakes worry you. I've been wandering around the African bushveld for many years now and have never yet had a snake make a pass at me.

The GIANT FOREST HOG, so far found only in Kenya, and whose existence was disbelieved in for many years by the armchair know-it-alls, is like an overgrown specimen of the ordinary bush pig. I've never hunted him.

The common ZEBRA is the curse of farmers and ranchers in Kenya and, to a somewhat lesser extent, in Tanganyika. He simply swarms on the great East African plains. In Kenya he's classed as Varmint Number 1. He carries and spreads all the ticks most abhorred by growers of livestock. When he gets to a fence, nothing will satisfy him until he gets under or through it: it doesn't seem to occur to him that he might be able to jump it. The result is that he tears down more fences than all the rest of the game put together. True, if a rhino gets hung up in a fence, he'll pull down half a mile of it; but then he very rarely does get stuck. In some places, however, you'd think the zebra actually goes out of his way to find a fence to mess up. There's nothing on one side of it that he can't find on the other; but the grass on the far side is always greener.

At one time sportsmen were restricted to so many zebra on their licenses; then the limit was raised (to twenty); after that, because of the squeals of the stock owners, the limit was removed entirely and sportsmen were told they could shoot as many zebra as they liked. But since there's little sport in shooting him, and his resemblance to a horse deters many men, few hunters shoot more than a specimen or so as a trophy. They do kill a certain number to use as bait for lion. However, the number shot has no appreciable effect on the zebra population—so little, in fact, that Percival said he'd like a clause in every lion permit specifying that for every lion a hunter should be compelled to produce, I forget whether it was thirty or sixty, zebra tails, since he figured each lion must kill at least that number of zebra a year. There is no question that lion prefer zebra to anything else. The African will tell you that that is because zebra meat doesn't stick between the teeth like other meats. I don't know if lion are bothered by meat's sticking between their teeth. I doubt it. But it's a fact that zebra meat *is* far less likely to stick than other kinds, though whether or not this is the case when it is eaten raw, I can't say.

Various attempts have been made to domesticate the common zebra, but they have all proved failures. A German, a Baron Bronsart, went in for this in a big way in Tanganyika. He had good horse trainers, both white and Somali, and they did everything they knew. But it was no good. Some cowpunchers brought over from the States described zebra as plain mean. That sums them up: they are vicious and mean and in the end spineless. They'll fight like hell and then just lie down and die on you. The very few that actually submitted to harnessing wouldn't work. They'd have a light spider or buggy where the going was easy but would refuse to pull if they came to heavier going. Somebody, it is true, used to drive three and a pony into Nairobi in days gone by and one of the Rothschilds used to drive one with three ponies in a light dogcart in London. And there was one that drew a light cart around the grounds of the London zoo. But taken all around, in view of the money spent on it, the domestication of the common zebra was an utter failure.

One government tried crossing zebra with ponies and burros, calling the resulting animals "zebroids." It was thought they would be tough and hardy. But they proved no better than their striped parents. They were supplied to an Indian division in one of the frontier wars in the northwest of India, to carry light mountain guns. The wind-up of it was that the men carried the guns themselves. The darned zebroids ran true to form and just lay down when the going grew tough.

The much bigger GREVY ZEBRA, which I don't think you find south of the equator, would seem a more likely subject for domestication. However, I can't remember ever hearing of anybody's attempting this. All were too disheartened, perhaps, by failures with the common zebra. There is no mistaking the Grevy species. Not only are they considerably bigger than the common zebra, but their stripes are quite different: they're much narrower and closer together, and run right around under their bellies. (The stripes on the common zebra are broad, wide apart, and stop short of the belly.)

Although zebra are considered a pest on the great plains it's not so elsewhere.

Zebra like lightly bushed veld where it's dry underfoot. They're very fond of having dust baths, and you will frequently come to circular dust-filled depressions to which they return for a roll. In this type of country you find them mostly in small parties of a dozen or so. They're not difficult to stalk and shoot. But they're tough; you needn't expect anything but disappointment if you try shooting with little copper-pointed slugs.

The common zebra are eternally fighting among themselves—you'll often hear them squealing. They bite and kick one another without apparent reason. Time and again I've heard a resounding thump as one of them lashed out with both hooves and they landed squarely on a companion's ribs. I remember seeing an old eland bull teach one manners at a water hole one time: There was a troop of six or eight eland, led by this old bull, and they were sedately enjoying their drink when a noisy party of some thirty zebra arrived. They were, as usual, behaving like hooligans. They barged forward and bumped into one another and the eland as they all struggled to get a drink together. They stomped into the water, stirring up the muddy bottom; they staled into it, making it sour and unpleasant; they fought and squealed. Finally one of them knocked into the old eland bull, and not for the first time. The old boy lost his even temper and decided to teach the ragamuffin manners. He suddenly wheeled around and butted the offender in the ribs with his horns and forehead. I clearly heard the thump and the zebra's grunt. He would certainly have been sent rolling had he not caromed into a companion. And he was truly astonished. When he recovered his balance and had scampered away to a respectful distance he turned and looked back at the old bull in amazement. But I noticed he kept his distance thereafter, and so did the rest of the ill-mannered crowd. It was for all the world as though a quiet dignified old gentleman had been rudely hustled and bumped into by skylarking corner boys in some big city and had lost patience with them and laid his cane across the shoulders of the nearest.

I have many times eaten zebra, but only when I've had nothing else. It's reasonably palatable; but the bright yellow of the melted fat, like melted butter that has had too much coloring matter mixed into it, puts most people off. Incidentally, the fat when rendered down remains fluid like oil. I've used it to cook with when I've had nothing else; but its color and slightly strong flavor are objectionable to most men. Still, there have been times when I was mighty glad to get it, because food cooked without any fat at all quickly becomes uninteresting.

Hunting for meat for my men one time I saw a troop of zebra scamper away about a hundred yards off through light scrub. I knew we weren't the cause of the disturbance and guessed it was a lion. I carefully stalked the place from which the zebra had stampeded and there, sure enough, was a lioness, heavy in cub, just commencing to feed. The zebra had halted when scarcely more than forty or fifty yards away, looked around to make sure the lion had all she wanted, and then re-commenced grazing as though nothing had happened. They knew she wouldn't interfere with them again. I wasn't interested in the lioness—this wasn't a man-eating area—and so fired directly over her at a zebra. I killed my beast; and it almost looked as though I'd killed that lioness with shock! She tripped over something as she tried to get away and rolled completely over. I let her go. That now gave us two freshly killed zebra—hers and mine—which was ample.

On coming away I picked up the spoor of a big lion and followed it for a spell. It was the mate of the lioness: he must have killed for her, she being so near her time, and then wandered off to look for something for himself. This surprised me somewhat as there was far more in the zebra than the lioness could have eaten. Maybe he figured she'd lie up by it and have several feeds from it. When she cleared she also picked up his spoor and followed him. I followed too until I came to where he'd halted on hearing my shot. He must have waited here for a while, doubt-less wondering if all were well with his mate. When she came along they both moved off together, in all probability cursing me heartily for giving the male extra work to do.

4

THE AFRICAN HIMSELF

15: THE AFRICAN AS HUNTER, TRAPPER, FISHERMAN, SERVANT AND PORTER

The African hunts solely for food—he isn't a "sportsman." By this I mean that he doesn't kill merely for fun or for trophies. An animal's hide is a secondary consideration and may be taken, but solely because in the first instance it covered the meat. In many areas the hide is cut up along with the meat, and both are dried together and used as food. Bechuanaland, and southern Africa generally, is the great place for karosses, or skin rugs and blankets. These are beautifully tanned, cured, and made up, the hair, of course, being left on. Elsewhere throughout the continent they seem to know little about curing and tanning. Yet the natives undoubtedly did know something about it in days gone by because before the lordly white man got the notion of increasing his country's trade in cotton piece goods by insisting on all natives' wearing clothes, those who wore anything at all mostly used skins, either loincloths or hides tied loosely over one shoulder. These skins would be soft and flexible and comfortable to wear, even when drawn between the legs. But you seldom see anyone nowadays with such a garment, other than an elderly fellow away out at the back-o'-beyond.

Hunting methods vary, naturally, from tribe to tribe. Different methods are attributable to varying types of bush and veld and to the different species of game encountered in them. Among the more direct methods of hunting, the spear deserves pride of place. Throughout the length and breadth of the continent, in the days when the African could hunt at will without fear of interference and prison sentences, those who went after the mighty elephant lone-handed, even though they were primarily eager for meat, nevertheless had the true instinct of the hunter—what we call nowadays the sportsman. Those heroes came to closer grips with their quarry than any other hunters. They did not throw the spear; it was a heavy broad-bladed two-handed weapon which they drove into the elephant's lungs, then legging it like hell out of the danger zone. Before closing on the elephant—in thick bush or grass, of course—they'd strip off every stitch of clothing they were wearing (if they were wearing anything at all) including even their belts and knives. These odds and ends they'd leave in the charge of a youngster, usually the hunter's own son, at the foot of a tree some little distance away and if possible so situated that the youngster could see exactly what was happening and thus learn his father's methods. Then, entirely unencumbered and with nothing on him that could possibly get hung up on a bush, branch, or trailing vine or creeper as he made his getaway, the hunter would creep silently up alongside the elephant and drive his spear in with all the force he could command. The broad heavy spearhead, almost as sharp as a surgeon's amputating knife and certainly sharp enough for an African to shave with, was not firmly attached to the shaft: the shaft was left loose to save it from being broken every time it was used, and also so that it wouldn't pull the head out of the lungs when the elephant stampeded through the bush. However, before it dropped clear of the blade it would have been knocking against plenty of things and would have worked the blade about in the lungs. The result was that the lungs were cut to ribbons and the elephant seldom got far; but a charge was almost a certainty as soon as the spear had been driven in. The elephant nearly always whipped around and tried to grap his assailant. And since the hunter was actually within trunk reach you can understand why he didn't want anything about him which might in the slightest degree impede his progress. Naturally he dodged away either down- or across-wind and just relied upon his natural agility and knowledge of the game to get clear. It was surely a man's game, that. But, as I've pointed out, those hunters were brought up to it from the time they were elbow-high to their fathers. This method of spearing was practiced in the past in every elephant district through which I've wandered. I know a number of men who killed elephant that way and have greatly enjoyed their reminiscences—and by all accounts remarkably few such hunters were killed or even injured.

However, I doubt if an elephant has been killed in that manner for many years. The great old spears are hung away like grandpop's musket or sword, just occasionally to be taken down, fondly handled, and gazed at with rheumy old eyes that once were clear and that still brighten when the elderly warrior relives some of those stirring hunts. The passing of the old elephant spears and the men who wielded them marks the end of an era.

Another method of hunting the elephant with the spear is practiced to the present day by the Shilluk in the southern Sudan. A party of them, stark-naked, will go out and eventually encounter a herd or troop of elephant. Closing in from both sides they begin throwing their light but very sharp spears, three or four of which every man carries—and nothing else, not even a knife: the spear blade serves as a knife when required. On feeling the bite of a spear the chosen elephant usually wheels around toward the thrower with the intention of attacking. But no sooner does he do so than the men on the opposite side throw their spears into him. He immediately wheels around toward them, only to have the first attackers get busy on him with another spear or two each. Bewildered, he tries to make a getaway, but these slim fleet-footed hunters can and do keep up with him on both sides. Their endurance is truly remarkable (and they don't undergo long periods of training beforehand like Western athletes—they're always fit). The hunt may extend for only a mile or two, or it may last many miles. If the hunters want more elephant after the first one has gone down they'll pick up the spoor of the remainder of the herd right away and get after them. They'll kill another, too, and as many more as they want. They can keep going for hours on end. Rarely does a man drop out and say he's tired. On and on, hour after hour, as tireless as the wild hunting dog. I like those fellows. They hunt all their game the same way, the throwing spear being their only weapon—it and their lithe greyhound physique and inexhaustible endurance.

The Masai and their cousins the Nandi are probably the best-known spearmen. There are no elephant in their country but they are famous for their lion hunts. They will also, when necessary, kill rhino and buffalo with their spears. When tackling lion they invariably start off by throwing one or more spears—each man carries only one—so as to provoke the animal into charging. Then they know he's theirs. They've encircled him, and when he goes at the man directly in front of him the others immediately rush in and drive their long narrow-bladed spears through him from both sides. I'm not sure that the Nandi aren't actually greater at killing lion than the Masai—they certainly seem to do a lot more hunting. They will even go out, just two together, to tackle a lion: they are entirely fearless. Generally speaking, they are slightly lighter colored than the Masai, with pleasant open features. But don't misinterpret this; you'll find superbly handsome men among the Masai, too. Both tribes have the same slim lightly boned bodies. They are fine fellows, and I have a great admiration for them.

I've already spoken of the hippo harpooners of the lower Zambezi. I have recently come across a somewhat different method of hunting hippo on Lake Namaramba in Portuguese East Nyasa. This is Yao country, and I find that at the upper end of the lake, where it's rather shallow, hunters go out in their little dugout canoes, one-man craft, find where the hippo are sleeping under the sudd, and then just spear them. They don't bother about harpoons; they merely drive their light spears down into the hippo hoping to find the lungs. The wounded hippo goes for his life and the hunters chase him across the lake, spearing him again if they get the chance, until they finally drive him ashore. (As I pointed out earlier, a hippo wounded in the body will always try to get the wound out of water as soon as possible. I've a notion that leeches and little fish worry them otherwise; and quite possibly, if they are wounded in the lungs, water is drawn in when they breathe.) I gather the men are seldom attacked; and when they get the hippo ashore he's easy money. A hippo on land is clumsy and has little chance surrounded by spearmen.

When you think of all the fuss and preparation there is, and all the excitement, before a party of whites, armed with the most modern of powerful high-velocity rifles, will venture out to hunt any one of these potentially dangerous beasts—well, you may despise the black man but if you're honest you will have to admit admiration for the naked "savage" who tackles these creatures with such primitive weapons without giving the matter a second thought. He doesn't consider it anything to write home about. Of the microscopic number who *can* write, I don't suppose one has ever mentioned such a hunt in any letter to his folks. No matter what or how many animals he has killed, he'll never boast about his prowess. True, if he's looking for a job as hunter with some white man he'll then boast that he's killed more elephant than there are leaves on the trees, and never missed a shot in his life—never learned how to miss. But that's a different matter. If he recognizes you as an old-timer yourself, knowing the game as well as he does, he won't try any such nonsense. And I've never heard a genuine native hunter boast among his fellows. When called upon to do so he will delight in recounting some adventure or hunt, but he won't stress his part in it. As a matter of fact, I've found that the best of the native hunters prefer to sit quietly and listen to others, and when asked for an opinion they are very soft-spoken.

Incidentally, it might be of interest to mention that the good native hunters who wear any clothes at all invariably choose black. Khaki is just another of those stupid white-man conventions. Black is far more suitable and practical. Khaki is all very well when the grass is dry but it's conspicuous when the land is burned over. (After the annual grass fires have swept through the country everything is black.) If you're wearing black clothes you're quite invisible the instant you stop moving. Even when moving slowly, you're not nearly so conspicuous as when you are wearing khaki. Moreover, all shadows at all seasons of the year are black or dark gray. If you're wearing black you've only to stop and you immediately become just another shadow. I found this out many years ago, and ever since have worn nothing but black or gray or a mixture of both —if I wear anything at all! It may be wondered, perhaps, just how dark an Irishman becomes, even after living not merely for months but for years naked under the Central African sun. Well, I have been taken for a native a number of times when seen from behind. Certainly I wasn't black; but then, many Africans are brown, ranging from the color of milk chocolate down through bitter chocolate to dull coal black and finally shiny jet black. I was certainly a good deal darker than the khaki drill usually worn by whites in Africa, and therefore much less conspicuous—and was darker, as a matter of fact, than many brown-skinned natives who had been living for some time in the shade, or continually wearing shirts. (It is not generally known, I think, that Negroes other than the very dark ones vary in shade depending on the extent to which they expose themselves to the sun.)

A favorite way to hunt, after the spear, is by bow and poisoned arrow. It's popular throughout Africa to a greater or lesser extent. Bushmen of the Kalahari Desert are great bowmen; but I think that today the Wakamba of Kenya are probably the primary exponents of the method, though the Wanderobo, from whom they buy or trade the poison, and who live solely on the proceeds of their hunting (meat and wild honey), must run them a close second.

There's a species of Euphorbia that rhino are very fond of, but curiously enough not until the young shoots and leaves begin to wither and dry. The Wakamba, in whose country there are plenty of rhino, well know this, and the hunter fells one of these trees, waits so many days, and then returns by night to sit up close by. By this time the young shoots are beginning to wither, the rhino will have found them, and the hunter will almost certainly get several shots before daybreak if he wants them. (Let me hasten to say that the African hunter does not kill more than he and his mates can conveniently handle—which is more than can be said in most cases of the rifle-armed whites.) The good thing about the use of the bow for this kind of hunting is that the wounded animal will *always* run some distance before falling. Depending on where you hit him, a powerful rifle can easily drop him in his tracks and thereby spoil the spot for the future—at least for a very long time. In the case of a water hole, it might ruin the place for years.

There are various kinds of arrow poison, some very much better and more powerful than others. If fresh they all kill with certainty. But in the case of a big animal, such as a rhino or elephant, the arrow *must* drive in. If for any reason it only glances and so inflicts a superficial wound it won't kill, though the wound will almost certainly fester and make the recipient very savage.

The Galla, from farther north in Tanaland, also use the poisoned arrow and fearlessly shoot leopard with it. There are some very big and beautifully marked leopard in that district, and they have the habit of waiting for the goat kraals to be opened in the mornings and then bagging a hungry goat that makes a dash for the bush to get its breakfast. The Galla hunter unhesitatingly follows leopard spoor into dense thickets and looses off from close range. In such circumstances a charge is almost a certainty where leopard are concerned. Many Africans, not necessarily hunters at all, are killed throughout the continent every year because of the reckless way they'll follow up and fearlessly tackle both lion and leopard if either of those big cats interferes with the goats and cattle. In all probability the fellow is hopelessly inadequately armed. But he surely sees red if something kills his precious goats or sheep.

The bows used vary: in some districts they are not very powerful, whereas in others it's a miracle how the men manage to draw them at all. The arrows, made from reeds and with very light heads, are not what you and I would call accurate. But the African has the patience and stealth of the true hunter and being both unencumbered and unshod can slip through the bush like a dark shadow. He relies upon the close approach. It's this that serves him so well when tackling elephant, either with his own old muzzle-loader or a modern rifle. As a marksman he might not shine; but when he is in the bush he gets so close that he must nearly scorch his victim's hide with the muzzle blast.

I've tried poisoned arrows quite often myself, using the native weapons. I found them so effective that when I got back from World War II and discovered all my rifles, ammo, and equipment stolen (or, rather, "disposed of," owing to a rumor that I had been killed in action) and almost despaired of ever getting new ones and shells for them, I was about to ask a friend of mine in the States to send me a couple of good bows and a bunch of hunting arrows. I mean that. I was quite prepared to hunt rhino and buffalo with the primitive bow and arrow—particularly if my arrows were dipped in fresh poison. The American hunting arrow, shot from a good American bow, is far deadlier than the uninitiated think. And with fresh poison properly added to the heads—or better still, with the heads slightly modified to carry the poison—I wouldn't hesitate to tackle elephant. I've never yet shot an elephant with a poisoned arrow but that's simply because I never found an elephant when I was so armed. I have shot buffalo and lesser game with them. And that wasn't a quarter of a century ago—it was as recently as halfway through the

econd World War, when I was no longer anybody's chicken and had
ong forgotten what it was to be agile.

If fresh (as I say) the better poisons kill in a remarkably short space
f time. I've seen animals receive the arrow, run a short distance, stop,
way, and collapse. There were some that looked dead before they
ouched the ground: there wasn't a movement out of them after falling.
"he poison seems to have a paralyzing effect on the heart or nerves—
'm not enough of a toxicologist to tell you which. When an animal has
een killed for food the flesh immediately around the wound made by
he arrow is cut out and thrown away; the remainder of the meat is quite
ll right. Anyway, the poison isn't a stomach poison and could doubtless
e swallowed without doing harm.

Just how good is the African hunter with a decent rifle? Well, as I've
lready said, he probably wouldn't put up much of a showing at Bisley
r Camp Perry. He's never had any experience of that sort of shooting, and
vhen he's hunting his natural instinct and ability as a stalker make him
et really close before attempting to shoot, so his actual marksmanship is
ot of primary importance. Anyway, it's naturally as a hunter that we're
hinking of him and want to know just how good he is when suitably
rmed. And the answer is that it all depends on what training he's had—
s you might expect. Mostly the natives get no training at all and are
iven any worn-out rifle and expected to kill with it. That's unfair; and
bservation shows that when properly trained and armed the African
s at least as good as any white man who has ever hunted elephant—
vith the possible exception of the great Karamojo Bell. The Africans
mployed by the Elephant Control section of the governments of
Jganda and Tanganyika have been extremely well trained and are well
rmed with rifles in which they can have complete confidence. Three of
hese men in Uganda were especially commended for killing three hun-
lred elephant between them in less than a year, while another killed
inety in nine months. Some of the Tanganyika men are just as good
nd no doubt have equally high bag figures. There are not many white
unters who have done as well, much less any better. One of the things
hat helps the African, of course, is his mobility and the simplicity of his
eeding arrangements. He doesn't need a string of men toting kit, bed-
ling, foodstuffs, pots and pans and kettles, cutlery and crockery, like the
ormal white man. It was learning to live and eat like the African and
Asiatic that enabled me to get around to the extent I did. Nevertheless,
hose of us with real experience at this game feel that for serious profes-
ional elephant hunting a gunbearer, cook, and six porters is the mini-
num satisfactory number for a party.

Personally, I have never employed a native hunter to shoot for me But nearly all the hunters of the past did. (Sutherland never had fewe than five, and usually double that number.) Those men who have na tives shooting for them don't hesitate to claim all the elephant as shot by themselves. Sutherland was usually referred to as the first man to have shot a thousand elephant—but no mention was made of his gang o native hunters. Bell was an exception: so far as I know he did all his own hunting—aside from the eight tuskers old Kilassa shot for him during hi absence one time. The real old-timer of the black-powder days shot hi own elephant, though he always had a reliable gunbearer trained to shoot if he was facing a charge and had a misfire—an all-too-common occurrence in those days. This, of course, was permissible in view of the unreliability of the guns and ammunition of those days, to say nothing o the smoke nuisance.

The best of the native hunters are entirely without fear. There have been several cases of their being knocked down by charging elephant or by trees felled by charging elephant and then having the courage to lie doggo, feigning death, as a trunk came feeling and smelling over the supposed body. The elephant then buried what he thought was the corpse under branches and grass and moved off. The hunter, who wasn't hurt, waited for a short while to be sure the elephant was really gone, then got up, picked up the spoor, followed the wounded bull and killed him. His very narrow escape hadn't shaken his nerve in the slightest. As I say, several of these cases are known—Blunt mentions one in which his Wemba tracker, Pemba Moto, was the central figure, and I have no doubt there have been many more of which the only record is in the memories of the men concerned. Incidentally, it's quite common for elephant to bury the bodies of those they've slain—that is, if they have left anything to bury! Presumably the notion back of it is to conceal their guilt. Elephant are fully capable of such thought processes and if this isn't the answer, then what is?

Other native methods of hunting, less direct, are nets and traps, pitfalls and snares. The nets are from a quarter to a half a mile in length, of strong cord, with eight- to twelve-inch mesh. They are stretched across a suitable place, and then the entire countryside is roped in for the drive. The game is driven ahead toward the net. Many of the bigger animals break back through the beaters or jump the net when they reach it, though they are occasionally caught. It's mostly smaller buck the natives hope to kill. These usually try to get through the net and entangle themselves in it. They are killed with spears, bows and arrows—not poisoned—knobkerries, tomahawks, rocks, or any odd thing that's andy. Every scrap of meat is scrupulously evenly divided among all aking part in the drive.

Pitfalls for game spell a lot of preliminary work. First of all a long ence of trees, branches, and grass must be built. It may be a mile to everal miles long. Deep pits are then dug here and there in gaps left along the length of the fence and carefully covered over. From time to ime an animal will drop through and be unable to get out again because the pits are narrow, and narrow still more as they go down. This means that the unlucky beast's legs are all bunched together so hat he can do little scrambling or jumping. He's killed with spears. Even buffalo are trapped in these pits. The trouble with the method is hat the natives responsible for the pits don't go out every day to see what they've caught. When the fence is new they do; but as time goes on they grow careless about daily visits, which means that sometimes a wretched buck dies of thirst before the men find him.

Pits were a regular method of killing elephant all over the continent in days gone by, but for them it was not usually necessary to build a ong fence. The pitfalls were dug on regular elephant paths, or else a ence was built around the lands with pits here and there so that any elephant that came raiding stood a good chance of being caught in one of them. In British territory this method of killing elephant has been igorously suppressed, and it's strongly discouraged everywhere. Except in parts of the Congo and French Equatorial Africa I've seen comparatively few elephant pits.

The native's muzzle-loader—"Brown Bess" Tower musket—he treasures more faithfully than his favorite wife, and before he turns his ace to the wall he hands it on to his eldest son. A few (a very few) affluent and much-to-be-envied individuals have two of these old guns and are looked upon by the less favored with that awe which American multimillionaires inspire when visiting Europe. Yet some of the real hunters who own these old gas pipes are surprisingly careless in their reatment of them. I know one, a very good hunter indeed who seldom lowers himself to shoot anything smaller than a buffalo, who was casually poling his canoe along an arm of the Lifumba one day in a place where I happened to know there was about two feet of mud on the bottom; and he was using his musket, muzzle downward, as a pole. When I asked if that wasn't a hell of a way for a hunter to treat a gun he merely shrugged a glistening ebony shoulder, flashed me an ivory smile, and replied that it wasn't loaded!

The men make their own powder for these guns—terribly coarse stuff hat belches prodigious clouds of smoke—but naturally prefer the store-

bought powder when they can get it. However, they're not primaril
concerned with the powder charge. What interests them is the projectil
—I hesitate to write "bullet" or even "ball." Rather, projectiles: the
like to load two, one about half the size of the other. Rarely does eve
the larger one touch the bore anywhere; and anything at all will do
provided it's heavy. They're fond of Sparklet bulbs, which they fill wit
sand or a stolen stick of solder if they haven't any lead. They have n
molds and will just hammer a lump of lead until it's reasonably roun
and use that. They use hammered telegraph wire in the same way, an
chunks cut off a bar of any old iron—not forgetting the legs of cookin
pots. I've recovered some of these pot leg slugs from buffalo I subse
quently killed myself. One big old bull had a chunk of iron bar abou
half an inch in diameter and an inch long right in the center of his live
and a chunk of a smaller iron bar that had driven clear through hi
intestines. It had punctured them in many places, but every punctur
had healed beautifully. The old fellow was in fine condition, with plent
of fat—which may give you an idea of African game's toughness an
tenacity to life.

Although the natives lose a lot of wounded game, nevertheless the
do sometimes kill with these old guns. Armed with them they hav
literally no fear at all. They think nothing of tackling buffalo and rhino
and if they only wound at the first attempt, they don't hesitate to follo
up though they know perfectly well they stand a very good chance o
being charged. However, fully realizing how often the big game get
away, unless they've plenty of powder and slugs they prefer somethin
smaller. Still, there are some, such as that fellow I've just referred to wh
used his gun as a punt pole, who scorn to tackle anything smaller tha
buffalo.

As trackers and gunbearers well-trained Africans are as good a
any on earth. A gunbearer is absolutely reliable—he will *never* let yo
down: scores of hunters would have come to a sticky end had it no
been for their staunchness. There are men who were grabbed b
wounded elephant or lion and are alive today solely thanks to thei
gunbearers who stuck by them and came to their assistance with a sec
ond rifle. Many and many a gunbearer, too good for the cowardly whit
whose second rifle he was carrying, has been killed when the self-style
hunter let *him* down, threw away his rifle and bolted instead of standin
to the charge. You don't hear a whole lot about these incidents—they'r
hushed up because of "white man's prestige." You say such incident
are rare? Don't you believe it! Why, only recently a pseudo "whit
hunter" who had undertaken the responsibility of guiding a visitin
American woman turned tail and bolted after throwing away his rifl

when a wounded elephant charged, leaving the woman and her gun-bearer, and his own gunbearer, to face the enraged bull unsupported! Be it noted—and remembered—that *both* gunbearers stood by the woman. I forget whether she killed the elephant or merely turned it—the point is immaterial. It is enough to say that she and the native boys stood to the charge, and she succeeded in saving her life and probably those of the gunbearers also.

When you hear or read of a man's complaining that his gunbearer bolts and is not there when wanted you can be sure it's because the man himself is unreliable and the gunbearer never knows when he's going to drop his rifle and bolt. *Why* should the gunbearer stand there if the white hunter runs? Most gunbearers don't know how to shoot. Now, I'm not just a seasonal hunter who goes out for five or six weeks during the easiest and pleasantest time of the year, like practically all other hunters of the present day. I'm the last of the old school of professional ivory hunters; I hunt right through the year, every year. Yet in all that time, although I've had many gunbearers at different times, I've *never* been let down. Never once has my lad failed to be there with my second rifle if I wanted it. These men knew perfectly well that I wouldn't let *them* down. Show your men that *you're* staunch and you'll have no cause for complaint.

Gunbearers have on many occasions fired a second rifle into an ele-phant or lion that has got the hunter down—thereby drawing his attention to themselves and causing the beast to forget the man he al-ready had. Sometimes they paid with their lives for their loyalty. And too often that was taken as a matter of course—they were merely "niggers," it was their job to see that the lordly white man wasn't hurt. There have been others who didn't know how to shoot who actually sneaked right up and thrust the second rifle into the hunter's hands—and he down under either elephant or lion—in the hope that he might be able to do something to save himself. Would you call that courage? Such action usually meant the death of the plucky fellow in question. In the late thirties Salmon of Uganda had his gunbearer killed in just such a man-ner, when he tried to save Salmon's life from an infuriated wounded elephant. A second gunbearer then fired Salmon's third rifle into the elephant's ribs, causing him to leave Salmon, who thereupon escaped without serious injury.

As for trackers—you can't train one. He either is one or he isn't. Most Africans are good trackers because of their keen eyesight; but some of the experienced ones are superlative. It's amazing how little trace there may be of the passage of so huge a beast as an African elephant—or even a troop of them. And it can be unbelievably difficult to sort out the most recent spoor in a place where the elephant have been camping for severa days or perhaps weeks, and last night's spoor is underlaid by yesterday' and that of the day before. Before you know where you are you'll fin you're following yesterday's trail and have lost today's. So back you g to where you know it was fresh stuff and try again. An ordinar tracker can be excused for going astray like this and will probably do i several times before finally getting you on the right track. But a reall expert tracker will never be at fault. It's an endless source of joy to m to watch such a man instantly work out such a problem. I had two o them one time. They were truly marvelous. They would track as fast a I could comfortably walk, when there didn't seem to be any visible spoo at all; and, had I not constantly slowed them down, they would hav tracked faster than I could comfortably walk when the trail was a littl clearer. Never once can I remember seeing them in error. They worke as a team. They had been tracking all their lives and had grown u together. They were inseparable, although both were going on towar middle age. They had even married sisters. They were with me for year in the Zambezi valley.

The Australian Blackfellow has the name of being the best tracke in the world, and the police out there would be pretty well lost withou him. The Sind trackers retained by the police in Peshawar (Pakistan also have a very fine reputation. But I honestly don't think that either ar better than really good Africans. Possibly the Australians, taken as : whole, are better than the general run of Africans; but then the Austral ian is still back in the stone age and relies solely upon his hunting whereas the majority of Africans are agricultural or pastoral, not, gener ally speaking, hunters. The only tribes known to me who live solel on the proceeds of their hunting are the Kalahari Bushmen, the Pygmie of the Ituri forest, and the Wanderobo in Kenya and Tanganyika. Ac cordingly it's unfair to take the African generally and compare him wit Australian aborigines.

Let it be clearly understood that when you employ trackers it' their job to track. It's your job to have your eyes constantly roving ahea in order to spot the game. (I have said this before.) Particularly is thi so if you're following a wounded and potentially dangerous beast. You trackers will do a better job if they know they can rely upon you in cas of a charge to see the quarry in plenty of time. You won't do so i you've been peering down with your eyes focused for close worl and tiring rapidly from the constant strain. Anyway, you won't spot th traces as quickly as will your men; but, just because your eyes aren' tired, you'll be of help to them if they're at fault. Then it's permissibl

or you to lend a hand, and you'll often find that it's you who pick up
he lost spoor. All right, don't get all puffed up because of it!

S TRAPPER

The African traps for meat—that is, for food—just as he hunts for meat.
've already spoken of his pitfalls, and he has several other methods of
aking game. First I might mention the common box traps he builds on
he outskirts of the kraal. These are primarily to safeguard his food
upply: they are for lion or leopard and he builds them only if he is
a livestock owner and the big cats have been getting in among his stock.
These traps are the essence of simplicity. They are oblong structures of
tout poles set well into the ground and strongly bound together. The
maller of the two compartments into which they're usually divided is
or the bait—generally a goat. The roof, also of logs, is weighted down
with all the heaviest rocks the stock owner can lay hands on and lift into
osition. A trap door with a trip cord to operate it is then arranged.
On the lion's entering, in the hope of getting to the live goat, he pushes
is head against the trip cord and so causes the trap door to drop down
ehind him. That's all. But I might also mention the excitement there
s next morning when the inhabitants of the entire countryside turn
ut for the kill. They jab spears in between the poles forming the sides
of the trap. The lion or leopard is roaring and snarling and trying to get
ut to tear his assailants to pieces: the spectators and participants are
yelling with delight and excitement: there's positive pandemonium.
Quite a few leopard are killed this way, and also hyenas, but not so
many lion. For man-eaters they build a similar trap, but instead of a trap
door the trip cord fires a gun or rifle tied vertically above the entrance,
with its muzzle directed downward in the hope that it will shoot through
he top of the man-eater's head or neck. Some considerable skill is needed
n setting the trip cord if a gun is used: one too loose may fail to fire
he gun or do so too late and merely wound the lion in the hindquarters
or belly, or he may be able to brush past it entirely. On the other hand,
if the cord is too tight the dew may cause it to shrink and fire the gun
before the man-eater puts in an appearance. Personally, I've always
advised the natives to use a piece of net instead of a cord. That's easy if
it's a fishing district. Otherwise there is no net available and probably no
one who knows how to make one.

Other methods of trapping consist of springles and foot snares and
a weighted spear slung above an elephant path and released by a trip
cord. This last is bound to a heavy log or something of the sort and

drives down into the elephant's lungs or spine. The spring for the sprin
gles consists of a strong sapling with a noose at the end. It's bent dow
and held by means of an ingenious arrangement of small sticks, wit
the noose just the right distance from the ground. When a buck, say
gets his head in through the rope the trip is released, the sapling spring
up, and the noose tightens around the animal's throat, frequently raisin
its forefeet off the ground and holding it like that. I once saw where
leopard had been caught, and how he had struggled to get loose. Ther
were deep grooves where his hind claws had torn up the ground. Bu
the trap held.

These springles are widely set around water holes during the dr
season, and there are tribes, such as the Azimba, who live on little els
than the catch from such traps. They dry their surplus meat and sell o
trade it over the border for grain, since their own districts do not grov
enough to support them.

The foot snare consists of a small round hole in a trail with a noos
set in it. It's concealed, of course, and the other end of the cord or rop
is secured. But in the case of a foot snare for an elephant, since he
would probably be strong enough to break anything firmly tied to a tree
the men usually secure it to a heavy log. This impedes the elephant's
progress by causing him to get hung up on things as he proceeds, beside
leaving a plainly discernible trail. Some tribes, like the Wanderobo
make unusually elaborate foot snares. Not content with a simple noose
they arrange a complicated system of sharpened bamboo slivers all facing
inward toward the center of the snare. When an animal—anything from
a small buck to an elephant—puts its foot into the trap these thin sharp
slivers, sloping downward, prevent its being drawn out again. The more
the trapped creature tries to pull out its foot the more do the slivers drive
into the leg, until they may eventually pierce or even sever tendons
Anyway, the animal is either held fast or unable to go far. Such traps are
very effective.

Youngsters are usually the only ones who attempt to trap or snare
birds. There's a very powerful bird lime obtainable in most districts, and
they set this on likely trees. It's strong enough to hold almost any bird
I've had many a feed of green pigeons so taken. Another method of
taking doves is to balance a large flat stone on edge, propped up by a
small stick, bait the place with grain, and then, with a long cord attached to the stick, lie concealed within sight of the trap. When a dove
or two gets into position the trap is released by pulling the cord and the
bird held by the falling rock.

Young boys also set numerous small snares along paths. They will
build a little fence of grass and twigs across the trail with a gap in it—and

in the gap a noose. Small animals naturally make for the open space in the barrier, and many birds and cane rats and such things are caught. Some of the youngsters are very fond of this trapping. I had one with me one time who was quite exceptional. His elder brother told me that he'd been an ardent trapper almost since he could walk. He traveled with me for years—he eventually became my cook—and he never seemed to be without several little birds or other small game impaled on sticks and stuck around the fire to roast. He was also the best shot with a catapult I've ever known. Time and again I've seen him knock a dove out of the top of a tall tree. He'd go on until he had at least one for every man in camp—not forgetting me. His ammunition consisted of round pebbles only. I often wondered how much better he'd do if he had a bag of ball bearings from an old truck. Incidentally, this same youngster—whom I called Friday—once killed no less than seventeen spur-winged geese with one shot from my three-inch chambered wild-fowl gun. (An African spur-wing is the heaviest of all geese: I remember downing a big gander once which turned the scales at better than seventeen pounds.) That seemed to me a mighty stout effort for the kid. My double 12-bore with its long barrels was pretty nearly as big and as heavy as he was but he stalked up with it behind a tuft of reeds to where the pack of spur-wing were feeding. As he knelt for the shot the geese all lifted their heads to see what was happening. The kid let drive and, as I say, killed seventeen of them clean. You should have seen his face when he came striding into camp followed by a string of potbellied little pickaninnies staggering under their loads of geese. I'd heard the shot and knew darned well he'd have killed something—but seventeen!

AS FISHERMAN

The African's fishing, like his hunting and trapping, is solely for food. Only once did I meet a native who really seemed to enjoy this occupation and liked to play his fish before landing him. He had no reel, but he definitely played his catch. Usually the native just yanks the fish over his head onto the bank the instant he gets a bite. This lad was with me for a considerable time, and he and I spent many happy hours together fishing in any fishable water in the locality. My one regret was that I didn't have a second reel to rig up for him. But his joy was great when I sometimes lent him mine.

Fishing as he does for food, the African uses the methods of professionals the world over, traps and nets: seine nets and float and drift nets as well as bottom nets and also, in most places, the cast net. He makes every scrap of every net himself from what the forest supplies. He sets his nets both by day and by night but naturally makes the best hauls after dark. The seine is usually hauled only by night. Naturally it cannot be used everywhere as there isn't always a suitable beach up which to drag it and dugouts are mostly small one-man craft. Down on Lifumba and on Lake Nyasa the seine net is extensively used, and some magnificent catches are made. Here in Lake Namaramba, however, there is too much sudd all around to permit seine netting (although there is one fisherman who habitually uses a seine net on a couple of very small beaches up his way). Furthermore, the canoes are, almost without exception, too narrow to kneel in—the men either stand or sit on the gunwale—so in this district they mostly use the long stake net and the lift net. Having set the former, they paddle off fifty or a hundred yards and then work slowly back toward the net walloping the surface of the water with poles to drive the fish into the net. It works, too. As to the lift net: in the evenings and at night when there's no wind the surface of the lake is simply dotted with the snouts of innumerable fish sucking down such things as insects. The lift net, a Y-shaped affair held out on two bamboos, is simply slid under a shoal of fish and lifted out of the water. That end of the net close to the fisherman is left loose so that the fish are funneled into the canoe when he raises the net.

I'm surprised that the cast net isn't used here—it is in most other places I've been. Perhaps lack of stones is the answer. The cast net is a circular affair weighted all around with fairly heavy stones. The cord by which it's held is attached to the center. Considerable knack is needed in the throwing of it, or you'll find yourself going headfirst into the water along with it. As a matter of fact, the real secret is in the gathering and folding of it *before* the cast. The rope is held in one hand and the net gathered and laid across one forearm; but before any attempt is made to cast it, it is essential to sling a large fold over the shoulder of the *throwing* arm. The cast is then made with a circular movement in which the whole body plays a part. If properly made the net swings out, revolving with the weight of the stones, and opens to its fullest extent just before reaching the surface of the water. It then drops flat on the water and the stones draw it down and around any fish. The splash of the stones all around them scares the fish into the center. The fisherman waits for a moment, until the stones have all come together, and then draws the net back into the canoe, lifting it straight out of the water. The weight of the stones will hold the net close together and prevent the fish dropping out. Used by day, you may cast it twenty, thirty, or forty times without netting a single fish and then, when your tail is dragging, you may haul in a dozen or more good ones. It's much more effective by night, and if you have a lamp of any sort, the rays of which can be thrown down onto the water, the lift net is better still: fish are attracted by the light. The African, however, doesn't use light. In the first place he hasn't got one, and in the second he'd be afraid of the hippo. If hippo have never been shot-up with the aid of a light at night they are likely to come right up to any strong light they see and might upset the fishermen's canoes. (If you are the first to shoot them by night you can kill as many as you want without any trouble. But they quickly get wise to the shooting lamp and thereafter go for their lives the instant they see one.)

Fish traps are made from bamboo or a certain kind of reed, depending on which is the more easily obtainable. They're of more or less conventional pattern and differ little throughout the continent, about the only noticeable variation being the matter of size, which is mainly dependent on the size of the fish to be caught. There's a good deal of work attached to the trapping of fish in lakes and estuaries. Although traps are sometimes dropped just anywhere, to be successful on anything but a very small scale it's necessary to erect a long fence of packed reeds and grass with openings here and there along it, and the traps laid in these openings. The traps dropped haphazardly are baited; those set in gaps in a fence don't need bait.

There's another more elaborate kind of trap the Africans set in estuaries and similar places. It consists of a fence built out from the bank or beach and at the end of it a large compartment or cage with a trap door. Bait is laid in this cage, and usually a long cord stretches from the door to the beach. At intervals the owner of the trap comes along and pulls the cord, thus closing the trap door. The fish caught in the cage are then scooped out with a large landing net.

These fisherfolk live entirely on the produce of their nets and traps. Buyers come fifty or more miles for fish, which they dry in the sun during the day and then place neatly on racks or trays suspended from the roof of the grass shelters they build for themselves and smoke over the night fire. When they have all they can carry, or all their money will buy, they tie them in great long grass-covered bundles and carry them away on their heads to sell at retail back home at a profit. Others, where there are better roads or paths, do a big regular business with the aid of their bicycles. They make long deep backets which they balance on grids over the rear wheel, load up all the fish they can pack in, and then ride as fast as they can right through the night to land the fish fresh on the market in some township first thing in the morning. It's really hard work, both on the riders and their machines and tires—and postwar bicycles and tires seem next door to useless. The Yaos are very keen on this kind of commerce and make quite good money out of it. Lake Nyasa is where they buy most of their fish.

From the point of view of the sportsman who fishes almost exclusively for pleasure, Africa is a fine place. The tiger fish of the Zambezi and other rivers, the Nile perch of the lakes, and similar fish, are as good fighters on rod and line as you'll find anywhere. They take only a moving bait. But when they're on the feed little finesse is required. They —particularly the tiger—are voracious critters and will take almost anything that moves near them: just a bit of red rag will do. I remember long years ago sitting on the bank of the Zambezi one blazing midday and watching three little native kids yanking tiger fish over their heads on to the sandbank almost as fast as they could bait, cast, and rebait their hooks. They were using a stout cord attached to the end of a pole, but it surely was bringing home the bacon. And I thought to myself, "Well, look now—there are plenty of men who would pay large sums of money for a place where they could catch fish like that; and here you are, my lad, without a fishhook in your possession. What about it?" Then and there I got my writing things and made out an order for some fishing tackle. I've done a good deal of experimenting since then and unhesitatingly recommend the Pal-o'-Mine floating plug in various sizes. I like the three- to three-and-a-half-inch one for the medium-size tigers and the heavy six-inch one for the big fellows that live in deeper water. But with tiger fish it's the medium-size ones that put up the liveliest and most spectacular fight, jumping repeatedly, their brilliant colors flashing in the sun. The runs the fish make are exhilarating, their jumps a joy to behold as they savagely shake their heads to try to free themselves from the hook. Curiously enough, the best time to take them is during the midday hours—say between ten and three. They seem to become ravenously hungry around that time, almost without fail—at least during the dry season. You get out on the edge of a sandbank then, right on the main channel, and fish there. But keep a wary eye out for crocs—don't allow your sport with the fish to cause you to forget them. And you'll have sport, all right, some of the finest sport you've ever known.

The beauty of these floating plugs I recommend is that they bring the fish to the surface: the take is in full view.

I've heard men say, and have read, that African fish are overrated, that they don't put up much of a fight, the boosting they've had to the contrary. But I discovered that at least some of these negative writers had been fishing with heavy two-handed big-game fishing rods—triple split-cane affairs with a steel center, deep-sea lines with a breaking strain of half a hundredweight, and reels more like a Kelvin sounding winch than anything else. Such a fisherman will have a stout wire cable for a trace and a massive hook of forged steel. In other words, he will be using

n outfit needlessly powerful for even a thousand-pound sailfish. How
ould he expect the fish to fight, or realize that he was fighting, with
uch tackle? Use reasonably light gear and give your fish a chance to
un and fight—there can be no sport otherwise.

The big perch like the deep water of the lakes. They are inclined to
ɔe a mite sluggish until you get them hooked so it's advisable to trawl
lowly and deep for them. But they give plenty of fun when they take
rou. Their fight is not so spectacular as that of the medium-size tigers.
However, they are powerful fish and will offer plenty of opportunities
ɔr testing your skill before they're safely on board.

The one disappointing thing about these fish is that they're almost
ɪneatable—unless, of course, you're a Negro with a Negro's perfect
eeth. They're a mass of Y-shaped bones scattered apparently haphaz-
ɪrdly throughout the otherwise excellent flesh. The African can and does
ɔick up a handful of cooked tiger fish, cram it into his mouth, and eat
ɪway as though there weren't a bone in the lot. (And in all the years I've
ɔeen among them I've never seen one of them choke himself with a fish-
ɔone and have heard of only one youngster's doing so.) Bell, to be sure,
;peaks of the tiger as the best of all fish on the table; but I cannot help
:hinking he must be confusing it with something else.

When all goes well you can, if you're so inclined, catch forty or fifty
tigers during the hot hours of the day. Possibly you could take more if you
wanted to. I've killed as many as that myself, both for the sport of it and
for my men to smoke and carry along with them. There is no such thing
as waste out here where foodstuffs are concerned. I recollect a fellow's
fetching a truckload of fresh fish down from Lake Nyasa to Southern
Rhodesia. They were packed in ice, but when he got to Tete on the
Zambezi he found the motor ferry broken down and the intense heat
there soon melted his ice. When his fish started to whistle he had no alternative but to dump them. He did so; but it was beyond the power of the
local natives to watch that load of fine fish float away down the river. They
chased around salvaging all they could and lugged them along to their
homes. If they had been white the entire countryside would have come
down with ptomaine poisoning next day; but it takes more than a bellyful of rotten fish to upset the African's digestion. Not a single one turned
a hair!

AS SERVANT AND PORTER

Some tribes, notably those of Nyasaland, make splendid cooks and servants. They are clean, honest, entirely to be trusted with the running of
the house. Once you show them what you want done you can there-

after leave it to them: you don't have to be eternally following them around to see what they've overlooked, deliberately or otherwise. As cooks they are second to none. I had a Yao cook for some years—Johnny from Fort Johnson on Lake Nyasa—and never before or since have eaten so well in the bush. What to me was astonishing was that he came and volunteered for the job when he learned I was an elephant hunter I naturally thought that if he were any good as a cook he'd want to stick around the towns where he'd have plenty of facilities (stores markets, proper cooking stoves) to enable him to show his skill. But he said he was tired of towns. How Johnny prepared the meals he served way out in the wilderness only he knows. I don't carry a lot of groceries around with me when I'm hunting; yet that fellow turned out meals that wouldn't have disgraced any hotel on earth. One of his favorite dishes was to bone two birds, stuff one with the other, and then fill the inner one with all kinds of delicious spices and herbs—you just sliced this down like a loaf of bread. (The first time he placed such a dish on the table in front of me I started to carve it like an ordinary roast bird but he quickly stopped me.) That sort of thing only is like what we get once in a blue moon back home on some very special occasion such as Christmas or New Year's; yet here was I enjoying it every time I shot a bird or two, and I away out yonder! The cakes Johnny baked would have made any normal woman green with envy, and I was never without at least one; and his pastry was something to dream about. I used not to care much about pastry but after I started in on his I learned what pastry *could* be.

When he first came to me I asked what pay he expected and how much he'd been getting before. He told me he'd like fifteen shillings a month but would be willing to work for twelve shillings sixpence. When I saw what a cook he was I felt unable to pay him such inadequate wages. His face fell when I told him I couldn't pay his rate, but he said it would be all right if I wished to start him off at ten shillings. When I explained that I would give him several times that if he behaved himself, he seemed overwhelmed.

His one failing was liquor, in spite of the fact that he was a Mohammedan. But much as he loved the bottle he didn't let it interfere with his work. If there were a beer drink in the offing, Johnny would scout around until he'd estimated how many days it was likely to last; that done, he'd prepare sufficient food of different kinds to see me through the period in question—without saying a word to me about all this—and most carefully drill and instruct his little helper in exactly how he was to serve each dish: this one to be warmed up, the other served cold, and so on. He'd then tell me that he was going visiting, and that I wasn't to

worry if he were a mite late getting back because he'd prepared everything and the pickaninny knew how and when to serve it. So off he'd
go. I might not see him for a couple of days; but I'd get my meals just as
I liked them all the same. I remember on one of these occasions watching
him come crawling home on hands and knees in the middle of the afternoon after being absent two full days. He couldn't stand; but he didn't
let that interfere with his determination to have me properly fed. He
questioned the pickaninny exhaustively as to just what he was doing
and then, satisfied that all was still well, and knowing the beer wasn't
yet finished in the neighboring kraal, he pulled himself to his feet with
the aid of the nearest veranda pole, turned around, fell flat on his face,
and started to crawl away again on hands and knees. When he came
back the following evening, partially sober with eyes like signal lamps,
and tried to ask me if all were well, he could scarcely speak he was so
hoarse from singing and yelling for three days and nights on end. But he
was a fine cook and servant. I remember he insisted I fire three other
servants I had who never did anything—there wasn't enough for so many
to do—and told me not to waste my money that way, he was fully capable
of looking after me on his own if I'd give him a youngster to wash the
pots, collect firewood, and draw water.

My good lad Aly, also a Yao, is just the same in that respect: he made
me sack two other lads who were sitting around eating their heads off
and doing nothing else, and said he'd look after me himself. That was
years ago; but he's never changed. Although he's my headboy now
that I'm back in the bush again and have other men on my pay roll,
nevertheless he still keeps an eye on my food—which he shares with
me—and generally supervises the work of all those in any way attending
to me personally. If we get some of our favorite ingredients for a meal
and he's afraid the cook may make a mess of things he doesn't hesitate
to do the cooking himself. I'm very fond of Aly. When times were lean
he worked for me for three years—three solid years—without drawing
or even asking for a single penny of his pay. It's true that I didn't have it
to give him, and he well knew that; but the vast majority of natives
would have asked all the same. When I did get a handful of cash one
time, from the sale of a magazine article, I suggested to Aly that he take
what was owing to him and, if he had sense, go look for another job.
He scoffed at the notion of leaving me; and when I tried to point out
that it was only for his own sake that I suggested it, that I certainly
didn't want to lose him, he said he was hurt that I should be capable
of believing he would ever desert me—especially when times were hard.
And mark you, that was a long time ago, when Aly didn't know me as
well as he does now.

But although Aly is exceptional, he isn't unique. Blunt relates how his good Wemba boy, Pemba Moto, volunteered to work for him without wages when times were hard, provided only that he be fed. And I knew an Australian-Scot, one McIntyre, whose boy used to lend him money between jobs when Mac was broke. Mac mostly drank the money, but the boy kept him going in spite of the fact that Mac used to beat him up and kick him around pretty generally. Finally, in one of his drunken rages, Mac beat the boy up badly and sacked him. Unable to get another good servant, Mac didn't last long with nobody to look after him, and he died without ever paying back the money that good lad of his had lent him. There have been and still are many such cases of staunch faithful service in Africa, though those who sneer at the African are careful to overlook or forget them. As I see it, honest faithful service is deserving of the highest recompense that God and man can bestow. But, the world and man being what they are, it's usually the worst-paid and most thankless job of all. However, now that things are looking up somewhat for me, it will be my main object in the future to show Aly that *all* white folks aren't base ingrates.

Beverly Nichols once visited India, during the time of the British raj, and when he got back he wrote his impressions. He described an occasion when he entered a railway compartment in which there was only one other occupant, an army officer in mufti. After the coolies had handed Nichols' suitcase in and he was searching for some small change with which to pay them he turned to his traveling companion and asked how one said thanks in Hindustani. His companion looked at him with exasperated surprise and exclaimed, "Thanks! In Hindustani! My dear sir, one doesn't. One simply doesn't. It's not done."

Nichols deplores the fact that "the British have been a hundred years in India and haven't yet learned to say thanks." If he'd come on to Africa he could have used the identical words. Admittedly the greater part of my life here has been spent in the bush without other whites around; nevertheless I have from time to time been in civilization and visited with whites, both male and female. Yet right now, offhand, I cannot remember ever hearing any white express any kind of thanks to an African no matter what service he rendered. Back home in Eire, the rock whence I was hewn, I was surrounded by good Irish servants and was taught as a child to treat them with kindness and consideration because they were as human as I was and made life a whole lot easier and pleasanter for me than it would have been without them. When I came to Africa I could see no reason to change that attitude toward servants just because they were unshod and had more pigment in their hides than those back home. I never have changed, nor shall I as long as I draw breath. But I may say this viewpoint doesn't go down well in British Africa and is the main reason why they take a dim view of me there. It is probably unnecessary to mention that the powers dislike even the mention of my name because of my poaching activities; but these pale into insignificance when compared with my crime of treating the natives like human beings. I do not exaggerate here. Admittedly there is no written law prohibiting decent treatment for the African, but there is most certainly an unwritten law to this effect, and to it the vast majority of whites subscribe. I know that there are a few— just a few, and widely scattered—who do not dislike natives. Unfortunately they haven't the courage of their convictions and are afraid to say openly what they think lest they be blackballed (or worse) by their fellow whites. On the other hand, I have never made any secret of my sympathy with the African; hence my unpopularity.

There is one infuriating trait I must mention in connection with the average native servant, and that is the casual way in which he attributes to his master superhuman powers. Of course the white man himself is to blame for this because of his eternal insistence on his superiority. But that doesn't prevent his getting mad at the results. One specific one is that your servant responsible for such matters will never tell you you're running short of something until it is absolutely finished and urgently wanted. It just doesn't occur to him to tell you it's time you renewed your supply of whatever it may be when you're at or passing a store. I have vivid recollections of canoeing up the Zambezi one time. We'd slept a night on the veranda of an Indian trader's store, a fellow I knew well. I ate with him that evening and left at daybreak after a pot of tea. When we pulled in to a sandbank for the midday halt I naturally wanted some tea; but to my indignation my cook came grinning to tell me that we'd entirely run out of it. Since we'd spent the night at a store where we could have bought some I asked why the hell he hadn't told me before. He replied that he'd forgotten until now. In exasperation I scrabbled my hands in the sand and asked him if he thought I could find some here? He just grinned again and reminded me that I was a white man! "I don't know, *Bwana,*" he said, "but you're a white man and you can do anything." Then he looked at me interestedly as though expecting to see some kind of conjuring trick that would produce a packet of tea. It was no good bawling him out.

But Africans *can* be trained to remind you in time. My old cook Johnny was very good that way; so was little Friday, the lad who shot the seventeen spur-winged geese; and I've never known Aly fail to tell me in plenty of time, or even remember himself when near some store and just go in and buy the supplies needed.

But then Aly is really exceptional. I've had some excellent and very conscientious servants at different times but never another to compare with him. Maybe some of them would have proved equally good if they'd been with me as long and gone through as much with me as Aly has. Well, I wonder. God knows there was little to laugh about during those three lean years, but Aly always found something: he'd wake with a laugh; all day he'd sing and give that gloriously infectious chuckle of his; he'd fall asleep still laughing. When he'd prepare our two meals a day, or frequently only one, of sour weevily meal for porridge and beans that were full of borers, and I'd turn up my nose but eat it because there was nothing else, Aly, bless him, would pretend he was thoroughly enjoying it, had never eaten anything more delicious, and hoped for nothing better. He'd frequently spend the entire night fishing to get me something a bit better—I was a mighty sick man at that time, after those military doctors had seemingly been unable to put things right. And, like all sick men who have never been sick before, I was captious and querulous, hard to please, never done grumbling and bellyaching. Aly must have had the patience of Job to put up with me; but he did. I surely did not pull my weight in the boat that time.

Speaking generally, the African, as I say, makes a good servant—*provided* you go the right way about showing him what you want done and have a little patience when he makes mistakes at first. After all, it's all new to him. You've been accustomed to having your bed made in a certain manner all your life, and you can't understand why he doesn't naturally fix it like that for you; but you must remember that quite possibly he has never even seen a bed before, much less made one up. All the multifarious possessions of even a poor white man, which he takes as a matter of course, are nevertheless astounding to the raw African who has never owned anything at all except perhaps a tomahawk and a stick. But the native is keen to learn and if you don't scare him too badly to start with he *will* learn. There are some, of course, who would never make good servants. Well, then, fire them or put them on other jobs—don't try the usual method of kicking them around when they do things wrong, in the hope that by the process of elimination they will eventually learn the right way. If you don't get yourself a bad name you'll never be short of volunteers. Why keep a boy who's incapable of learning? Sign on another—Africa's full of them.

By the way, little pickaninnies (boys) make excellent nursemaids. You'll see one in sole charge of one, two, or more white children pretty nearly, or even quite, as big as he is. The mother wouldn't dream of allowing her darlings to play in the park unattended but will leave them in the charge of a black youngster of tender years and go off to her bridge or tennis without a moment's uneasiness. If there's no hill in the park or the immediate vicinity, well and good; but if there is, those little black nurses will have the time of their lives: they'll be having chariot races with the prams and gocarts, their young charges screaming with delight as they go hurtling down the hill at anything up to a dozen miles an hour, four or five abreast, with their black jockeys standing on the back axles and leaning flat down over the body of the pram, whooping and yelling. But their ears are as sharp as their eyes, and at the first indication of an automobile's approach they whip the chariots off the road and long before it's close will all be sitting sedately in a circle on the grass like a group of professional white nursemaids, gossiping. Apart from these little peccadilloes they're very good and love their little charges. And can you blame them for their skylarking? They're human, they're young, they enjoy fun as much as other youngsters the world over.

I've always reckoned the job of porter one of the worst on earth. I should hate it. But there are some Africans who excel at it. The Swahili of the East Coast have long been famous porters. They've had plenty of practice—right from the bad old days of the Arab slave raiders. The Achikunda—or Anyungwi, as they like to call themselves—of the Zambezi valley are also exceptionally good porters. Sixty pounds was the regulation load in East Africa, but the porter would always be carrying more than that because he'd have his own blanket and sleeping mat and various other odds and ends as well. It naturally depends greatly on the shape and composition of the load how comparatively easy or unpleasant it is to carry. The African carries loads on his head, so the weight is distributed straight down his back to his heels. From time to time he'll shift the load to his shoulder, and when he does that he'll carry his stick over his other shoulder slanted back under the rear of the load balanced opposite. In this way he distributes the weight evenly.

Twenty miles a day is plenty with heavily laden porters. If they can average fifteen to twenty miles a day for long spells with heavy loads, you certainly have no reason to complain. It's all very well for you to finish your twenty miles without feeling tired. Don't forget you've been carrying nothing but a stick, there's no reason why you shouldn't be able to walk another fifteen miles before complaining; but just try it with a fifty- to sixty-pound load consisting of an awkward sharp-cornered packing case and see how you feel after the first twenty miles!

Bear in mind too that your porters will now have to make some sort of clearing for the night's camp, pitch your tents if you have any, collect firewood and water, and cook their own food. It's outrageously inconsiderate of men to keep their porters going until dark before halting for the night. If the halt is near a kraal, as it probably will be for the sake of water, the villagers will usually have long ago collected all firewood close by: your men will have to wander away into the darkness of a strange locality to search for wood. Have you ever had to do that yourself? Then they've probably been sweating during the day. They would have liked a bath. If you want one, some of them will get the water for you; but there's nobody to get it for them. You don't have to coddle your men, and they don't want to be coddled; but you can show them consideration and common decency. Although beasts of burden, they are human beings and deserve treatment as such. And it takes so little to keep them happy.

A point frequently forgotten is that if it weren't for the porter there would be little or no elephant hunting; and since the type of game you can reach by car is comparatively limited and found only in certain districts, that dream trip of yours would, without porters, remain a dream.

It's when things are all going wrong, and the rain's found you unprepared, and the food's damp and soggy and your blankets soaked, and the firewood's soaked too, and you're cold and miserable and wretched, that you'd expect the African porter and servant to let you down if he were ever going to. You'd maybe expect him to sit huddled up in a wet blanket, shivering his soul out, unable to do anything. But it's precisely now that the African shows his worth. A dry bit of wood will somehow be found; he'll get a roaring fire going under extreme difficulties; somewhere he'll find a dry truss of grass or a bucket or two of dry sand with which to make you a sleeping place; he'll rig up a roof of branches or something which will at least partially keep the rain off; before you know where you are someone will bring you a steaming mug of tea or coffee. Your hot food will follow shortly, and if necessary two or more of the men will stand in the cold rain holding something over you while you eat. You don't tell them to do any of these things: this is where the African uses his own initiative. I've even had two of them sneak their blankets onto my bed, without saying a word to me, because they were less soaked than mine. The fact that their blankets might be lousy wouldn't have occurred to them—they were warm and fairly dry weren't they? and wasn't that what I wanted? Never once in all the years of my wanderings have I heard even one man grumbling or blaming the white man for one of those foul nights—and I've experienced many of them. For an occasional one I *was* to blame: I'd insisted on trekking against the advice of my men; yet it didn't occur to them to blame me for all the unpleasantness we suffered. In short, they'll make a joke of the whole wretched business in such situations and find something to laugh about. The African doesn't bear grudges, he doesn't worry his head about causes, he just takes things as they come; and since he's wise enough not to expect too much out of life, he's seldom disappointed. If something good comes his way he makes the most of it—it may not be repeated. He's a firm believer in old Omar's advice: "Take the cash in hand and waive the rest. . . ."

16: THE AFRICAN'S PHILOSOPHY AND OUTLOOK ON LIFE

The African's philosophy can be summed up in a very few words: "Leave me alone." Just leave him alone and he'll leave you alone. He doesn't want to be interfered with; he wants to live his own life his own way: the way he likes things, the way he's lived since the world began— long before the first white man set foot on African soil. Among themselves, Africans never attempt to interfere with one another: each lives his life in any manner he pleases, just so long as it doesn't interfere with others. If some fellow does things the others don't do they never try to stop him, they merely shrug and say, Well, if that's his way of enjoying himself, let him go to it—it's his affair and doesn't concern them so long as he doesn't try to make them do likewise. Let him alone!

It's a very simple philosophy, and one with which I emphatically agree.

But the white man, with his eternal insistence on trade, trade, and ever more trade, can't let well enough alone. At first the trade consisted mostly of ivory and native produce (including slaves); then gold was discovered, to be followed shortly by other valuable minerals. Towns began to be built and shops opened in place of the old trading stores. These shopkeepers wanted a cash business. It was found that the country was in large measure suitable for cotton growing. That was the beginning of the rot. The next thing was to find a big market for all the cotton piece goods. That was easy: natives were no longer permitted to enter even a small township without wearing clothes. They wanted to enter the township to trade their surplus produce and perhaps buy something like hoes, knives, possibly in the colder areas a cheap cotton blanket. So now they had to work for months, for a pitifully meager wage, in order to get the necessary money to pay for the clothes they didn't want and never had needed. Then their womenfolk had to be clothed also—more work. Never having worn clothes they didn't suffer from heat or cold and had never been ill if there were no epidemic raging. But now things changed. They had not been lousy in the past because they'd had no clothes to harbor the lice and scrupulously removed all body hair. But with the advent of clothes they began to become lousy and also became less scrupulous about body hair. In other words, they became less clean. Moreover, when they were naked it did not matter if they became wet— they were dry again in a very few minutes. Not so when wearing clothes; and they didn't and don't realize the necessity for removing wet things. The result is a serious increase in the sick rate.

But by far the worst things were the filthy compounds and locations in which the Africans were herded when working in the towns and mines —places in which no decent man would house a dog he cared even slightly about, and certainly wouldn't consider a moment for his valuable cattle or other livestock. But it was good enough for the "kaffirs," the "munts," the "wogs," the "niggers." The whites forgot or overlooked— or even more probably just didn't care about—the inevitable effect such conditions would have on the mental state of those compelled to live therein. Throughout the world the slums of large cities have been breeding places for crime. The big mines were no better until the Americans opened up some of the copper mines. Those fellows realized they'd get more and better work out of healthy laborers than they would out of sick and ill-fed ones; they further realized that the mines had a long life before them and would be wanting many millions of laborers as the years rolled by. They built decent compounds under hygienic conditions; they saw to it that their men were soundly and scientifically fed—that is, with a diet adequate for active, hard-working men. Proper medical attention was provided, and suitable housing for the wives of those who brought them along. The men were encouraged to bring their wives, too —and they were also supplied with good rations—because of the problem of prostitution and all it meant in having workers off sick. The larger British mines were now compelled to improve conditions also. Otherwise they'd get no labor. It goes without saying that this policy has paid the Americans handsomely—as it deserved to. But what of the boasted British "trusteeship" that allowed things to go on so long in such a manner (and without doubt would still be doing so if it hadn't been for the example forced upon them by American businessmen)? The

Americans hadn't done any hypocritical prating about being in Africa for the benefit of the native inhabitants; they didn't tell the world that they were here solely as "trustees." They were businessmen who knew their business, that's all, and treated their native laborers as human beings because it was sound policy.

You may well be wondering what all this about labor conditions has to do with me, a hunter; but if you will bear with me a moment I'll tell you.

You'll hear the old-timers and those who'd like to be thought old-timers constantly telling you it's the missions which ruin the African. "Don't have anything to do with mission boys," they'll tell you. "Without exception they're cheats, thieves, rogues, and liars." They're wrong. I hold no brief for the missions. But the African doesn't have to go anywhere near a mission to become a most accomplished cheat, thief, rogue, and liar. All he has to do is enter British "civilization" for six months or so—that will do it. He'll come back a suitable applicant for admission to any rogues' gallery.

Maybe you'll say I'm allowing my freely admitted bias against the British to take control, that I ought to say Western or European civilization. Not so. I've been most careful in my choice of words. Wait just another moment. Then, whether you're Anglophile or not, if you're honest I think you'll agree with me.

When I first arrived on the Zambezi there were neither motor roads nor motors. I found the natives living around Tete unclothed except for a small white loincloth, and one hundred per cent honest. The Portuguese had been there for upward of three hundred years—long before the first Britisher arrived in Africa—so these natives had had ample experience with European civilization. Yet, I repeat, they were utterly and absolutely honest. If a youngster picked up a small coin outside my tent or anywhere about the camp he would bring it to me with a shy little smile and hold it out saying: *"Bwana,* I think this must be yours. I found it outside." I could leave money or anything else lying around on tables or boxes without giving it a thought. So it remained for years. On one occasion my men had built me a small grass shelter on the river bank opposite the township of Tete. It had no door. In it were three large tin trunks chockful of almost brand-new European clothes: I'd recently been back home in Eire and my parents, particularly my mother, were very particular about my being well dressed. So I'd a lot of junk in those trunks, nearly all new because I'd spent only about three months at home. Now I'm one of those Irishmen who always lose keys. It had happened again not long before, and I'd had to burgle my own boxes. This meant that when I went away elephant hunting I had to leave the boxes in that little grass shelter without a door, and they not locked. I was away for some eight months, and when I got back I wondered vaguely if I'd been left even one of the boxes. I didn't care about the clothes but had use for the containers. When I arrived I found the three trunks untouched. It wasn't that the local natives didn't know they were there: they'd been in and out of the hut to get an occasional empty beer or wine bottle. They didn't consider that stealing, and neither did I, because they knew they had only to ask and I would have given them— being empty they were of no use to me. But there wasn't a single footprint in the sand of the floor anywhere near those boxes of mine, showing that not a single solitary native had even been sufficiently tempted to see if they were locked.

Now up to that time these natives had had no dealings whatsoever with Britishers, except for the very occasional hunter or prospector. Then came the motor road, up from Southern Rhodesia to Nyasaland and Northern Rhodesia. And also came a demand from Southern Rhodesia for more and more labor. The demand became so insistent that the Rhodesian government put a fleet of covered trucks on this road with the word *Ulere* painted on them in large letters. This means "free." The notion was to encourage natives from the north to get aboard for the free ride to Southern Rhodesia in exchange for a twelve-month contract to work and a free return trip guaranteed by the Rhodesian government when the twelve months were up. Tens of thousands of these natives have been going down there ever since. And today you can't let a thing out of your hand down Tete way but it's whipped away before you turn around. Well? These natives were pagans and would have had no dealings with missions; besides, they were on contract to work, and you can bet your life the Rhodesians would have seen to it that they *did* work after getting that free ride, for which of course the Rhodesian taxpayers were paying.

There may be others, and doubtless are—one sincerely hopes so— but I've met only *two* out of all the hundreds if not thousands of Tete boys I used to know who've been down to Rhodesia and returned with their honesty and decency unimpaired. These two are of that very rare breed you'll find here and there throughout the world who, irrespective of race or color or creed, seem to be quite uncontaminable.

I could give you many personal incidents to substantiate my statement that it's the British influence which ruins the African—not the white man in general. If the British weren't eternally shouting about their honor, and their justice, and their fair play (which exist solely in their own imagination), it would not be so bad; but when the raw African comes in close association with these awe-inspiring self-styled supermen ne not unnaturally looks for something out of the ordinary. His reaction when he finds them is that if this is the way superior folk act—why, it must be the correct thing to do. He comes home where he was honest before, and where his tribe are still honest, and finds he can live well by practicing the cheating and stealing he has learned. It's easy, where others are honest and treat you as though you were also.

I personally caught red-handed a British South African stealing native regimental police lads' blankets when they were on night duty. He planned to sell them so that he could buy more beer. And he was one of the loudest-mouthed shouters about white supremacy, keeping the nigger in his place, and upholding the white man's prestige.

Nyasaland is different. It's a native protectorate with only a handful of whites—about twelve hundred or thereabouts. The two main tribes, the Anyanja and the Yaos, make such excellent cooks and house servants that they are usually snapped up for these jobs when they get to Rhodesia. Indoor work in one house and with one family does not lead to the same contamination as the others are subjected to. But the Angoni take on most of the heavier work and very quickly learn to cheat and steal—and so do those of the Yaos who take on similar jobs.

There are so few whites in Nyasaland and they all make so much money exploiting the natives generally that there is little incitement to barefaced dishonesty—except, of course, for the general wholesale dishonesty of the widespread exploitation. But this is on such a gigantic scale that the native is unable to appreciate it and realize he is being cheated with every breath he draws.

I remember a man not so long ago who knew all about upholding the white's prestige among the blacks, as he never tired of telling me and anybody else who would listen. He'd been running a tobacco estate for some years and wanted to retire. He had a big labor gang working for him and owed them from three to six months' wages when he quit. He packed up and cleared off in the night in his truck without paying any of them. Not only that—he'd sold the plantation as a going concern, including the house as it stood. (The buyer was an Indian.) Yet he had his men remove the iron roof and load it onto his truck the night he left. And he has the gall to prate about the white man's prestige!

Lest you still think I'm allowing my Irish bias too loose a rein, let me remind you that the great Karamojo Bell devoted the final chapter of his *Wanderings of an Elephant Hunter* to a comparison of the different European methods of administration in Africa. He'd had no experience with the Portuguese but had with the British, French, and German systems. He placed the French system at the top of the list as by far the best, and equally definitely placed the British methods at the bottom. So much so, in fact, that he wound up the chapter, and the book, with the following pungent sentence:

"Far better clear out and let someone else try."

Nothing ambiguous about that sentence!

If you had known these people when they were jolly, clean, willing, courteous, helpful, and utterly honest, when they could and did look you fearlessly in the eye since they had nothing to conceal and therefore nothing to fear; if you then came back and found them unable to look at you frankly—knowing perfectly well what they'd become and knowing equally well that you knew what they were—you'd realize what a tragedy it all is. I don't blame them; how could one blame them? I lay the blame where it belongs.

But there are still a few places where this damnable influence hasn't yet been felt, places where the native is as he was at the beginning: naked, clean, courteous, hospitable, willing, helpful, and absolutely honest. For the African is not naturally a thief. The tribal native is not worried by burglaries. A hungry traveler may pass through a goodly field of mealies but nothing will induce him to tear off even one cob if it is someone else's crop. If you ask him why not, he'll look at you with horror in his eyes and reply, "It belongs to the owner."

Africans are generous to a fault. They have little but will willingly share what they have with you or with any stranger passing through. If you give some child a biscuit or cracker or piece of candy he'll break it into pieces and share it equally with all his little pals until there is scarcely a taste or smell of it left for himself. Such natives simply can't do enough for the rare white man who passes through their country. When he and his porters arrive at a kraal a clean mat is placed under a shady tree for him; and then the villagers come with fowl, eggs, tomatoes, anything they have they think the white would like. They will bring him a scrupulously clean pot of beer, or it may be palm wine, and a huge pot of the same for his men. The women and girls will troop off to the water hole or river and return with clean water for all hands, to save their having to get it for themselves since they are probably tired. If there is a prospect of rain a clean hut will be prepared for the white man and another one or two for his men. The families will double up, the men in one hut and the women in another, so as to make possible this hospitality. Nothing is too much trouble, all are highly honored that you should deign to visit them! This is the real Africa, the Africa I love. What's more, it's the Africa that all the genuine Africans themselves prefer in their heart of hearts. When they get their first taste of civilization they reckon it grand, now they'll also be white folks. And they squander their paltry wages on shoddy ill-fitting clothes and strut around in them looking and feeling hideously uncomfortable. But that phase soon passes in the majority of cases—always excepting, of course, the semi-urban native who is utterly detribalized, having been born and brought up in the slums of a big city without the benefits of tribal traditions and training in decency, honesty, and courtesy.

Those who don't know speak of the African as "savage," implying something bestial. How they expose their ignorance! The African is kindly and considerate, respectful and courteous to age always. Africans are almost excessively polite to each other in the kraals and especially when in strange kraals—far, far more so than are whites in either America or Europe. Yet they're "savages."

There is a historical case on record in which the governor of a certain British colony, all dolled up, complete with gray topper, was addressing a large gathering of both whites and blacks on a special occasion—it may have been a king's birthday or something—I forget—and suddenly in the middle of his speech the wooden platform which had been erected for him collapsed, and in all his portentous dignity he disappeared from view. I've already mentioned how nothing tickles the African so much as seeing somebody unexpectedly fall, and you would have expected a full-throated spontaneous roar of laughter on this priceless occasion—but only if you didn't know the African and his innate courtesy. There wasn't a sound, not a murmur; not a single smile showed. Instantly every man and woman in that vast throng dropped the curtain behind his or her eyes and assumed that wooden, blank, expressionless look of which the African is such a master. Youngsters clapped both hands to their mouths lest their white teeth show and crouched down behind their elders in positive agony holding in their desire to laugh. I considered it a perfect example of "savage" good-breeding and restraint, in what anybody must have considered excruciatingly funny circumstances.

If you give a native something he will always hold out both hands for it no matter how small it is. This is not greed; quite the contrary. It's to show he accepts your gift with his whole heart. In the same way, if he's giving or handing you something, he will always at least touch the other hand to it: this is to show that he does not grudge it but gives with his whole heart. If you give a child something his mother will watch him carefully and if he doesn't hold out both his little hands she'll scold him for his boorishness. Does he want to shame her for her upbringing of him that he doesn't know better than to accept the white lord's offering with but one hand, as though he didn't really want it at all? She'll show every trace of confusion, and if she were of a different color would without doubt blush deeply. Yet both she and her child are "savages."

You will almost never see either parent chastising the youngsters. Just occasionally, almost always in or close to a town, you may come across a father who, in a drunken rage, will beat his children; but this would be an outstanding exception. Normally, all that's ever offered or needed is a mild oral rebuke. African parents are kindly and indulgent; they love their children and the children love them—especially their own mothers (they may and usually do have several stepmothers). The whole family gets along without friction. And after the child has passed infancy there is no coddling and precious little caressing; the African has a curious dislike for any display of affection. If a favorite son has been away for a long time and returns home again he'll greet his mother in apparently the most casual way, as though he'd little or no interest in her—though actually he's been longing to see her again—and she, after the one cry, "My son!" literally forced out of her, will also pretend to have little interest in him. But if you watch closely you'll see that her eyes are seldom off him. There is a yearning look in them. She'll slay her choicest fowl and with trembling hands prepare for him all the particular dainties and relishes she remembers he prefers. And from time to time you'll see a tear trickle down her face, hastily wiped away with the back of her wrist before he sees it: it might embarrass him. There is love here between these two; but there must be no outward display of it. That would be unseemly. The African does not kiss, unless it's in the privacy of his hut and under the kindly cloak of night. It would be unthinkable to kiss in public, either his mother or his wife. Yet they're called "savages"!

You will frequently hear it said that the African doesn't know the meaning of the word love, that marriage with him is merely gratification of his animal instincts. Nothing could be farther from the truth. Every honest man who has lived among Africans must marvel at their remarkable continence. (Bell does so in unqualified terms.) Compare the faces of any representative group of Africans, especially those from the eastern side of the continent, at any age from puberty up to and including middle age, with those of a similar group of natives from any other part of the world—say New Guinea—and see the difference. The latter look as though they had no more control over their sexual urges than baboons; whereas on the African faces, or, if you see them unclothed, on their sex organs themselves, you won't see the slightest trace or indication of over-indulgence or excess. Quite recently I had a youth acting as my cook. He was an extremely good-looking lad. One day a girl came to the kitchen and stayed there with him for some hours, chatting. She was a most beautiful creature by any standards. I later asked Aly who she was. He told me she was a whore who came from these parts and was then living with a Portuguese. My cookboy evidently fell in love with her, and seemingly she did with him. A few days after, she said she had to return to her white man. My cook came to me and told me he wanted to leave. When I asked why he replied that he loved the girl and wanted to follow her and get a job with her white man so he could be close to her. He hoped to persuade her to leave the white man and marry him. Naturally I did nothing to dissuade him and made no criticism of his quitting so abruptly. For some months he worked for the white man whose mistress his sweatheart was. Finally I was glad to hear that he had his way and she left the white man to marry my ex-cook. In due course she presented him with a child and now there's another on the way. They make a splendid pair and are very happy together. Well, is that love or isn't it? The girl was so beautiful that she could have lived in a city and gone far in her original profession. She preferred to produce a family for the man she loved. Moreover, that man was quite prepared to continue working for the white man so as to be near his sweatheart even if she refused to become a homemaker, and did not hold it against her that she was a whore before she married him. The African looks at such matters very differently from the white man. Furthermore, the African does not cruelly sneer at a child whose mother cannot name his father. The child is welcomed as he deserves to be welcomed, and is not held responsible for the faults of his parents. It seems to me that these "savages" could teach self-exalted white men—and women—a thing or two.

To what extent has "civilization" got hold of the African? With the exception of certain unfortunate urbanized natives I honestly don't think there is one African in a million who would shed a tear if every white were to drop dead tomorrow and "civilization" disappear from the face of the continent. The European brought many things with him, but mostly foul diseases and endless trouble and interference. Except only for his medicines, he had nothing with him that Africans wouldn't have been happier and better off without. And if it were not for the unnatural life he's been forced to live, the native wouldn't be needing all those medicines.

Malnutrition is to blame for many if not most of the African's ailments. In South Africa in particular, but also in parts of East Africa, it's not merely malnutrition but the effects of steady and prolonged semistarvation. This is directly due to the white man's having grabbed all the decent land, turned the tribes off it, and reserved it for white settlement. There are hundreds of thousands if not millions of square miles of magnificent farming land lying idle in Africa—awaiting nonexistent white settlers, while right alongside the natives are slowly dying from the effects of prolonged semistarvation because they are forced to live on land that's too poor and infertile to support them. That's called "trusteeship." You've only to compare those miserable starving tribes with the healthy well-nourished people among whom I'm living right now, their black hides glistening in the sun. But then I live in Portuguese territory and while admittedly there are aspects of the Portuguese administration which might be improved, at least they let their natives alone and allow them soil capable of supporting them. (And they don't prate about being here solely for the benefit of the original inhabitants.) If the British were actually using all that fine land it would be a different matter; but it's lying idle, has been lying idle for more than half a century, and there doesn't seem reason to suppose there will be settlers with the necessary capital to open it up for the next half century or more.

The African outlook on life is quite different from that of the ordinary white man. He is gifted with certain attributes, feelings, wishes, and desires and quite reasonably figures he's expected to make the most of them —he'd be a fool if he didn't! For instance, most Africans with the exception of Mohammedans, to whom it's forbidden, have a liking for alcohol, though they don't normally get enough of it to harm them. Since their beer takes quite a lot of preparation and calls for a good deal of grain it's mostly a seasonal affair. And anyway, the ordinary native doesn't get drunk so much from the actual amount of alcohol he consumes as from the psychological effect of knowing he's at a beer drink. But he won't hesitate to imbibe when the opportunity presents itself. Indeed, far from looking with scorn on the white man who sometimes overindulges, he considers him crazy for not doing so more frequently since he has both the money and opportunity. He may occasionally feel a twinge of envy, but the white man is so far above him and the white man's way of life so unattainable that he doesn't upset himself with vain wishes. Although, as I say, that is his opinion of the white man it doesn't imply that the African would be merely a drunkard if he had plenty of money. I've already referred to his extraordinary continence with respect to sexual indulgence, and no doubt he would show reasonable restraint in his other appetites if he were in a position to indulge them. But he just *can't* understand the white man's being abstemious in any direction. He figures there must be something the matter with him; and he certainly reckons there's something wrong with him for not having a bevy of wives. He can well afford them—can't he? The native can understand a bachelor far more easily than a monogamistic white man.

As for all this shouting you hear in Rhodesia about the "black peril," I haven't the slightest hesitation in declaring that it exists solely in the imagination. *There's no such thing as black peril in Africa.* The Africans know me so well by this time that they openly discuss before me, or with me, that which they don't even hint at with other whites, whether they understand the colloquialisms or not. The African doesn't want anything to do with white women—he prefers his own. There's something cold and unapproachable about white women that doesn't appeal to him. You must remember that he looks upon white folks much as whites would look upon the inhabitants of another planet who unexpectedly arrived among them. Their appearance (possibly light green) is unattractive, and their way of life utterly different and unappealing—they've developed their brains to such an extent that all they do is press buttons and everything is done for them by electronics. They just lie around in long chairs moving switches on the arms—that's life for them. It wouldn't be for you, and you would have no wish to associate with them other than momentarily to see what it is like. That's much the way the African looks upon white folks. He scarcely considers them human beings—at least, not normal healthy human beings like himself.

On the very rare occasions when some native is roped in for interfering with a white woman it is likely the white woman who was to blame —who, in plain language, either seduced or attempted to rape the boy. I have proof positive that it was so on five different occasions that came under my own personal observation and I know of several others in which I'm convinced of the boy's innocence. But this is an aspect that is never, *never,* even hinted at or suggested in Africa. In the interests of justice it's quite time it was; still, maybe I'm getting beyond the scope of my book here so we'll leave it at that. I'll just add this: if my own sister, with whom I was always on excellent terms, landed out here with the expressed intention of walking across Africa from east to west I shouldn't dream of attempting to dissuade her. I would happily see her start off, entirely unaccompanied except by her African servants and porters, nor should I lose a wink of sleep worrying about her even though twelve months or more elapsed before I heard of her again. There have been several white women who have undertaken just such lengthy safaris through "Darkest" Africa, quite unescorted, and I've yet to hear of one who regretted it.

If you are sufficiently interested to read back through the writings of the very earliest pioneers, explorers, and hunters in Africa you'll find that they met with nothing but kindness and welcome and help wherever they went. An unprovoked attack was something that just didn't happen. If one of them was attacked it was entirely his own fault: he either lied to the chief or king, or tried to cheat him over some deal. Failing that, he tried to assert his white supremacy in too gross a manner, or attempted to interfere with the women. This last was responsible for not a little if not most of such trouble as has arisen. But the others, those who did not do these things but treated the natives decently, experienced no trouble whatsoever. Livingstone had his wife with him from a very early date—she was without doubt the first white woman tens of thousands of those natives had ever seen. Moffat, pioneer missionary of the Rhodesias, did likewise. These pioneer women were never molested.

And this inevitably brings me to a discussion of: his attitude toward the missions.

I've often been asked the question: "Just how does the African react to the missions and to Christianity? Does it mean anything to him? Why are mission boys scorned by the old hands?"

It is not an easy question to answer—there's too much involved and the reply must inevitably arouse mixed feelings. Maybe you'll say I'm not a suitable person to attempt an answer. But possibly by not belonging to a Christian church I'm in a position to take an impersonal, unbiased view of such matters.

Let me say at once that for a man to adopt the calling of missionary in Africa simply because it's a job, a career, giving him an assured social standing because of his "cloth"—a standing to which he otherwise might not be entitled—is, in my humble opinion, one degree short of criminal. The African is as clever as a monkey but in many ways his mind is like that of a child. However—and you'd do well to remember this—his mind works with all a child's simple unanswerable logic. He wants a straight answer to a straight question. It matters not whether the answer is direct or takes the form of a parable (he's fully capable of appreciating a parable); but the answer must be one that he can understand. The African, as a direct person himself, does not like matters that are too involved. "Do as I say and not as I do" may be all right in the case of the ordinary white man. But it does *not* do for the missionary. If the missionary hopes to win the African's respect and following he must practice what he preaches. Doubtless there are many missionaries who would like to have but haven't the courage of their convictions: they're afraid to go against public feeling, to say nothing of the opinion of their superiors in the mission. And so they all too often drop into the accepted attitude. The African cannot understand it.

The African doesn't object to white superiority as such. He is satisfied to accept it as preordained that he should be the hewer of wood and drawer of water for more exalted beings. But what he can't comprehend is the missionary standing up there in his pulpit on Sundays telling him that they are all, black and white, God's children and exactly alike in God's eyes—and then, coming out from church, expecting the natives to take off their hats as he passes. If any of them wish to speak to him when he's sitting on his veranda they may not step up on the veranda to do so but must stand on ground level with their hats in their hands and peak up to him. He doesn't offer them a chair or a cup of tea. They wouldn't expect that of an ordinary white man but it seems strange, this standoffish attitude on the part of the preacher a bare ten minutes after he has told them they are all equal in God's sight.

I have on three different occasions, occasions separated by years and hundreds of miles, heard pagan youths speak of their mission experiences and the conclusions reached as a result. In spite of the different languages the three spoke there was little difference in the remarks they made. They were speaking to their comrades, not to me; but they were sitting close enough for me to hear what they said. I found it most interesting:

"Listen, brothers, all this talk of the white folks at the mission about their God, and that if we're good we also can go to heaven because we also are God's children—do you know what it is? It's quite clear we can't also be God's children, because God's white—naturally, because he's the white folks' God; and anyway, I saw a picture of him in one of the teacher's books. All his angels are white too. They wear long white *kanzus* like the Swahili and big white wings like pelicans; also they wear a kind of round brass hat. Well, don't you see, brothers, the notion is that if they can persuade us to do what they say and we also go to this heaven of theirs we'll just be their servants there as we are here. They naturally want servants to wash those white clothes of theirs and perhaps comb those long wing feathers. And they'll also want those brass hats polished. They're only cheating when they say we're all children of the same father: how can we be? We're black—aren't we? No, brothers, if we had a white father we'd be brown like the half-breeds—wouldn't we? They're just cheating in this matter, as they cheat in other matters. I'll be working for them down here all my life, that's enough. I'm not going to heaven when I die to work for them some more."

There are plenty of Africans who think along those lines but attend the mission because they're eager to learn. They particularly want to be able to read and write. But the missionaries insist upon their attending church services—if they don't they won't be received in the mission school. I personally saw a missionary (American Methodist) once come out of a church during the service, get a sjambok (hippo or rhino hide whip), and flog a youth who had played truant that Sunday. Every soul in church must have heard the whip falling and the yells of the victim. When the beating was over the missionary threw down the whip and returned to his place in the pulpit. Perhaps that's what they call Militant Christianity. But can you imagine its effect on raw pagans? It's hardly in accord with the teachings of the Nazarene, or with the Sermon on the Mount.

Don't misunderstand me here. I'm not suggesting for a moment that such is common mission practice; it just happened that I actually saw this myself. Maybe it was unfortunate that I happened to be there, but I can hardly forget what I observed with my own eyes. Kicks and cuffs and occasional floggings don't upset the African unduly. He accepts them as part of the predestined scheme of things where white folks in general are concerned—but *not* missionaries. *They* should be mild-tempered and forgiving.

The snag in mission education is that it goes just so far and no farther. The semi-raw native emerges with the belief that since he can now read and write and speak a little English he's almost "white folks" himself. After all this education he's surely above mere manual labor. He wants an easy clerk's job in which he can wear good clothes and lord it over the common uneducated native. This was the tragedy in India also under the British raj. The rulers educated thousands of Indians and then were unable or unwilling to provide suitable jobs for them. All the best positions they reserved for themselves. Is it necessary to point out that these more or less educated and very dissatisfied black and brown folk are ideal fodder for Communists and other disturbers of the peace?

The education of the African throughout the continent is left almost entirely to the missions. The various governments take little or no part in it beyond making grants to the missions in accordance with the number of pupils they can show on their books. Education rarely goes beyond the elementary stage. The natives are then expected to go out and look for jobs. There are two—I repeat, *two*—colleges in which government takes an interest: one way down in South Africa and the other, opened in the middle or late thirties, way up north in Uganda. In these institutions a somewhat higher form of education is possible for those lucky ones in whom somebody takes enough interest to send there. But even when students qualify in, say, medicine and surgery, as to my knowledge four or five have done, taking their final degrees in England, what openings are there for them in which to practice their profession? They are given—grudgingly—positions such as sub-assistant surgeon in some district considered too unhealthy for a white medico. They are little more than glorified dispensers, at very small pay; yet their qualifications are just as high as those of any white physician in the country.

I know a native dresser in one of the Nyasaland hospitals. He's been a dresser for many, many years, and assistant in the operating room. On one occasion he performed an appendectomy under the supervision of the white surgeon who was too shaky from malaria to operate himself. The operation was entirely successful. That man is as keen as mustard to be a surgeon—it's been his secret ambition for years; but when I asked why he didn't apply for Makerere College he replied that he had asked his boss but had been turned down for no clear reason. I take it the boss didn't want to lose his services.

That the African is fully capable of assimilating all branches of higher education, and then taking on any job for which he's qualified, is proved by the situation in West Africa. For many years West Africans have been completing their education in England. There was one who returned as a lawyer not so long before the recent war. His wife also had qualified in law. She was appointed magistrate soon after her return to West Africa. The British say that the East African natives aren't yet ready for higher education. How can they be ready if the British won't educate them beyond the elementary stage? What are two colleges among Africa's millions of natives? What the British want is for the *status quo* to continue as it is indefinitely so they can continue to hold down their easy fat supervisory jobs with an abundance of cheap labor. Whatever fancy names they choose to give it, it's barefaced exploitation. For many years the Governor General of French Equatorial Africa, above all the white provincial governors, was a full-blooded African Negro and the whole country mourned for him when he died, for they considered him the best governor that vast territory had ever had. Under the French flag there's no discrimination whatsoever, and there you see how easily and pleasantly the African can be assimilated by white civilization when he is treated as he deserves and has a right to be treated—that is, as a human being.

My talk about African education may seem at variance with my previous statement that the African wouldn't regret the disappearance of the white man and his civilization from the face of Africa. However, while "civilization" is here he'll try to rise with it and become of it. Let it go, and he'll revert to his former condition: you'll see it in a small way in the bush. When a man returns home after a year or two in a town he will for a while parade around in the clothes he brought back with him, to let his folks see them and how far he's risen; but he'll soon start giving them away to his brothers and friends and when they're worn out he'll don the loincloth and live as his fathers lived before him. He has no regrets.

Civilization spells possessions and worry. The African doesn't like either. Some of the happiest and most carefree folk I've ever met were domestic slaves on board the Arab dhows. Out of curiosity I asked several of them about their lives: why didn't they just desert when they touched at some port on the African coast, and so be free?

"Free, *Bwana,*" they laughed. "What is freedom? Free to be kicked around by some white man for a small wage and given food no decent man would give a dog! Free to die in the ditch if we're sick and can't work! Free to be thrown into jail if we haven't a pass to say we're work-

ing for some white man! Free to rot or starve when we're too old t
work any more! Thanks. They can keep their freedom. As slaves we'r
valuable property. We have nothing to worry about: our master feeds u;
clothes us, houses us, and treats us kindly. Why should we desert an
leave him? 'Freedom'! Not for us. We've seen too much of it."

That was the reply I got every time. I had spoken to their master first
asking him if he ever had desertions when touching at port. He ha
shaken his head with a smile and said, "Never." It was he who suggeste
I ask the men themselves what their feelings were.

You say there's no slavery nowadays? Isn't there! If some strange
comes prying around, or a uniformed official asking questions, not one c
those men will admit he's a slave—he's afraid he might be taken awa
and freed. But they're slaves, right enough; and happier than many fre
Africans.

One bad point about the missions, and one that almost invariabl
arouses wrath when I criticize it, is their absolute refusal to countenanc
or recognize a Christian with more than one wife. This is directly respon
sible for a great deal of prostitution. Again you may think that I'm goin
beyond the scope of my book in touching on such a subject; but it's im
possible to consider the African and his outlook without also considerin
his womenfolk. To the African his womenfolk are in very large measur
life itself. Existence without them would be unthinkable.

His god was good to the African in arranging matters so that wome:
outnumber men. For the native this was pretty much essential. You mus
remember that the African woman has no nursemaid or pram or any
thing of that sort to save her having to carry her infant herself whereve
she goes. Her daily chores keep her fairly busy in a mild way, in additio:
to her duties nursing and looking after her child. It's obviously out of th
question for her to be given another baby to carry around until the firs
one is able to look after itself—say when it's a couple of years old a
the minimum. Well, now, whatever else he may be, the red-blooder
African is no long-term celibate. If he can't take unto himself anothe
wife while his child is growing sturdy, he'll inevitably start looking farthe
afield—to someone else's wife or daughters. If he's away working for
white man he'll turn to the prostitutes and soon be diseased. Besides, i
there were no polygamy what else would there be for all the spare wome
in Africa except prostitution? The African female is as red-blooded as th
male and makes no silly secret of it. She *wants* babies. A woman of child
bearing age without an infant on her back or slung over her hip is some
thing remarkable. And something she will quickly proceed to rectify.

But the missions flatly put their feet down and won't permit more tha one wife. They must realize they're wrong. Damn it, they can't *all* be stupid. But you won't get them to admit it.

Prostitution "outside"—that is, away from town life—is something unknown. True, if a young woman has been married to an elderly man she will almost certainly have a lover of around her own age. The old boy doubtless knows or suspects it but provided things aren't too blatant he's mostly wise enough to turn a blind eye. But the girl won't be promiscuous; and her favors will be for love, not for money. When a baby appears on the scene the old husband will pat himself on the back, telling himself there's still a tune left in the old fiddle. And his friends will play up to him: never by word or look will they express a doubt as to the father of the child. Thus all are happy. Can you criticize them?

Of the different brands and denominations of missionaries in Africa the White Fathers are held in greatest respect. This is because, in African eyes, they live more in accord with their teachings than do the other denominations. They don't have new bungalows with all modern conveniences; they don't float around in fine new sedans. With their beards split by the wind and their white cassocks girt up around their waists they're a familiar sight bumping around in antiquated old motorcycles. And they don't take six- or eight-month vacations home every three years; Africa is their home and their lives are devoted to Africa and the Africans. They are permitted only one vacation in the whole course of their lives; they do all their own work with their own hands: they build all their own schools, dwelling places, hospitals and dispensaries. When instructing their pupils to be good artisans and craftsmen they don't stand off and just tell them how to do things, leaving the rest to a capitao or headboy—they *show* them. They take the tools—bricklayer's trowel, carpenter's plane or blacksmith's hammer—and work away alongside their pupils, chatting with them, joking with them, jollying them along, setting them right when they make mistakes, all in the best of humor—and not through the medium of interpreters but in the boys' own language, using familiar colloquialisms. They aren't standoffish; they never give a thought to their "dignity." They are just perfectly natural and clearly enjoying their work. These are all things the African can and does appreciate.

Furthermore, the White Fathers seem to have a better insight into the African mentality than do other missionaries, if only because of their knowledge of the languages. Certainly they seem to have a more practical way of dealing with that problem of polygamy and Christianity. They cannot officially recognize a second wife or permit an African Christian to marry more than one; but they are wise enough, if an African gives his wife a handmaiden, to refrain from peeking and prying and asking questions. This is also something the African wholeheartedly appreciates

The result is that, as I say, the White Fathers have greater influence with the African throughout the continent than any other denomination and fully deserve the appellation they are universally given—The Beloved White Fathers. They comprise all nationalities, incidentally, including Americans.

Next in power, influence, and respect undoubtedly comes the Salvation Army. I've seen so much of the fine work these people do in both Africa and Australia that I feel the highest admiration for them. I may have my own opinion as to the desirability of blowing trumpets and banging drums on street corners, but I forget that when I think of all the good done unobtrusively in dark places. It's improbable that the inhabitants of such places ever tell the story, because they are not given to wielding pens. The things they habitually use are different: knives, knuckle dusters, lengths of lead pipe, bottles. But all that doesn't deter the Salvation Army from quietly going about its work. Men and women come and go unmolested. Raucous liquor-hoarsened voices may occasionally taunt a man, but never a woman. If an attempt were made to interfere with a bonneted girl there would be serious trouble from the slum dwellers—real violence. Which, I think you'll agree, is a pretty convincing commentary on the respect accorded the Army.

17: THE AFRICAN'S CUSTOMS, BELIEFS, SUPERSTITIONS

So many of the African's customs are bound up with beliefs and superstitions that it is almost impossible to discuss them separately. This is not the case, however, with tribal markings and ornamentation. Most of the markings take the form of raised cicatrices. Small cuts are made in the skin, and various substances are rubbed in. Finely ground charcoal is usually the principal ingredient. The women like the cicatrices well raised; the men have them mostly flat. With men they may be just three black stripes, vertical or horizontal, immediately in front of each ear; but ie women like to cover their cheeks and foreheads with blobs or crosses, nd they ornament bosoms, backs, and bellies with the same patterns. hey frequently make similar marks on their infant sons—on the bellies, ot elsewhere. It's rather strange to see how, in the case of two brown omen standing side by side, the one who is covered with these markings as come to look natural, whereas the one without actually looks quite aked: even though neither of them is wearing anything in the way of lothes.

Other tribal markings take the form of extraneous ornaments. For instance, in one tribe, the Shangaan, both men and women wear a single arring; in another, the Anyungwe, all the womenfolk wear a metal stud hrough one nostril. The style of hairdressing, too, used to be distinctive of he different tribes; but with the steady creeping forward of civilization any of these customs are dying out. The Asengz used to fit a round flat isk about the size of a checker piece through the upper lip of their omen. In other tribes farther north this disk and another, even larger, hrough the lower lip were gradually increased in size until by the time a oman was elderly she had two things the size of plates through her lips nd had to lift the upper one with her hand in order to feed herself. he ignorant used to scream with laughter at this notion of "beautifying," ut the idea was quite the reverse. The mutilations were for the express urpose of making the women ugly. The custom dates back to the days of he Arab slave raids: those people happened to live in the raiders' hunt- ng grounds and hoped that if they were sufficiently hideous the raiders ould let them alone since they couldn't hope to find a market for such omen. The African is not stupid. It's absurd to suppose he derived leasure from seeing his womenfolk deliberately making themselves orrible—for many of these African women are truly beautiful by what- ver standard you judge them. (Incidentally, it might do those hooting vhite women no harm to hear the remarks of African men and women on he idiocy of stumbling around on four-inch heels.)

Marriage customs throughout the continent vary only in detail. In nost tribes the youths choose little girls who strike their fancy to sleep vith but must not take their virginity. They can have two if they like— he Masai generally take two, but elsewhere it usually works out at only ne. This is because if a lad casts eyes at another, his first little girl vill inevitably make life miserable for him. If all goes well, and the two atisfy each other, the boy will usually marry the girl in time—that is, vhen he's managed to rake up the necessary bride price. This used to ake the form of cattle or goats, but nowadays cash is acceptable. If the ould-be bridegroom has difficulty collecting the required amount things re generally made easy for him and he is allowed to pay the fee in in-

stallments. If a young man takes a girl's virginity he is usually compelled
to marry her. After he's given her the baby she wants she won't then object to his taking another wife. But even though the two may have more or
less agreed to marry, all must follow established custom. The prospective
bridegroom would not think of approaching the girl's parents himself; instead, he'll have a friend act as go-between. This groomsman arranges
everything, even to handing over the small sum that always goes to the
girl's mother as proof that the matter is serious and not merely talk. The
relatives are all told and there is much talk about the forthcoming wed-
ding.

The actual marriage ceremony merely consists of the happy pair'
entering their hut together that night and remaining therein for the ensuing three, four, or even five days and nights. This is to ensure that the girl
gets well and truly accustomed to her husband. From time to time food
and drink will be brought to them by an elderly female relative; and when
it's necessary for either of them to leave the hut they'll slip out by a
back entrance that has been especially prepared for that purpose. If
there's no back entrance a sleeping mat will be hung over the front door
and they will slip around under the eaves and so away out to the bush
at the back of the hut. Everyone in the vicinity will studiously keep eyes
averted so as not to see either of them during these little excursions. When
at long last they emerge it will be toward evening and the old women of
the kraal will have arranged things for them. They'll take the pair to a
selected place, strip them naked, seat them side by side on a clean sleeping mat, and then wash them from head to foot in—beer! This completes
the marriage ceremonies. Thereafter the pair are expected to take their
normal place in the tribe as a married couple.

As far as childbearing is concerned, it worries African women even
less than a hen seems to be worried about laying her daily egg. They will
do their daily chores right up to the last minute, or at least up to the
last hour. I knew a native cookgirl working for an American missionary's
wife who asked permission to go home one morning around eleven
o'clock because, as she said, she wanted to have a baby. The missionary's wife realized that matters had progressed farther than she'd realized
and gave the required permission, at the same time bewailing the fact that
the girl hadn't told her sooner so she might have got in a substitute: the
occasion was inconvenient because she was expecting company that afternoon. Still, as the mother of a family herself she could see there was no
alternative. But the girl only smiled, told her not to worry, and that she'd
be back soon. Sure enough, she *was* back, with a little black bundle on
her back, in time to prepare afternoon tea around four o'clock that same
afternoon.

The native bush telegraph is something people are eternally asking me about: Does it exist? And if so, how does it work—by drums, or what?

Let me say at once that it undoubtedly exists. In some places drums do play a part in it; but in others—vast tracts of desert and uninhabited country—drums can be ruled out because there aren't any.

West Africa and the Ituri forest in the Belgian Congo are the best-known areas for drum signaling. On many occasions drums have called medical assistance to hunters or travelers in the Congo and have even brought help in the shape of motor trucks when a party has broken down miles from anywhere. But in the areas more encroached upon by civilization drum signaling is dying out. Nevertheless, I have on many occasions heard two drummers talking to each other up and down the Zambezi during the night; and there is no mistaking the warning drummed out if a man-eater attacks some kraal during the night watches. The rolls and taps of the drum are extraordinarily like a lion's singsong roar.

On one occasion I returned from a short trip overseas. I disembarked at Beira, went by rail to Murraça on the lower Zambezi, and there launched a fast motor launch I had brought and started upriver to my headquarters at Tete. When scarcely halfway there my propeller shaft broke and thereafter I had to pole up. When I arrived in Tete I found all my old servants waiting to welcome me on the river bank. I asked them how they knew I was coming and they told me they had heard of my arrival on the river and then of my breaking down. They had followed my voyage upstream and so knew when I was due to arrive. But they couldn't tell me *how* they knew. Drums had almost certainly played their part in it—I had heard them nightly—but the boys knew only that first one and another had started talking about my coming.

Blunt relates how on his return from Europe he found his servant waiting for him on the wharf when the ship docked. The boy couldn't explain how he knew—he just did.

It's historical fact that the natives in West Africa knew all about the annihilation of the British forces by the Zulus at Isandhlwana long before the news reached the authorities. Moreover, there is an interesting case on record in Northern Rhodesia: during one of the not infrequent skirmishes in Somaliland some askari (native troops) were killed. It was before the days of radio, but word was sent by telegraph as quickly as possible to the native commissioner of the district in which these men had their homes. On receiving the list of names he dispatched the news to the wives and other relatives. But when the messengers arrived they found the families already in mourning!

Now in neither of these two cases could drums possibly have conveyed the information—more especially in the Somaliland one. What is the explanation? Telepathy? Your guess is as good as mine. That certainly appears to be the most obvious answer. Even cold material science has had at last to admit the existence of telepathy—the experiences of so many people seem to have proved it.

There have been numerous cases in Africa like the ones I have described—practically any man who has wandered there extensively could tell of others. *Semper aliquid novi ex Afrika,* even to the present day—although actually there is nothing new about these things.

In days gone by African superstitions gave fiction writers great scope, but in many cases they allowed their imaginations too free a rein—even those who really did know something about Africans. For instance, the late Sir Henry Rider Haggard, the man who first turned my thoughts to Africa, made a total eclipse of the moon a major feature of his famous *King Solomon's Mines,* and had the natives panic-stricken with the thought that the end of the world was upon them. The first time I saw a total eclipse of the moon I was camped on the bank of the Zambezi. I expected considerable excitement among the local natives, but to my astonishment they took not the slightest notice. I drew their attention to the phenomenon, but except for a casual glance, out of politeness to satisfy me, they showed no interest whatever. In fact, the only African I've ever met interested in things astronomical is my good lad Aly. A few years ago—in 1946 I think it was—there were two total eclipses of the moon several months apart. Aly and I saw them both. On each occasion he grabbed my old binoculars and studied the eclipse carefully for a long, long time. One, the first, took place around midnight early in the year; the other, later in the year, started scarcely half an hour after sundown. The full moon was only a little above the horizon when Aly drew my attention to the fact that another eclipse was starting. But, I repeat, he was the only native I noticed who bothered even to look at the thing.

However, on another occasion some years ago when there was a total eclipse of the sun one afternoon I reckoned surely those same natives would show at least awe if not consternation. I was visiting with my old friend McKenna, an Irish-Australian, across the river from Tete. We were sitting on his veranda sharing a bottle of wine when I noticed that it was becoming curiously dark. There wasn't a cloud in the sky, though there was plenty of haze around the horizons. Surely, I thought, it can't be sundown already; but it gradually became so dark that I went out to have a look around. I then saw the dark shadow that had crept almost entirely across the face of the sun and remembered having read somewhere that there was an eclipse due and that scientists from all over the world were hastening to someplace in South America where they figured they would get a good view of it. Well, they could scarcely have had a better one than ours there on the bank of the Zambezi. But once again, to my astonishment, the natives took not the slightest notice; neither during the eclipse nor when, in due course, the sun shone brightly once more for an hour or so before sundown. I remember wondering what Rider Haggard would have had to say had he been there and seen the Africans' entire disregard of such celestial manifestations.

These matters, and comets and shooting stars, leave the African quite cold. They are all so remote from him that he just doesn't bother his head about them. He certainly doesn't let natural phenomena scare him—though occasionally you'll see a youngster shrink into himself as he waits for the crash that follows on a near flash of lightning.

This reminds me of a rather amusing incident that occurred one time when I was encamped close to a government post in Angoniland. I was sitting in my tent watching the rain pouring down, and just across the way my twenty-five porters and servants were camped under a long open shed with a corrugated iron roof. Suddenly there came a blinding flash of lightning and I felt as though somebody had swiped me across the ear with a sledge hammer. It knocked me flat on the bed but otherwise didn't hurt me, except that my ear rang for a considerable time afterward. Since it must have struck very close, as the crash of thunder was almost simultaneous with the lightning, I struggled up and looked anxiously out to see if my crew were all right. To my horror I saw that each and every man was flat out! I ran over in the rain to see if there were any life left among them, anything I could do. Even as I reached them I saw one head raised and then another. Eyes like saucers gazed vacantly around until they saw each other. The men then rubbed their eyes and looked again—at their recumbent friends, at themselves, to see if they were in one piece, and at their surroundings. By this time all were stirring: wide-open eyes stared in astonishment to see where they were. There was absolute stillness until someone laughed—I think it was I. Then there came a simultaneous yell of wholehearted laughter from the entire twenty-five that pretty nearly lifted the roof off the shed. They rocked and rolled with utterly uncontrollable laughter, the tears pouring from their eyes as they gasped for breath. Not a soul had been hurt. It must have been a pretty close shave, but near misses don't worry the African.

Much the same sort of thing happened a couple of years ago. I was sitting on the veranda of a native hotel and eating house across the river from Tete. Another of those blinding flashes of lightning came, and the proprieter of the hotel, a couple of truck drivers, and myself were all knocked off our chairs. We got up, sat down again, and continued the conversation as though nothing had happened. There was a bit of a laugh as we got up, but nobody worried. Misses don't count!

Only a few days ago, with the first rains of the season, three terrific thunderbolts pounded their way toward us for all the world like a stick of bombs. As the last one struck I felt a blast of warm air on my bare arms and shoulders and a jolt right through me from my feet to the top of my head. On looking out I saw that a tall tree on the outskirts of my camp, about thirty paces away, had been shattered. But my men weren't particularly interested.

Throughout most parts of Africa where there's any large stretch of water, such as a big river or lake, you'll hear tales of an amphibious monster. This legendary creature varies slightly, but only slightly, in the different places where you're told of him. On the lower Zambezi he somewhat resembles a whale but isn't a whale: if you can picture a whale with short legs and a definite neck you'll have a fair impression of how the description runs. In the swamps around Lake Bangweulu he more closely resembles a gigantic water rhino—he's described with one if not two horns sticking up from his face. Along the upper Zambezi, west of the falls, the description is much like that of the prehistoric dinosaur. In all the accounts this beast is definitely carnivorous—hippo providing his favorite dish (he's said to be able to take a full-grown one at a bite), though he will also swallow a canoeful of men if he happens along. On Lake Namaramba, where I'm typing this, they don't know exactly what he looks like, but all are satisfied of his existence and of the fact that he eats hippo.

I think there can be little doubt that these legends have come down through the ages from the time the great swamps were of much vaster extent than they are now, and warmer, and probably contained degenerate descendants of the great dinosaurs of prehistory. It seems improbable that man could have seen a true dinosaur, as the age of reptiles goes way back into the dawn of time, and, unless I'm mistaken, the creatures had been extinct long before our first ancestors appeared on the scene. But in view of the widespread legends and the rather remarkable similarity to a dinosaur in the animal's appearance wherever he's spoken about, there can be little doubt that some sort of weird monster once lived in the great African swamps.

Several deposits of fossilized dinosaur bones have been uncovered in different parts of eastern Africa, indicating that the monsters were once numerous there. Moreover, Professor Leakey, curator of the Corydon Museum in Nairobi, has for many years been unearthing fossilized and partially fossilized bones and skulls of giant hippo and giant eland. The last time I had the pleasure of visiting him he kindly invited me into his workroom at the back of the museum and there showed me his then

atest discoveries. The skull of the giant hippo was at least 50 per cent
bigger than the biggest I've ever shot and the skull of the giant eland
proportionately bigger than the biggest of that species wandering around
the veld today; which tends to support my view that the legendary
swamp-dwelling monsters have some basis in fact.

It's essential that those who set themselves up to govern should be
thoroughly familiar with the customs and beliefs of the people under
their rule; and this naturally implies knowledge of local languages and
dialects. You cannot know a people until you speak their language. And
by "speak" I don't mean merely making yourself understood. I don't
consider I'm conversant with a language until I automatically think in it
and speak it without translating from English as I go. More than that—
I don't really call myself at home in a language until I find myself
dreaming in it at night. Then, and only then, do I say I know it. A
language must be spoken not merely according to the book, but idiomatically and colloquially—as the people born to it actually speak it themselves. Africans don't use slang but they make great use of idiom—far
more than is ever shown in handbooks or manuals. They also have local
colloquialisms which you can become familiar with only by living in close
contact with the natives. Few white men in Africa at the present time
are really fluent in any native language. They do everything through
African interpreters. Comparatively few of the native commisssioners
nowadays can speak even *one* African language. The main trouble is that
they're constantly transferred from district to district. That's all wrong.
It doesn't give the fellow a chance to become familiar with either the
local dialect or the local natives; and the African, besides, dislikes
change. He wants to get to know the "boss," his likes and dislikes.
Constant changing of commissioners makes it impossible for natives to
find out just where they stand, because each man has different notions
about how this or that should be done.

A district commissioner ought to find his job intensely interesting—
responsible as he is for tens, possibly hundreds, of thousands of natives.
He should be allowed to spend his whole life, his entire period of service,
in one district. But to all too many of these men the job is merely a
job. They have little real interest in the people they're supposed to be
governing. They're mere timeservers, waiting for their pensions. And the
various colonies and protectorates are governed from the Colonial Office
in London through the medium of a resident governor who is transferred
all around the Empire. He's essentially a bird of passage, hoping that
each transfer will be to a more important colony. As such, he cannot
possibly know anything about the aspirations and hopes of the people

for whose welfare he is responsible. In actual fact, his only real concern is with his own future welfare. That's empire-building!

If such men had the honesty to admit they knew nothing about the natives' customs and beliefs it wouldn't be so bad, but that's something they won't do; and they govern the Africans precisely as though they were governing their own people back in Europe. No consideration is given to the native's different outlook on life and his different beliefs and customs. For instance, in British law murder is murder and that's all there is to it; if the accused is found guilty there is only one sentence the judge can pronounce, "You will be taken to the place appointed and there hanged by the neck until you are dead, and may the Lord have mercy on your soul." If the jury is so inclined, and can be bothered, it may add a trailer recommending mercy, and when such a case comes up for review in Africa consideration *may* be given to that and the sentence commuted to penal servitude for life. If the trial has aroused any public interest—which it won't unless there's a white concerned in it —the papers may even be sent to the Colonial Secretary or someone. But what on earth can *he* know other than what he reads in the official evidence; he won't have had any personal experience among Africans.

There was a case in Tanganyika during the thirties in which three Masai youths were indicted for murder. They had been "blooding their spears" in the time-honored fashion. They all three pleaded guilty. (In the past a Masai youth remained a boy until he'd blooded his spear in the body of an enemy and could not take his place among the men and warriors, or marry a woman, until he'd done so. Nowadays, under the *Pax Britannica,* the blooding usually takes place in the body of a lion.) But owing to some legal quibble one of the youths was found not guilty and discharged. However, he was ordered to witness the execution of his comrades so that he could tell his people all about it. What do you imagine was the tribe's reaction to that?

One of the traits I admire in the Masai is their staunch refusal to be civilized. Where most Africans are forced to work and wear clothes, the Masai resolutely refuses to do so. Natives from other tribes are likely to be arrested if they enter a town without clothes, but you'll see a Masai stalking grandly right through the center of Nairobi, the capital, with no more on than he wears on his own plains—just a bit of cloth tied loosely over his right shoulder and otherwise hanging free to blow as it likes in the wind. The police, black and white, turn their heads, pretending they don't see him. He looks neither to the right nor left; he has no interest in the shopwindows or in the goods displayed therein; his eyes stare right through the tall buildings without seeing them. If there is an expression at all on his face it's one of lofty disdain mingled perhaps with slight contempt. He stalked across the plains where Nairobi now stands without hindrance in bygone days: he doesn't permit the town or what it represents to hinder his passage now. Who knows but that in days to come he'll still be stalking across those same plains when Nairobi is only a memory and the white man and his civilization self-blasted into oblivion.

Perhaps you'll think that I harp altogether too much on the question of clothes. But nobody who hasn't wandered among these entirely nude peoples to the extent that I have could appreciate what a misery enforced clothing is. The great African tragedies of the past were the slave raids. When those were stopped there came the hideous atrocities of the "Red Rubber" days in the Belgian Congo, which ran up through the first decade of the present century. When they were exposed there was a violent uproar and the Belgians were forced to bring in reforms. But I contend that this business of forcing the African to wear clothes is every bit as bad and even more widespread—but it's an insidious evil, insidious because its effects aren't so apparent. That does not mean that they aren't there. You have only to live for a spell among one of the totally nude tribes and then return to one of the partially clothed ones to see it. The nude peoples are delightfully natural, totally unself-conscious, as unaware of themselves and their bodies as any small children playing on a beach or sharing a bath, and no more naked than such. They're not naked because they don't know they are; there is no such word as "naked" in their vocabulary. Immodesty is unknown among them— immodesty came in only with clothes. Those who wear clothes are eternally adjusting and settling them so as not to expose themselves and are, if they only knew it, really drawing attention to themselves and what they are trying to conceal. If for any reason they have to divest themselves of their clothing all eyes are instantly and automatically focused on them, to their great mental distress.

The stupid, exaggerated, totally needless "modesty" which the African so surprisingly develops when he takes to wearing clothes can be positively infuriating at times. A man will shrink from allowing even his own brothers to see him when he's having a bath at a stream. He will do anything rather than strip off his loincloth or shorts when wading a river or swamp on safari; although there is nobody within miles he's afraid somebody might see him. You will observe a porter with one hand covering his genitals while the other precariously clutches at your precious loads: he fears one of the other porters might get across first and turn around and see him! I've had loads dropped in the river because of that stupid modesty, loads containing such perishables as sugar, salt, tobacco, and watches. If there were any reason under the sun why they should be ashamed of themselves, or, rather, of exposing themselves, it might be understandable; but the African possesses a more perfectly proportioned body than any other human being on earth. There is certainly no reason to be ashamed of it.

Africans generally are firm believers in the transmigration of souls. Not general transmigration: they have no definite ideas as to what happens to the bulk of the population after death. But chiefs, kings, and other important individuals come to life again as lion, croc, hyenas, etc. Some decide beforehand the shape in which they'll return and tell all who are interested—which means everybody. Others don't seem to care particularly in what guise they will be reborn but are quite certain that reborn they'll be. Curiously enough, though, reincarnation in human shape doesn't seem to have occurred to them.

A lad working for me at one time had to go home to attend his father's funeral. (If a close relative doesn't get home shortly after a death he's afraid he'll be accused of killing the deceased by witchcraft.) It was a very hot district and it took this youth some days to arrive. By the time he reached home decomposition of his father's body had commenced. When he returned to work for me in later weeks he told gaping audiences that his father's skin had come up in large blisters, that he pressed his finger on one of them, it burst, and, sure enough, there underneath was the coarsely spotted hairy hide of a hyena! His father had always assured his family that he'd return as a hyena.

Down along the Zambezi valley you'll frequently see on the outskirts of some kraal a neat little hut with two doorways but no doors. This is for the late chief or headman, now a lion, to sleep in should he return to his old home. There will usually be a raised sleeping place in it, nicely mudded over and smoothed. I remember arriving at a kraal one evening with heavy rain threatening. It was only a small kraal and I had many porters; clearly there would not be accommodation for all of us, so I said I'd sleep in the lion hut. Oh, but that was impossible! Unheard of! The lion would surely kill me if he found me sleeping on his dais, and then they'd be blamed by the authorities for allowing me to sleep there. I only laughed and told them the lion wouldn't worry me; if he came there would be plenty of room on the dais for the two of us and if he didn't like that he could sleep on the floor. The women crossed their hands on their breasts and moaned at my daring to make light of such a serious matter; the men hugged themselves with their hands in their armpits and implored me to reconsider. But I was determined to sleep there. It wasn't mere bravado—the hut was new and had of course never been used, it was scrupulously clean and would certainly be free of bedbugs, fleas, cockroaches, and similar unwelcome pests.

Two of my boys, who had been whispering together, pluckily volunteered to sleep with me in the hut, the idea being that if the lion came he would take one of them and not me. I thanked them and said if they wanted to sleep in the hut with me they would be welcome, but I certainly wasn't ordering them to. It was really an extremely brave gesture on their part, because they believed in the danger as firmly as the locals.

The three of us went to bed in the small hut, and at daybreak next morning the entire kraal—men, women and children, and those of all the neighboring kraals who had of course heard about it—flocked around to see the remains. They could scarcely believe their eyes when they found us still alive. They looked with awe on my two companions of the night: this would indeed be something to talk about for many a long day to come. As far as I was concerned it wasn't remarkable: I was white and there was no accounting for white folk, they ran slap in the face of everyone's pet superstitions, they flaunted all omens, they didn't believe in witchcraft (or said they didn't), they didn't seem to believe in anything (except themselves), and could and did do things that nobody else would dare to do; but how account for those two African youths? The only answer seemed to be that I must have a powerful medicine, sufficient not only to keep me safe, but also able to protect those in close contact with me. The villagers stood around and discussed the matter endlessly.

In most parts of Central Africa you'll see tiny huts built close to the paths approaching the various kraals. Under the shelters, only about three feet high or less, will be small bowls and gourds and platters containing food and water. These are for the spirits of the dear departed—those who haven't changed into hyenas and such—should they come drifting back to their old homes and feel hungry or thirsty. The food and water are renewed frequently at first but gradually stay there longer and longer until eventually no one goes near the little place, just as in other lands flowers appear on graves regularly and frequently in the beginning but slowly and inevitably diminish.

Some tribes won't eat the flesh of animals that have white markings on the face. If you ask why not they'll simply tell you that it would "make them sick in the stomach." But the vast majority of Africans get so little meat that they will relish any. Their staple diet is porridge cake with whatever is available—meat, fish, vegetable, what-have-you—as relish. They are brought up mostly on one meal a day, served in the evening. At certain seasons they'll have snacks during the day, such as corn on the cob, peanuts, pumpkin, watermelon, and so forth; but generally speaking they are accustomed to only the one meal in twenty-four hours. So it's not really astonishing that one practically never sees a fat African.

Incidentally, what have dentists to say about the African's perfect teeth? I remember having been told by dentists in the past—and I've read it many times—that plenty of chewing is necessary to keep teeth and gums in good condition. But there's no chewing in the African's porridge cake, or the fish or vegetable that goes with it. Moreover, his meat, if he has any, will be cooked like the rest of his food in earthenware pots, and there's no pot that cooks meat so tender as a clay one. Yet there are no people on earth with teeth so good as the African's. The only cleaning they get is a wipe with a finger after a meal and in the morning. Occasionally someone will chew a certain kind of stick until the end frays out like a brush and will then rub that round his teeth; but it's only done as a sop to convention and months may elapse between such "cleanings." Besides, I've never noticed that the teeth looked any cleaner afterward than before. African teeth are so superlatively milk white anyway that they could hardly be improved on.

The African, in spite of his happy nature, is hag-ridden by witchcraft. The night is full of evil spirits waiting to grab him. He makes no window openings in his hut and plasters the walls with mud right up to the roof so as to keep these spirits at bay. He hates sleeping alone; he and his fellows will, if possible, always roll up two or three together at night for mutual protection. There are bogymen everywhere waiting to reach out hands and clutch him by the ankle as he passes. Probably we all, as children, were frightened by certain places in the dark. But the African lets his scare remain with him much longer: he's not ashamed of it as we used to be. If he has to pass a place he doesn't like, he doesn't hesitate to ask a friend to accompany him.

Other than in the case of sheer old age there's no such thing as natural death to the African: it is always witchcraft. Apart from the general practitioner—the resident rain maker and fortuneteller, who is fairly harmless—there is the real witch doctor, the big shot, the traveling magician. Even chiefs stand down for him. He doesn't lower himself to consider petty matters: he's the expert, the specialist, the smeller-out of evildoers, the caster of spells; he can control the lightning and has the power of life and death—particularly death. If for any reason he curses a man, be sure that man will wither and die no matter how far away he may be or try to go. There are innumerable cases on record of just such inexplicable deaths. There was one that took place within the walls of a prison in British territory: a prisoner just curled up and died after saying he'd been cursed by a powerful witch doctor. Power of suggestion, self-hypnotism, you can call it what you like; but it's very real in Africa—and elsewhere. You say it effects only ignorant superstitious savages? Would you describe a belted earl and his scientific companions as ignorant superstitious savages? Then what of the mysterious deaths of Lord Carnarvon and some twenty-one members of his expedition after they'd violated King Tutankhamen's tomb in Egypt?

I saw one of the big-shot witch doctors in action one time. He gave a truly remarkable performance.

I was camped in that remote and lonely valley to which I've previously referred, where no white man ever came because sleeping sickness was prevalent and the natives were described as outlaws and runaway criminals—though I found them much like natives anywhere else, and pathetically grateful that I'd come among them and didn't cause trouble. The rains were on, and I'd been sitting reading and writing in my tent all day. Shortly before dusk the rain stopped, and the red ball of the sun blazed across the rain-drenched valley. Its rays picked out a strange procession wending its way out of the fringe of the forest and making toward the kraal by which I was camped. The villagers, who had been huddled under the eaves of their huts out of the rain, came out and stood around in little clusters, watching curiously. Two young men were in the lead, and then came a very tall thin fellow, well past middle age, who stalked along with his eyes on the horizon. He was followed by two more younger men, and then a string of heavily laden porters. They strode straight to the palaver house in the center of the kraal—a conical thatched roof on poles without walls—swept it clean, unpacked a mat, and laid it carefully down in the center for the tall man to sit on. Then the porters placed their loads in a semicircle around him—I could see that most of them were just about all the men could manage.

While this was taking place the villagers, contrary to custom, had just been standing there gawking instead of making any attempt to welcome the strangers. It was they who ought to have swept the palaver house and generally made things clean. But there was something awe-inspiring in these silent new arrivals. Africans are unaccustomed to people who are so quiet. It was a mite frightening. It was unnatural. They like folks who laugh and talk as they go about their work.

Presently, when the tall stranger had seated himself and, cross-legged and motionless as a bronze statue of the Buddha, was staring straight into the flaming orb of the setting sun, the villagers egged on their headman to do his stuff. After a bit of shuffling he went slowly and reluctantly toward the palaver house, regretting for probably the first time in his life that he was the headman. He saluted the stranger, who took not the slightest notice, and then sat gingerly down just under the eaves of the roof. One of the assistants or servants took it upon himself to acknowledge the greeting, and then entered into conversation with the shy chief. He gradually raised his voice so that others might hear what he was saying.

One of my fellows who had slipped across to learn what it was all about came racing back greatly excited to tell his comrades. They clustered around him and I could see that every now and then all eyes were turned toward me. It was clear that they didn't quite know what to do: should they tell me or not? But since I could speak their language as fluently as they could themselves and since, when Africans are excited, they carry on a conversation as though they were half a mile apart, I already had heard as much as they had: that the tall thin stranger was a powerful witch doctor. As it developed, the local villagers were even more perturbed than my men. They knew well by now that I didn't interfere with them. However, this was something very different: they knew that all white men frowned darkly upon witch doctors: could I be expected not to interfere here? How could they prevent it? They daren't *tell* me not to—you can't *tell* white folks to do or not to do things. They do what they like; but by the same token they certainly couldn't tell the witch doctor not to do things if he wanted to do them. If I attempted to stop him he'd certainly blast me with a curse—and then there'd be hell to pay! The authorities would inevitably blame them, they wouldn't dare say that it had been a witch doctor or he'd sweep them and their relatives off the face of the earth—no matter how far away he might have gone he'd know about it the instant they spoke. They were in a serious predicament.

I called one of my men across and told him not to worry; I hadn't the slightest intention of interfering, I wasn't a cop, all this was no concern of mine so long as the fellow didn't interfere with either me or my party. Everyone was greatly relieved and assured me the witch doctor was only practicing white magic—there were no evildoers to be smelled out, there would be no curses, no spells cast. But would I please give each of my men two copper coins. I could deduct the money from their wages. They would need these next morning to pay for the charms the witch doctor would undoubtedly give out to ward off evil eyes and other ills for evermore. I gave them.

Nothing developed that night. Next morning I was awake as usual when the first cocks started crowing. The rain had recommenced and was drumming steadily on the fly of my tent. There wasn't a breath of air stirring, so I knew the downpour would continue for some time. As we had plenty of grub in camp there was no need for me to hunt for more and I presently enjoyed the luxury of early-morning coffee in bed. The dawn was late because of the rain and came from nowhere in particular: the day

ust gradually broke, gray and wet. And through the grayness and steady
downpour I gradually became aware of a rich rolling bass voice, clear
and resonant, intoning some chant in a language I'd never previously
heard—nor have I ever heard it since. It was a glorious voice, a voice like
that of the great Negro singer, Paul Robeson. Robeson had not, I think,
even been heard of in those days, but I well remember that when I first
listened to him sing, my thoughts immediately flew back over thousands of
miles to that lost valley and the wonderful voice which came rolling
through that dreary dawning.

I looked out under the open flap of my tent and saw a tall figure,
naked except for a small strip of tightly bound loincloth, standing out in
the rain as though utterly unaware of it. There wasn't an ounce of super-
fluous flesh on him but under the sleek brown hide every muscle was in
its place and rippled and wove and knotted with the slightest movement.
He was a sculptor's dream, that witch doctor, a physical-training instructor's joy; he was perfection even though, as I have said, he was past middle age. His face was seamed and deeply lined, the burning eyes deeply
sunk in hollow sockets. But as he lifted his face to the heavens, so that
the rain ran down it and down his splendid body, I could see that those
eyes were clear and bright—too bright: they were the burning eyes of a
fanatic. I've seen the same light in the eyes of a Christian monk in a mon-
astery; I've seen it in the eyes of an Indian fakir and in the eyes of a
dervish in the Sahara. And, like this Negro, these other men too had given
the impression that they were being consumed by the fires of their own
fanaticism.

The man was a showman, assuredly he was a showman, and knew
all the tricks of his trade; but I don't doubt that, however it may have
been originally, he had gradually developed a sure belief in his own powers. The villagers came sleepily from their huts and huddled under the
eaves out of the still teeming rain to watch the performance. The magician
took no notice of them whatsoever. His chant continued, rising and falling,
rising and falling, monotonously but never tiresomely. Spellbound, the
villagers watched him. He slowly commenced to move, weaving and twisting and turning, around and around, faster and faster, his drenched body
glistening and gleaming in the pouring rain, the long muscles weaving
like snakes under brown satin. And then he was dancing: leaping and
jumping, twisting and turning, faster and faster, until it almost made me
giddy to watch him. The villagers' eyes became glazed and vacant, but
they followed his every movement. There isn't the slightest doubt in my
mind that he had the lot of them hypnotized—he might have had me
hypnotized too if I'd been closer. It was an extraordinary performance.
His endurance must have been inexhaustible. How long this terrific dance

went on I don't know; but suddenly he stopped and froze. At some period of the dance he'd snatched up a small assagai, an ornamental dancing spear, and now stood with this in his right hand, his body bent, his head cocked sideways as a man will sometimes cock it when listening intently. There wasn't a sound from him or his audience, no movement but the heaving of his abdominal muscles—like a double string of good onions they were—as they pumped air into his straining lungs. Then he suddenly straightened, his whole magnificent body tense and rigid, his left arm straight down along his side, the fist clenched, his right arm raised and the point of the little assagai directed to the heavens. For a long moment he stood like that—like a superb statue, *Energy in Leash* or something of the sort. His chant had long ceased; it had stopped when he commenced dancing. But he now loosed a great wordless cry, his face upturned to the skies. And without the slightest warning came one of those blinding flashes of lightning; for a moment I could have sworn that it emanated from the point of the little spear. To the rest of his audience there could, of course, have been no doubt of it.

There was a gasp of astonishment from all—even from some of the witch doctor's assistants and servants. (I sometimes wonder if he didn't almost gasp himself at the incredibly lucky coincidence. I know I did!) Instantaneously came one of those ear-splitting detonations like the voice of a big naval gun—no rumbling before or after. For another long moment the man stood there; then slowly bringing down his arm with the little spear in it he swung around on his heel and stalked away. The rain had stopped at once with that one clap of thunder, not merely as though someone had turned off a tap, but rather as though an immense sheet of iron had been drawn across the heavens. If ever a showman had a stupendous curtain, that fellow had—and did he know it! However much he must have been glowing inwardly at his luck, by no slightest indication did he allow a shadow of awareness to show. He just strode off as though he'd arranged the entire performance beforehand, even to the abrupt stopping of the rain. Not a soul in the place doubted that he had.

I've already said this man was a fanatic, that his eyes proved it, and I still wonder to what extent he'd hypnotized himself into a belief in his own powers. Did he honestly think he had called down that vivid flash of lightning? Perhaps. I've seen Indian fakirs walking barefoot across glowing coals: they were convinced they wouldn't be burned, and they weren't. I've seen them stripped and reclining apparently quite comfortably on a pile of dry thorn bushes covered with needlelike three-inch thorns. I had not been hypnotized—I had felt the heat of the coals and pricked myself with one of the thorns. I've seen a dervish in the Sahara catch up a wild cobra—not a semi-tame one from which he might have removed the

poison glands—allow it to bite his tongue, and swing around in circles so that the snake, attached to his mouth, was stretched out at full
length. To those who can concentrate on it sufficiently, the human mind
undoubtedly develops a strange power over matter. Faith healing is scoffed
at by conservative medicos. Yet they all practice it themselves to a certain
extent. As I have said, my late father was universally acknowledged one
of the great surgeons of his day, and he would certainly have scorned the
notion of faith healing as sheer quackery—I've heard him do so. But he
practiced it himself, though he gave it another name, "bluff," or "boosting
the patient's confidence," or something of the sort. I'll give you an example.

Jack, an old friend, was in need of an abdominal operation. Had he
come along earlier it would have been simple, but he kept putting it off
until his strength was badly depleted. It was now a much more serious
business. My father performed the operation and shook his head gravely
when I asked him how it had gone. "I've done all I can do, all any man
could do with knife and needle. It's up to Jack himself now."

He was wrong. Maybe he couldn't have done more with knife and
needle but he undoubtedly saved Jack's life by sheer bluff. He was called,
after the operation, in the middle of the night. Jack was very low. Now
my father was a specialist. For years past he would undertake big operations only when it was a matter of life or death. Anything else he handed
over to a younger surgeon. In other words, he wouldn't be called out of
bed unless matters were really serious and the resident house surgeon was
unable to cope with them. Accordingly, when the phone rang after midnight and my father asked me to get one of the cars out and drive him to
the hospital it didn't look hopeful for Jack.

The Rolls-Royce horn—the only Rolls attending the hospital—had
a deep baying note that was unmistakable, and my father had a cough
which had developed into a habit and which was equally unmistakable. I
sounded the horn as I drove in through the hospital gates and my father's
characteristic cough rang out as he entered the hall. Jack, whose bed was
close to one of the windows, heard both the horn and the cough and told
me later that he nearly collapsed then and there. He'd been feeling
deathly ill and the sister on night duty had called the house surgeon a
short while before. They had stood at the foot of his bed talking quietly
and looking at him for a while, then had gone away still talking quietly.
And then when, not long afterward, Jack heard my father's Rolls, and
then the old man's famous cough, and realized the doctor had been called
late, he *knew* it was because of him.

But my father was an expert. He realized that if he made straight for
Jack's bed it probably would be the end of him; so he just took the house

surgeon by the arm and walked him around the halls and landings of the hospital for a quarter of an hour or so, coughing from time to time. He then arrived outside Jack's ward and stood talking for a few moments, after which he strolled casually down the length of the ward still talking quietly to the house surgeon. Jack's bed was immediately behind the door, and my father didn't even glance over that way. He took a casual look at all the other patients and then came strolling slowly back. When he was almost at the foot of Jack's bed he again halted, finished his conversation with the house surgeon, said good night, that he'd be getting along to his bed, and that he'd only looked in because he happened to be passing. With that he swung around and made for the door, but, happening to glance over Jack's way, he stopped and exclaimed: "Good God! Jack! Why of course you're here. I'd forgotten all about you."

He sat down on the side of the bed then and brought his hand down heartily on Jack's thigh. (Jack told me later that he felt as though one foot were in the grave already and that clout pretty nearly knocked him all the way in. All the same, it bucked him up. He decided he could hardly be as bad as he felt or his own surgeon wouldn't manhandle him that way.)

"Well, how are you feeling, Jack?" asked my father. "You're not looking so damned bad, anyway," he went on without waiting for a reply. "Get some sleep now. We'll be having you dining with us at home a week from today. Good night."

And he *was* dining with us a week or two later. But as we drove away from the hospital that night my father was still grave when I asked him what Jack's chances were.

"Don't ask me, son," he said. "He's as weak as a cat and I had to be very careful not to frighten him. But I think I succeeded in bluffing him into the belief that he isn't really so bad as he feels. It was all I could do."

It was all he could do; but he did it so well that, as I say, Jack never looked back from that moment. It was amusing to listen to him later when he told us how foolishly low he felt that night. To this day he doesn't know that he was bluffed out of the grave—though he will if he reads this.

It's a long stride from Africa to Eire and perhaps at first glance there may not seem to be much connection between that yarn and the story of the witch doctor; yet both are actually part and parcel of the same thing, examples of the power of mind over matter. Does it really make much difference whether that sorcerer did stop the rain, or only seemed to? His audience (excepting me) believed he did. Is that not what matters? The world is, to ordinary men and women, what they conceive it to be; but such conception is based upon interpretation of what the objective

nses—hearing, seeing, feeling, smelling—tell them. To you or to me,
onder field is green; yet to someone who is color blind it may look blue.
nd as far as he is concerned, it *is* blue. As far as concerns those villagers,
he witch doctor *did* stop the rain. Anyway, I have wandered too far and
en too much to scoff, as other whites scoff, at anything attributed to
frican witch doctors. Admittedly there are many charlatans among them,
any cheats and frauds; but there are also, here and there in their ranks,
ome very wise men.

As I have stated before, *Semper aliquid novi ex Afrika.* And yet per-
aps there is nothing new under the sun—not even under the African sun.

APPENDIX

There are two or three very important matters I want to discuss, but since they concern hunters only I've reserved them for this Appendix. First I want to stress the enormous importance of becoming thoroughly familiar with your heavy rifle before you ever set foot in Africa. And by that I don't mean simply getting accustomed to handling it but to shooting it.

Quite recently a man who'd read one of my books on rifles suitable for African game wrote to say my knockout values were all nonsense, that he'd fired at an elephant broadside-on at 30 yards' range and the elephant hadn't even been knocked down, much less knocked out—though I had stated a bullet from a .450 even if it missed the brain by a small margin would nevertheless knock out an elephant for close to five minutes. What about it? He knew where to hit an elephant on the side brain shot because he'd once killed one with a 9.3-millimeter Mauser.

I invited him to come to see me, bringing his .450. When he arrived I put up a target I'd prepared consisting of a bull 4 inches square in the center of a board some 2 feet square. We then stepped back 30 paces— the range from which he said he'd shot at the elephant—and I told him to let drive at the target. He did, and I saw where both shots went. He was quite certain they were in the black. However, when we examined the target I showed him where his first shot had hit it at 1 o'clock, some 9 inches from the center of the bull, and the second at 9 o'clock, about 8 inches from the center. I thereby convinced him that he hadn't hit his elephant anywhere near where he thought he had and that's why it wasn't even knocked down. He blamed the rifle, so I took it and from the same distance placed both barrels in the bull.

There are some sportsmen who buy heavy rifles and have them shipped out to Africa from the shop, or borrow heavy weapons out here which they've never fired in their lives before going out to shoot something. The inevitable result is that they fail to kill. I wrote a correspondent of mine in Texas that if he could get only 100 rounds for his .465 he would de better to expend 90 of those over there at home getting thoroughly fa miliar with his big gun, and coming out here with only 10 shells—than to fire only 10 there and bring 90 with him. He had no difficulty in getting all the ammo he wanted, and he took my advice and did plenty of shooting with the .465 over there. The result was a most satisfactory safari. He had complete confidence in himself because he knew he could place his bullets where he wanted them. He didn't lose a single beast fired at, and very very few of them needed a second shot.

My advice is to put up a target like that I've described above and then step back just 10 paces from it and try to put a bullet from each barrel into the center. (I suggest 10 paces only to start with for the purpose of boosting your confidence.) Then go back another 5 paces and do it again; then another 5; and then another, and so on, until you're standing 30 or 40 yards from the target. If at any stage you fail to get both barrels into the bull, don't go back farther until you succeed. I consider this a much better method than that usually suggested, which is to start at 30 or 40 yards, going close if you don't succeed at that distance. My system gives you confidence right from the first shot you fire. Naturally, you will fire from the standing off-hand position, just as you'll be firing when you get your shot at elephant.

When you read of some amateur sportsman's shooting a buffalo fairly through the shoulder with his .470, and the buffalo's just walking away as though untouched, you now know why. Since it's impossible for an animal to walk away after receiving a bullet through the shoulder this clearly shows that the fellow didn't hit the buff anywhere near where he thought—probably because he hadn't accustomed himself to his heavy rifle.

This brings me to the second point I want to mention: Where to hit an animal. As I believe I have said before, nearly every writer on the subject recommends the neck shot—so much so, in fact, that it almost seems they are copyists, each afraid that if he doesn't follow the general line his readers will doubt that he is really experienced. The same criticism applies to that fatuous advice, "Aim lower for the heart shot on a buffalo than on any other species of game." This totally incorrect rule has been responsible for more disappointments and dangerous follow-ups than anything else. In spite of all you may hear in the way of claims there are precious few men in Africa today with much experience buffalo hunting. I say that emphatically for the simple reason that if they *were* really experienced they could never give such advice.

A wealthy American sportsman on a safari in Kenya had a lot of trouble trying to kill a buffalo and lost him in the end. He stated in his account of the incident that he'd aimed "for the lower shoulder region," presumably on the advice of his two guides. Since these guides were young fellows, and since there had been no hunting during the war owing to lack of ammo, it stands to reason that they couldn't have had much experience with buffalo and so merely passed on the advice they themselves had received or heard others giving. On the other hand, another American on safari in Tanganyika listened to me, with the result that he had no difficulty whatsoever in killing his buffalo.

My advice is this, as always. No matter what the animal you want to kill, anything from elephant down, if you slam your bullet slap through the shoulder centrally, he's yours. The shoulder is the largest, steadiest, and most vulnerable target on all game. An animal moves his shoulder less than any other part of his body. The most vital area lies *between* the shoulders. It doesn't matter a hoot where the creature's heart is. Your bullet doesn't have to puncture the heart to kill: the big main arteries are located above the heart and offer you an immense target. Your bullet on the shoulder will bring the animal down instantly in his tracks with spinal concussion and he'll be dead from rapid internal hemorrhage within not more than one or two minutes. *He will not get to his feet again.* I've shot thousands—I mean thousands—of animals of all species, the vast majority of them through the shoulder in the manner I'm advocating, and I cannot remember a single one that didn't collapse instantly where he stood. I can't remember a single one getting to his feet again. I can't remember a single one that needed a second bullet. I don't suppose one of those animals actually received my bullet through his heart—but they were all killed instantly without the slightest trouble.

So, since Africa is still a more or less free country—for the white man —it's your privilege to decide whether you'll accept the advice of those with little actual experience shooting on their own, or follow my advice and kill clean.

As to the neck shot, personally I don't like it and never take it if I can get my bullet into the shoulder. And I'm glad to be able to point to Elmer Keith of America, an infinitely finer marksman than I am, who has stated both orally and in print that he has long abandoned the neck shot because he had so many disappointments when trying it. Now, Keith really *can* shoot; he has the well-deserved reputation of being probably the most experienced and best game shot in the United States.

There's another important point to remember when you are shooting at very close quarters, and that is that your bullet is traveling *below* the line of sight for the first twenty-five yards or thereabouts from the muzzle.

With iron sights the first intersection of the bullet with the line of sight usually occurs at about 25 yards. This is because the axis of the bore is about three quarters of an inch below the line of iron sights and, of course, is anything from an inch and a half to two inches or more below the line through a scope sight (depending on how the scope is mounted). Only a fool would be using a scope at less than 25 yards' range by day, but perhaps you'll be using it at night. Now this may become a matter of very great importance. My best way of making it clear is to remind you of the extremely unpleasant time Jim Corbett had when he shot the big tiger known as the Bachelor of Cowalgarh. Corbett was lying down in the open and the tiger appeared about 10 yards away. He was standing behind a bush looking over the top of it, so Corbett had to shoot for his eye. But Corbett either forgot or didn't realize that at that close range his bullet would hit the tiger at least half an inch lower than he was aiming. Corbett says he aimed an inch below the tiger's eye because he was shooting slightly upward. But that meant that his bullet took the tiger at least an inch and a half below the eye, with the result that it passed below the brainpan and so failed to kill. Corbett should have placed his fore sight slap in the eye. Then his bullet would have taken the tiger in the bottom of the eye and killed instantly. You would be well advised to bear this in mind, especially—as I say—if you're using a scope sight at night. I would suggest that you test your rifle so sighted at a target 20 yards away and see just how much lower the bullet hits than you were aiming. As a matter of fact, if you expect to be doing any night work I'd suggest having your scope specially zeroed for 25 yards. Then you'll have nothing to remember.

There is a point about the use of shooting head lamps that should, I think, be repeated and emphasized here. When you are wandering around you must keep the lamp in the center of your forehead so that the light will shine wherever you look; but when you catch an animal's eyes and close in for the shot you must pull the lamp around until it's over your *left* eye if you shoot from the right shoulder, and over your right eye if you shoot from the left shoulder. This may sound odd, but try it and see. If game haven't been shot up much by night, they'll usually give you plenty of time to make this essential adjustment. If you don't make it you'll be firing blind because the ray of the lamp will be directed way out to one side and will no longer shine on the animal's eyes. If you make the proper adjustment there is absolutely no excuse for failing to kill clean. It's the necessity for this adjustment that makes these shooting head lamps a nuisance.

I know I have given this same advice about lights at night earlier,

n the body of this book, but it seems to me sufficiently important to in-
corporate it again here.

You'll occasionally read fantastic accounts of shooting by night without the aid of any sort of lamp, and it's because I know one young fellow
who was led badly astray by believing such yarns that I mention the myth
here as a warning. One writer tells how he shot an elephant on a dark
moonless night in the depths of the Ituri forest by means of the glint of
the starlight along the barrel of his .416, and that when he fired for the
brain the muzzle flash so lit up the elephant that he was able to get in another shot and then another by means of the flash of that one, so killing
the elephant. Then there is another man who tells of killing a man-eating
tiger somewhere in Malaya in dense jungle on a dark night. He was
armed with a powerful double rifle. He says that he waited until the tiger
approached the bait and then fired one barrel into the air so that the flash
would light up the tiger and thus enable him to kill it.

The only assumption one can come to after reading this twaddle is
that neither of those two men could ever have fired a shot by night.

The muzzle flash of any firearm is not a flare but an instantaneous
flash. Moreover, the pupils of one's eyes are dilated to their maximum extent at night. Any light will cause them to contract immediately so that as
soon as the light is gone one is temporarily blind—what we call being
dazzled. Under the conditions described by the two writers cited above
they wouldn't have been able to see their targets, much less their sights,
for quick following shots.

Bell also speaks of shooting elephant by night. But he encountered
his elephant under the most perfect possible conditions for night work:
out in the open on a dry river bed, the sand of which was very white, and
with a grand full African moon to light things up. Bell wasn't using a
powerful rifle burning a large power charge: he was using his little
7-millimeter Mauser. He says the moon enabled him to see his sights perfectly for the first shot; but *"what a flash even a small rifle makes when
one's pupils are fully dilated."* He saw the first elephant drop and then
fired a shot into the second one's ribs *"and hoped for the best, because I
couldn't see my sights."* (Italics mine.) And don't forget, that wasn't in
heavy forest or deep jungle in the dark, but in the open under a full moon
with the added advantage of white sand all around.

What it boils down to is that Bell was a genuinely experienced hunter
and had ample material to fill a most interesting and informative book
without needing to call upon his imagination; and even if he had wanted
to invent adventures, he had sufficient experience to guide him so that his
imagined escapades would seem authentic.

I've done quite a bit of night shooting, both with and without shooting lamps, and my experience is similar to Bell's: it is impossible to aim a quick second shot if one hasn't a light to show up one's sights.

I feel compelled to say something about grass fires because the fantastically exaggerated accounts of them one reads in books and outdoor magazines give inexperienced readers a false impression of their danger and the damage they do. My reflections are occasioned by reading recently an account by a man who claimed to have been hunting elephant right here in Portuguese East Africa in a district well known to me. He presents a hair-raising account of the devastating effect of a holocaust which swept down on his camp. He describes the terror-stricken animals—everything from elephant to porcupines, not forgetting lion and snakes—fleeing blindly past on both sides, taking not the slightest notice of one another. He mentions the panic-stricken helplessness of his native servants and porters as they ran around in useless circles, screaming and moaning. He tells us how he had to abandon everything except the light rifle he happened to be carrying and, after a terrible run with his men (surrounded by desperate wild animals), how he was only just in time to jump into a creek and submerge everything but his nostrils. He was all but suffocated as the fire swept right to the high bank of the stream and leaped across to continue its havoc on the other side. When at last he deemed it safe to climb out, he and his men went back over the blackened country to see if there were anything they could salvage; but there wasn't. Everything was burned. And he gives a harrowing account of the roasted carcasses of animals on all sides—even elephant—and the fierce anger he felt toward the cruel naked savages who obviously must have set the fire to kill game and who were now to be seen through the smoke, gathering for the feast like demons of the nether regions; and so forth and so on.

Buncombe! This sort of thing is either a deliberate attempt to arouse the reader's ire against the natives—and thereby draw attention from the real slaughterers of game—or else it shows a total lack of understanding and equal lack of reasoning power. This business of the African natives' burning game is brought up regularly at frequent intervals. I would like to ask those who write so irately whether they have ever seen the Africans doing it. Never have I come across anyone who has actually *seen* it with his own eyes. Invariably it transpires that the report is mere hearsay; and like all hearsay it inevitably becomes more exaggerated the farther it goes. Natives *may* very occasionally ring-fire a herd of elephant or buffalo if they happen to find the game in a saucerlike depression full of long dry grass and there is no breath of wind stirring—one hears of such things, though I've never seen them. But it's absolute rot to speak of natives' burning game in a straight-out cross-country fire. Haven't the game noses or legs? I have here and there seen the natives use fire to drive game into a long net. They know the animals can easily outrun the fire but set the net in the gap between two hills where they will have plenty of time to spear whatever becomes entangled, and also time in which to take up the precious net before the fire reaches it. That net took a lot of work to make, they certainly aren't going to let it burn in the first fire in which they use it.

Let us be rational. Grass fires are a regular feature of Africa every year without fail. I can see no reason for supposing that they haven't been a regular annual feature of every dry season since the world began. They sweep right through Central Africa uncontrolled year after year. If they were really as devastating as we are asked to believe they would have roasted every beast on the continent long ago. The game are thoroughly accustomed to the fires, know just how dangerous they are, can hear and smell them coming long before any man can, and *understand perfectly well how to avoid them.* In all my years of wandering around the African veld the only evidence I have seen of living creatures that might have been caught by a fire has been of tortoises. And at that there is no certainty that the fire killed them: they may have been dead long before the fire came. In fact, in all cases something else was probably the death agency, because the shells were old and there was no roast meat in them. It seems likely to me that only very small animals are ever caught and killed by these grass fires for the simple reason that one sees only hawks following on: I can't remember ever seeing vultures, and if the annual fires habitually killed a large number of animals the vultures would have known about it long ago.

Ever since the white man commenced exterminating game with his beloved magazine rifles and expanding bullets he has tried to find a scapegoat to bear the blame. The African wild hunting dog and the African native come in handy for this purpose: neither of them can answer back; neither of them can read or write; if either of them did try to write a defense no one would publish it.

Then, with regard to one's native servants' panicking and running around uselessly when they see a grass fire approaching the camp, and not knowing better than to let all one's kit be burned—this is calumny. The African is as much accustomed to annual grass fires as the game; he knows just as well how dangerous they are; he understands what to do when he sees one approaching camp or kraal. (If he were given to losing his head he would have been burned out of hut and home aeons ago, and there are still millions of Africans in Central Africa.) If he hasn't done so before, when he sees a fire coming the African proceeds to burn a fire break on the upwind side of camp. This will creep back against the wind and when the main fire reaches it it must—having nothing to feed on—subside. If the grass is long and the wind strong, so that there is doubt that the fire break will creep back sufficiently quickly to make a safe wide stretch of burned-off ground upwind of camp, the African most certainly won't lose his head. He will do as any experienced bushman would do: fire the grass on the downwind side of the camp. This blaze will sweep away just as fast as the other fire approaches, and camp equipment can then be moved to the burned-off ground. What is there to worry about? And yet there was a grown man who claimed to be an experienced elephant hunter who told us how he lost all his possessions in a bush fire. (It was he who lost his head—not his men.) It is in just such circumstances that the African shows his worth. He will make a joke of the whole thing: he'll be whooping and yelling and shouting and laughing as he dashes backward and forward through the smoke saving your precious kit and gear. (Screaming and moaning in dismay, indeed.) You won't lose a single thing. One of your men may drop his knife without noticing and have it burned, and later you'll see him looking ruefully at the bare blade minus handle; but he won't come whining to you begging for another because his was destroyed in your service. If anything does get burned in one of these seasonal fires the African takes it philosophically. I have been thirty-three years here and in that time have been through I suppose about thirty seasons of grass fires (I may have been away for perhaps three, but not more) and I cannot remember having a single thing of mine burned accidentally.

Of course this maneuver of a backfire presupposes matches; but what kind of bushman doesn't carry with him the means of making fire? Not that there isn't an occasional hunter of such sort. Not long ago I met a man who had spent some forty years in the veld as hunter and prospector, and he told a hair-raising story of a fire in which he and his gunbearer were very nearly burned to death. I asked him why on earth he hadn't lit the grass in front of him, and he looked at me in astonishment as he reminded me he was a nonsmoker. It seems nonsmokers are prohibited from carrying matches! As to the speed of these grass fires, I'll just say this: my men and I have on countless occasions when returning to camp strolled along in front of such a fire, although we were walking downwind; and I cannot remember ever seeing the men look back to see if the fire were overtaking us. They know perfectly well the fire will not overtake a man walking unless the grass is *very* long, exceptionally dry, and even then it would take an unusually strong wind to cause the African native to look back apprehensively. Yet some writers expect us to believe that elephant and buck are overtaken and burned to death.

And now let me issue a word of warning:

There are certain high-speed small-bore weapons being widely advertised for all game in all parts of the world because they're capable of blasting a half-inch hole through a half-inch slab of armor plate, even with a soft-nose bullet. I admit that when I first heard of this I was puzzled. But my friend Henry Kohlbacker of Buffalo, New York, who has devoted a lifetime to experimenting in this direction, enlightened me. It seems the whole thing relates to the properties of armor plate—a complex subject into which I've no intention of delving here beyond saying that it's a question of time/speed. There's a certain critical velocity of around 3650 feet per second. If the bullet is traveling at not less than that speed at the moment of impact, it punches, or shears, a button out of the plate before the plate can assert its physical effect; but if the bullet's speed has dropped even 50 feet per second below that critical velocity, it will scarcely mark the plate, which now will stop the bullet before it can do any damage. But, and this is the important point for the hunter of heavy game to remember, *in both cases the bullet disintegrates.* No trace of these bullets has ever been recovered—a point that is totally ignored by the boosters of the weapons. Take note that even when the bullet succeeds in blasting a hole through the plate, *it does not pass through that hole.* It's essentially a punching operation, not a drilling of the hole. And no matter whether a hard-nose or soft-nose bullet is used—either will disintegrate.

If an elephant's brain lay concealed behind a slab of half-inch armor plate it's just possible that one of these weapons would occasionally kill, because the button of steel blown out of the plate, provided it remained in one piece (but it often shatters into small pieces), packs quite a punch of its own. However, elephant's skulls are not made of armor plate, and if you attempt to fire a small light ultra-high-speed bullet of any factory make, either soft-nose or hard-nose, it will blow up long before it reaches the brain. The *only* high-speed bullet we know that will stand up to the terrific strains imposed on head shots at African elephant is made of homogeneous bronze in the smaller calibers, and either bronze or brass in calibers running up from .400. Such a bullet will definitely not deform or lose direction on or after impact, provided it has a suitably shaped nose.

I cannot warn you too strongly not to think of tackling any potentially dangerous game at close quarters with any small-bore rifle. Remember, it's by no means always the animal at which you're firing that constitutes the danger: there may be another one there of whose very existence you're unaware. Just because these small weapons are used safely and satisfactorily on the open plains where men shoot at 200 and 300 yards' range does not mean that they can be used safely in the bushveld, where the ranges are very much closer. It's one thing to shoot a lion on a short-grass plain with a scope-sighted high-speed small bore at 150 or 250 yards and it's quite another to shoot at a range of 20 or 25 yards in the bush veld. Even though you kill your lion stone-dead, as you ought to be able to, what if he has a mate concealed in the grass, with you unable to see her until suddenly she comes open-mouthed at you from 20 paces away. You'll be very likely to regret you haven't a man-sized weapon for a man's work—that is, if you live long enough to regret anything.

ABOUT THE AUTHOR

For more than thirty years John Taylor has hunted in Africa. He is often out of touch with civilization for as long as three and four years at a time. "I did not learn of World War II until some of my men went in for provisions and brought back tea and salt wrapped in old newspapers. Where I am there is no radio and I never see another white man."

Mr. Taylor—Pondoro to the natives—was born in Dublin, son of Sir William Taylor, K.B.E., C.B., D.L., one of the great surgeons of his day. Lady Taylor was an American from Louisiana. Young John Taylor struck out for Africa after a conventional upbringing at one of "the big five" of English public schools, and in Africa he has remained: for the most part in remote sections of the continent, naked like the tribes around him, living entirely by hunting and bartering what he shoots. Since the thirties he has been the only regular professional ivory hunter left in Africa.